To Great Health

Dietitian Jane

Flax Your Way to
Better Health

Flax Your Way to
Better Health

Jane Reinhardt-Martin, RD, LD

This book is intended as an educational and informational resource. The publisher and author expressly disclaim any responsibility or liability in connection with the use of this book.

Cover design by Foster and Foster, Fairfield, IA. Interior design by Nancy Gratton and by Publishing Professionals, New Port Richey, FL, Sylvia Hemmerly.

Cover photographs by the Flax Council of Canada.

Dedication

To Beth, whose life provided me with the inspiration to write this book.

Acknowledgments

I would like to thank Nancy Gratton, my editor, for her constant faith in this project and for helping put my thoughts in print; to Sylvia Hemmerly and her Publishing Professionals, especially Kathy Connor, for turning the manuscript into a finished book; and to George Foster, of Foster and Foster, Inc. for taking my vision and making it come alive so vibrantly with his design for the cover.

Thanks also to Kelly Laschkewitsch and Anne Lund, dietetic students, at the University of Wisconsin-Madison, Madison, Wisconsin, for kitchen testing my recipes; and particular thanks to my reviewers: Robert A. Flowers, MD; Jack F. Carter, Ph.D.; Diane Morris, Ph.D., RD, and President of Mainstream Nutrition; and Paul Stitt, M.S., CNS, and President of ENRECO, Inc.

Thanks most of all to my family, friends, and colleagues, for their constant support and understanding. Most especially, my love to my most loyal fan, Michael, my husband and soulmate. Thank you for your unconditional faith and support. And to my sons, TJ, Sam, and Alex, for putting your tastebuds to good use and being my "honest taste-testers."

Table of Contents

Foreword

After years of trying out home remedies, prescription drugs, and fad diets in our efforts to improve our health, isn't it time we all learned the simple truth that "we are what we eat"? As a physician, I like to encourage my patients to take charge of their health by giving them choices based on science, not fads, and backed up by ongoing research. Flax represents one such option.

Flax is an old food source that is currently being rediscovered by scientists in the lab, by the medical community, and by nutritionists. As Jane Reinhardt-Martin explains in this book, choosing to add flax to your diet is one way to help improve your heart's health, and it has benefits for fighting cancer, renal disease and other health problems as well.

As Reinhardt-Martin makes clear, a big part—but by no means all—of the benefit from flax comes from its oil. In these "anti-fat" times, recommending the addition of a food that is high in oils may seem counterintuitive, but it is not. The use of oils can actually be healthy. Monounsaturated cooking oils such as canola and olive oils have established their reputations as heart healthy alternatives to corn and other vegetable oils. Now research attention is being directed to grapeseed and flax oils to discover their benefits as well.

What are the benefits? Flaxseed and its oils have been shown to help raise HDL-cholesterol (the "good" cholesterol) while lowering LDL-cholesterol. This is good news for your heart, and it can contribute to your healthy longevity.

Reinhardt-Martin provides you with a solid grounding in the current state of research knowledge about the benefits of flax, but she doesn't stop there. She knows that most of us are unlikely to incorporate a new food in our daily diet unless we can do it conveniently, so she's tracked down a host of sources where you can get the product. She also knows that we generally don't make a particular food a regular part of our meals if we don't know how to make it taste good. With that in mind, she has taken the trouble to put together some tempting recipes, all of which incorporate flaxseed. Think of them as "the proof in the pudding." So read on, and remember you are learning to make better choices.

Robert A. Flowers, M.D., Internal Medicine

Introduction

Most people who know me will agree that I practice what I preach. As a Registered Dietitian, I am truly passionate about my work. My interest in nutrition began when I was a severely overweight teenager in high school. I learned about the profession of dietetics from my Home-Ec teachers. When attending college, I thought that if I could help myself with my weight problem, then maybe I could also help *others* become healthier—and feel better about themselves. Since graduating from the University of Wisconsin-Madison 15 years ago, I have had the privilege of making that dream a reality. Over the years, and after working with hundreds of patients, I truly came to understand how difficult it is to make simple lifestyle changes, for I still battle my weight every day.

So, how did all this lead me to becoming interested in flaxseed? In 1998 I was working for Coram Healthcare, and an important part of my job was to do cancer-and-nutrition presentations, teaching patients and their families about how changing their diet could help them in their recovery, as an adjunct to chemotherapy or other medical treatments. In the course of this work I often found myself doing on-line research for my patients, which is how I met Diana Dyer, a three-time cancer survivor. Diana, herself a Registered Dietitian, had posted information on-line telling about how, after her last breast cancer diagnosis, she had become intrigued by the anti-cancer properties that flaxseed is known to have, and had started using it in her own diet. She passed along to me much of the information she had gathered about this remarkable food, and I quickly became fascinated. (You will find one of Diana's recipes in Chapter 7.)

The more I learned about flaxseed, the more impressed I became. Soon I was sure that I wanted to share what I'd learned with people in the Quad Cities area (Moline and Rock Island, Illinois, and Davenport and Bettendorf, Iowa) where I live. As a regular guest on The Paula Sands Live Show on KWQC-TV 6, a NBC affiliate, I did a segment introducing flaxseed to the viewers. But I didn't stop there. I offered flaxseed classes at Greatest Grains, a health food store in Davenport, Iowa. The response was overwhelming! I could barely keep up with the requests for flax-based, low-fat recipes and meal plans. I spent the next few months collecting information and ideas from a variety of sources, with the idea of printing up a brief handout to give to my clients. Soon, however, it became clear that I had enough material to justify an entire book!

I might never have taken the project any further, however, if it weren't for my good friend Beth, whom I met in my sophomore year in college. Beth was first diagnosed with cancer as a child, and her mom had gotten heavily into health-food store products, believing it would help keep Beth well. When Beth went off to college, her mom always insisted that she keep lots of this kind of food on hand in her dorm room. At that time I thought it was strange—back then there were very few studies showing the correlation between nutrition and cancer. I lost Beth to her cancer eight years ago, but I have come to believe that her mom's health-food "care packages" were part of the reason that Beth was with us for as long as she was.

Today's nutritionists have come to know what Beth's mom instinctively believed about health foods: There are some powerful health benefits available in the foods we eat. Flax, in particular, has enjoyed a recent surge in popularity for very good reasons—as you'll soon see when you read about the latest scientific research on the subject. And it's clear that the benefits of flax go far beyond helping cancer patients; flax appears to be helpful in combating a wide range of diseases and disorders, from arthritis to some of the less pleasant symptoms of menopause.

The more I researched the dietary benefits of flax, the more I felt the need to make the results of my studies known to a broader audience. Even more, I am inspired by Beth herself, who was a gentle person who always considered the needs of other people over her own. Writing this book is, in part, my way of working through my sense of loss now that Beth is gone. It is only fitting, therefore, that I dedicate this book to the memory of my good friend Beth.

The Research Promise 1

You may never have heard of flax but, believe me, you will during this new millennium. The products of this plant can have a big impact on your health, from lowering your cholesterol to helping with your rheumatoid arthritis. More and more scientific studies are finding this out, and food industry executives and health-food stores alike are listening—and delivering more flax-rich foods to your table.

Flax Comes of Age

I first began seriously teaching about the benefits of flax in 1998. Right about then, I was getting lots of questions about the health benefits and nutritional importance of omega-3 fats, and I knew that flax was one of those little-known foods that contained a lot of these substances. Then, one day, I watched a broadcast of the *Oprah Winfrey Show*. Bob Arnot, M.D., and the author of *The Breast Cancer Prevention Diet*, appeared as a guest, and he mentioned flaxseed several times. In fact, he went so far as to call it a critical component in any woman's diet.

What a difference a little high-profile publicity can make! After that show aired, I got a call from Candice, the marketing director of a local health food store, Greatest Grains, in Davenport, Iowa. She was astounded to report that the store had sold *65 pounds* of flaxseed— in just three days! Clearly, Dr. Arnot's message had gotten through to a receptive audience. But my experience in the nutrition field made me cautious about drawing conclusions from these amazing sales figures, so I asked her "Do you think your customers know what to do with it once they get home?" Candice replied: "I don't think so—even *I* don't really know how to use it."

I could just imagine bags of flaxseed sitting on kitchen counters all over Davenport, all going to waste. I just couldn't bear it! So, I offered to teach a few flaxseed classes through the store. I had no idea if anyone would show up for those first classes, but it turns out that I needn't have worried—I got an amazingly large turnout. Even more astonishing, however, was the *nature* of my audience: these students were not regular health food consumers, dropping in to learn about the latest intriguing food product. Instead, my audience consisted of the kind of people who probably were more comfortable in the aisles of a conventional grocery store. They had come, not out of curiosity, but because they had specific health goals. Some wanted to lower their cholesterol; some were hoping flax would be useful in preventing or treating cancer; some were looking for help with their rheumatoid arthritis; and some were hoping to use flaxseed as a form of natural estrogen therapy, to ease the symptoms of menopause.

My usual experience with classes is that people start falling asleep as soon as you start off with "Studies have shown . . ." but not *this* crowd! No matter what their individual goals, all of these students shared one thing in common: they all wanted to know how such a small seed could live up to Dr. Arnot's claims about its powerful health benefits. They wanted to really understand some of the amazing results that have come from research studies.

Needless to say, this set of classes was not my last. During the course of my teaching, I've learned that consumers really *do* want more information about foods that are good for them. Even more, they want the "how to's"—instructions for applying this information quickly and easily in their own lives. After all, learning that a food is good for you is not enough. You need easy principles to help you incorporate this food in your diet. Otherwise, it simply won't end up on your table.

But let's not get ahead of ourselves here. Before we get into how to use flaxseed, let me tell you a few things about this remarkable plant and its distinguished history. From the ancient Egyptians to our own forebears of a generation or two ago, the usefulness of flax is something that's long been understood.

A Brief History of Flax

One afternoon before class began, one of my students, Virginia, shared a very interesting story. She told me that she was already familiar with this little seed, because her grandparents had grown flaxseed in their fields. She recalled the fields bedecked in beautiful blue blossoms, and she told me of how her "Nana" had so *many* uses for the harvested seeds.

Some of the uses that Virginia's grandmother made of flaxseed were new to me—I knew it best as a food item back then. But they have a very real presence in the folklore of people who have grown this plant throughout the world. For example, like many others who are familiar with the plant, Virginia's Nana used the seeds to heal injuries. Virginia shared stories of how, whenever she got a scrape, her Nana would apply a small pinch of flaxseed to the wound, confident of its curative powers.

Whether you are first learning about flax right now, or have used it for years, you're a newcomer in a long tradition of human use of flaxseed. As far as historians and archaeologists can calculate, humans have grown flax since about 9,000 B.C. The seed has gone through some changes as the centuries passed, as people domesticated the plant and developed newer, larger-seeded variants, but its fundamental health-promoting properties remain. Here are just a few of the highlights of flaxseed's long and illustrious history:

- In biblical times flaxseed was a very important crop. Flax is mentioned several times in the Bible, and it was credited with having a variety of uses. The seeds were eaten plain, or they were pressed to extract an oil that was used for cooking. The flax stem itself was used as roof thatching and to make cloth.

- By about 5,000 B.C., Egyptian doctors commonly carried flaxseed in their medical bags for use in cures.

- The Babylonians cultivated the plant as well, and the archaeological record shows that they had domesticated it by 3,000 B.C. Here and elsewhere in the world, art found in burial chambers depicts flax cultivation and clothing made from flax stem fibers.

- In 900 B.C., hundreds of thousands of flax seeds were left at Deir Alla in Jordan, according to Dr. Gillian Vogelsang-Eastwood of the National Museum of Ethnology in Leiden, Netherlands. She states that "the seeds were probably used for planting for the next year's crop, and as oil for lamps, as well as for human and animal food—possibly as a mixed grain bread."

- In 650 B.C., Roman physician Theophrastus wrote a recommendation for the use of flax mucilage as a remedy for coughs.

- Archaeologists excavating the peat bogs in England discovered the bodies of people buried about 2,000 years ago. The tannic acid of the bogs preserved everything—including the stomach contents, so we know what they ate for their last meal! Autopsy reports revealed that one "bogman" had eaten barley, flaxseed, gold-of-pleasure, and other cultivated plants.

- In about the first century A.D., Tacitus praised the virtues of flax to his Roman readers.

- In about the 15th century A.D., Hildegard von Bingen, an early Christian abbess and renowned healer in Germany, used flax meal in hot compresses for the treatment of both external and internal ailments.

Even Hippocrates, in whose name all modern doctors swear their professional oath, knew well the value of flaxseed. In approximately 650 B.C., he wrote of its value in the treatment of abdominal pains. And, in the 8th century, Charlemagne was so convinced of its importance to good health that he passed laws requiring his subjects to consume flaxseed regularly.

The archaeological record makes it clear that the many uses of flax, from fabrics to lamp oil, were apparent to people of all cultures, throughout time. The medicinal qualities of the seeds were recognized by peoples throughout the world, from the early Greeks to the people of Western Europe. But people have equally recognized their nutritional value: one recipe used in ancient Greece calls for combining flaxseed with barley, salt, and coriander; roasting and grinding the mixture; and then storing it in earthenware jars for future use. For a time, widespread recognition of the health-giving properties of flax fell out of fashion, at least in Western Europe. Now scientific research is once again demonstrating the medicinal importance of flaxseed.

What *Is* Flax?

"When flax fields are blooming, it looks like waves of water in an ocean" says Paul Stitt, owner of Natural Ovens, of Manitowoc, Wisconsin. The blue-flowered crop is grown world-wide, in North America, South America, Europe, Asia, and Africa. Wherever it is grown, flax is primarily prized for its stem and seeds. It is from the stem that we get the fiber used to make linen cloth and fine quality papers. The food and medicinal value comes from the seeds.

The seeds, which can be a shiny reddish brown or golden yellow, are not very big—in fact, they're only a little larger than the sesame seeds you see on bagels or multigrain breads. As is true with many cultivated crops, there are "grades" of flax, largely based on issues of consistency of size and shape, and on the way the seeds are processed. Flaxseed used for human consumption is of the highest grade: uniform in color and shape, and processed so that there is no extraneous matter (bits of leaf and stem, for example) included in the product. Lower-grade flax and flaxseed are used in the manufacture of non-food items.

Flaxseed has a crisp, chewy texture, and most people describe its flavor as "nutty." Many people simply eat the seeds whole, but the seeds can also be ground or crushed to express their oil, which can then be used for cooking. And flaxseed makes its way into your kitchen or workshop in non-food form as well. A quick peek at the ingredient lists on the packages of many common household products will probably turn up several that contain linseed oil— another name for the oil that comes from crushed flaxseed. You'll find it listed as an important ingredient in paints and coatings, linoleum, and a great many other products.

Nutrient Composition of Flaxseed

Clearly, flaxseed has been with us for a long time. Only recently has there been a resurgence of interest in this unassuming little seed. And the claims made in its behalf are nothing short of amazing! Remember what Dr. Arnot told Oprah: this is one food that is supposed to help you cope with disease as well!

The question is, how can such a small seed do all this? The best place to start looking for an answer to this question is to take a look at the nutrient composition of a single tablespoon of flaxseed. When you examine it closely, you can begin to appreciate how and why flaxseed can have a significant impact on your health.

Nutrition Composition of Flax (per tablespoon)

Nutrient	GROUND (8 grams)	WHOLE (11 grams)
Calories	36.0	50.0
Protein (grams)	1.6	2.2
Fat (grams)	3.3	4.5
Dietary Fiber (grams)	2.2	3.0
Calcium (mg)	18.9	26.0
Magnesium (mg)	34.5	47.4
Phosphorus (mg)	49.8	68.4
Potassium (mg)	66.5	91.4
Folic acid (mcg)	9.0	12.3

Protein

Flaxseed is a wonderful, rich source of plant protein—the building block for muscles and tissues in your body. Flax protein is similar in composition to the more familiar protein found in soybeans. For people who are trying to reduce the amount of meat in their diet, this is very important: high quality protein like the sort found in flaxseed is necessary for a balanced diet.

Fat

Fat has gotten a bad rap these days. Americans are obsessed with their consumption of it, perhaps because they're consuming too *much*—specifically, too much *saturated* fat, which contributes to raising blood cholesterol levels and increasing the risk for heart disease. But not all fats are terrible for you, and some even have beneficial effects. What's important is to know the difference.

Fat Composition of Flaxseed Oil

Polyunsaturated fats	73%
Omega-3	57%
Omega-6	16%
Monounsaturated fats	18%
Saturated fats	9%

As the table shows, flaxseed contains only 9 percent saturated fat. A much larger portion of the fat in flaxseed is polyunsaturated, a full 73 percent. And most of that comes from omega-3 fatty acids. Why is this significant? The omega-3 and omega-6 fatty acids are known as "essential fatty acids" which the body cannot make for itself—you must eat them or do without! But you can't very well do without them because they are necessary to several important body functions. For example:

- they maintain the structure of cell membranes, necessary for the efficient regulation of the nutrients that pass in and out of your cells;

- they form the basis for more complex substances, like prostaglandins, which affect blood clotting and constriction of blood vessels; and

- they enable the transport and metabolism of cholesterol in the body.

Flaxseed is unique in the plant world because it is one of the richest sources of omega-3 fatty acids. In other leafy green plants, a substantial portion of their polyunsaturated fats are omega-3s, but since the *overall* fat content of leafy greens is low, they cannot really contribute significant amounts of omega-3. Omega-3 fatty acids have been cited as beneficial for people suffering from rheumatoid arthritis and other immune-system ailments, so any food source that offers you a good supply of these nutrients is something to be prized. Many people are aware that they can get omega-3s from fatty fish, like salmon and tuna, but do not realize that there is a bountiful supply in vegetable form. If you are following a strict vegetarian diet, adding flaxseed will give you a good start at increasing your intake of omega-3 fatty acids.

In addition, there has been a lot of talk recently about the importance of getting the right balance between omega-3 fatty acids and their cousins, the omega-6s. In the past few decades, the American diet has shown a dramatic increase in the consumption of omega-6s, with omega-3s consumed at a much lower rate. Why is this important, you ask? Some researchers believe that having too much of one can interfere with the actions of the other kind, reducing the beneficial effects of both. For example, the omega-3s you consumed with your fish at dinner may not be as effective lowering your cholesterol if your overall diet is higher in omega-6 fats. Can flaxseed help with this? You bet! The extraordinarily high omega-3 content in flaxseed gives you an immediate boost, providing you with a better ratio of omega-3s to omega-6s and improving the efficiency with which your body can use both!

Dietary Fiber

Flaxseed, with its 2 to 3 grams of total fiber per tablespoon, is a great source of this necessary substance. Even better, it contains a mixture of both soluble and insoluble fiber. As with fats, the different types of fiber serve different purposes in your body: soluble fiber dissolves in water and has been shown to decrease blood cholesterol levels and to help regulate blood sugar levels; insoluble fiber—what your grandma called "roughage"—is fiber that is not absorbed by your body. Insoluble fiber helps prevent constipation, because it increases fecal bulk and reduces transit time as wastes pass through the bowel. About one-third of flaxseed's fiber is soluble, the rest is insoluble. Both provide important health benefits.

Lignans

This term may be brand new to you, but it's something you'll be hearing a lot about in the future. Not that lignans are, themselves, anything new. It's just that we're only beginning to recognize their importance.

Lignans are phytoestrogens—plant compounds that have been found to act in humans like a weak form of estrogen. In recent years, scientists have become more aware of the usefulness of phytoestrogens in the treatment of cancer as well as their ability to offset many of the discomforts associated with menopause, particularly hot flashes. Soybeans and other legumes, seeds, and some whole grain products are more familiar sources of these compounds, but flaxseed is by far the *richest known plant source* of lignans.

Vitamins and Minerals

Like any other seed, flaxseed contains vitamins and minerals essential to good nutrition. More important, however, is the sheer *amount* of these important elements. For example, flaxseed is very rich in potassium—just four tablespoons of flaxseed contain as much potassium as a small banana, and one tablespoon of flaxseed contains as much folic acid as a slice of whole wheat bread. Clearly, you can increase the vitamins and minerals in your diet simply and easily, just by incorporating flaxseed in your cooking. You'll learn how to do this later on in this book.

Safety Issues

Whenever you consider adding a new food to your diet, it's a good idea to really check it out. We've all heard the recent warnings about those "designer" sports drinks, enhanced with additives from ginseng to ginko biloba—some of them are only guilty of making outrageously excessive claims for themselves, others are making a few researchers a little worried. Are there safety issues regarding flax you should know about? Here are a few:

- Flax contains cyanogenic glycosides. These are natural substances found in flax, as well as more than 2,500 other plant species including lima beans, cassava (also known as manioc and tapioca), and the seeds of stone fruits such as peaches, plums, cherries and apricots. Plants that contain this substance can release cyanide, a poisonous compound, under certain circumstances. So should you be worried? *No!* The cyanogenic glycosides in flaxseed do not pose a risk to well-nourished populations. In fact, cooking destroys the enzyme that metabolizes the glycosides, thus rendering them harmless.

- Flaxseed, like any other seed, can cause problems for people who suffer from diverticulitis, if bits of seed become trapped in pockets in the intestine. The solution? Make sure your seed is finely ground before using it in a recipe.

- The high fiber content of flaxseed, while good for cleaning out your system, can take some getting used to. To avoid the possibility of problems, make certain to add flaxseed gradually, and make certain that you're drinking an adequate amount of water every day.

But What Do I *Do* With It?

Learning how to use flax is, after all, the key to making it a regular part of your diet. This point was made to me explicitly when I was counseling a woman named Millie. Millie had come to my office for help in losing weight, but she also wanted to lower her cholesterol. Of course, I introduced flax to her. After all, by this time I was fully aware of its potential in this area. Millie was interested in learning about flaxseed, but she was very practical. The first thing she asked was: "How can I fit this into my meal plan?"

Millie's question prompted me to sort this out. I had by then become pretty knowledgeable about the nutrient value of flax, but I hadn't really thought through the best way to integrate it into a healthy diet. And I hadn't worked out a good, clear, and simple way to present flax as a natural part of my clients' day-to-day life. Obviously, if I wanted people to begin making regular use of flax, I was going to have to help them get a firm grasp on how and why they *should!*

One thing I knew was that most people are familiar with the USDA Food Guide Pyramid—most of us were introduced to it during our grade-school years. But that was a long time ago, right? So, before we go any further, let me refresh your memory and do a quick review of just what the USDA Food Guide Pyramid tells us.

As you can see in the illustrations below, the USDA Food Guide Pyramid is based on servings of food, not on calories, fat grams, or other forgettable numbers. With a few exceptions, the food groups make sense, offering similar nutrients in each category. These divisions aren't perfect, for instance, cheese is placed in the dairy group but it fits just as well in the protein group (meat, poultry, fish, dry beans, eggs, and nuts). And beans and nuts, although high in protein, are in other ways very different nutritionally from animal protein, so they could just as logically be placed in a category of their own.

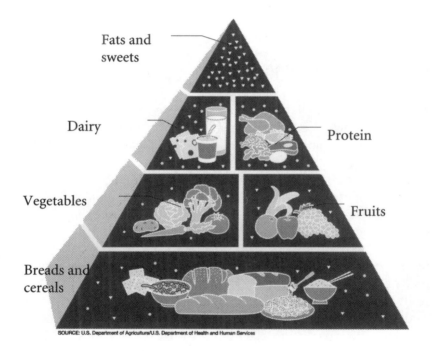

SOURCE: U.S. Department of Agriculture/U.S. Department of Health and Human Services

The Pyramid makes clear what foods you should be eating and the number of servings from each food group, but there's another crucial bit of information you need to make this information useful: what's a serving size? Take a look:

Serving Sizes for Food Group Items

FOOD GROUP	A SERVING IS:
Bread, cereal, rice, and pasta	One slice of bread; 1/2 cup cooked pasta, rice, or other grain; 1 oz. cold cereal, or 1 cup hot cereal, or any 80-calorie complex carbohydrate.
Vegetables	1 cup of raw leafy vegetables; 1/2 cup other vegetables, chopped or cooked; 3/4 cup vegetable juice.
Fruits	One medium apple, orange, or banana; 1/2 cup chopped, cooked, or canned fruit; 3/4 cup fruit juice.
Milk, yogurt, and cheese	One cup milk or plain yogurt, 1-1/2 oz. cheese
Meat, poultry, fish, dry beans, eggs, and nuts	2 or 3 oz. cooked lean meat, poultry, or fish (about the size of a deck of cards). Foods that count as 1 oz. meat: 1/2 cup cooked dried beans, one egg, 2 tbsp peanut butter, 1/3 cup nuts.
Fats, oils, and sweets	No serving size given. A good rule of thumb: keep added fats (those you smear or drizzle on like butter or salad dressing) between 4 and 6 tsp. daily and added sugar between 1 and 5 tsp. daily.

Now, to lose weight on the pyramid, you have to stick with the lower-fat foods in each food group, and for some groups, go with the lower range of servings. The next table shows what 1,500 and 1,700 calories look like on a low-fat pyramid plan—pretty generous, huh?

Low-fat Pyramid Plan : Servings and Calories

	1500 Calories	1700 Calories
Bread group servings	6	8
Vegetable group servings	3	3
Fruit group servings	2	3
Milk group servings	2–3	2–3
Meat group servings	2	2
Added fat (in teaspoons)	5	5
Added sugar (in teaspoons)	4	4

With a good understanding of the USDA Food Guide Pyramid, let's discuss where flax would be found. Foods prepared with flaxseed, such as cereals, muffins, breads, and waffles, would obviously be placed at the bottom of the pyramid. Flax-based foods could help with controlling your weight, due to the high fiber content and sense of fullness you get from eating these foods. I would recommend that at least one of your servings from this group be a flax-based food. Flax oil, on the other hand, would be at the top of the pyramid. Remember, keep fat servings under control!

Well, trying to decide where flaxseed (whole or ground) belonged on the pyramid was a bit trickier than I thought it would be. After a great deal of comparison, the most appropriate place to put it would be in the meat, poultry, fish, dry beans, eggs, and nuts group. Now, I realize that we're not likely to be eating handfuls of flaxseed for a protein serving. And many of the other foods in this category (meat, fish, and the like) have no fiber content, while flaxseed is abundant in fiber and other like nutrients. But, in the end, this group seems to be the most sensible place for flax to be added to the pyramid.

Alright, now that you know where flaxseed and flax products fit into the USDA Food Guide Pyramid, you can begin to see how to build a food plan that uses them in your regular meals. But if you're still feeling a little unsure of yourself, don't despair. In chapter 5 you'll learn lots more about how to use this helpful little seed. And in the final part of this book you'll find lots of recipes that will have you cooking with flax in no time.

But before we get started in the kitchen, let us devote the next few chapters to taking a closer look at the health benefits of flaxseed. From fighting heart disease to combating cancer, and beyond, you'll soon discover just how easy it can be to flax your way to better health!

A Quick Review

- Flax has been important throughout human history as a food and medicinal substance.

- Recent research makes it clear that the nutrient composition of flaxseed provides important health benefits.

- To increase the consumption of flax in your diet, it helps to have a clear and practical plan for incorporating it in your everyday meals.

Flax Fights Cancer

2

Cancer and Nutrition
Loads of Lignans
Cancer, Chemoprotection, and You
A Lignan Primer
The ALA Factor
Breast Cancer
    Prevention
    Help for breast cancer's early stages
    Flax and late-stage breast cancer
Colon Cancer
Other Cancers
Some Anecdotal Evidence
How Much Should I Take?

T he ancient Greeks recognized long ago what we are just starting to rediscover: flax may have medicinal qualities. In ancient times, there were no scientific data to back up claims from the medicine men—there was only experience. In fact, only recently has it been possible to do a scientific study of flaxseed. Today we know scientific research has uncovered this "lowly" seed's tremendous potential as a powerful anti-cancer agent, in test tubes, animal studies, and most recently human studies. The promise for protecting humans against cancer is tantalizing, but the research that supports this promise has only just begun.

Cancer and Nutrition

Before we enter the labs, let's look at how people in various populations around the world have, over the centuries, learned how to eat. Believe it or not, this offers us clues to how flax may have helped to prevent cancer—and how it may continue to do so today.

In countries with diets rich in plant foods that share many of the same components as flax, cancer rates are lower. For instance, the Japanese and Chinese—cultures that have a lower rate of breast and prostate cancer than Americans—eat a vegetarian or semi-vegetarian diet high in soy foods, fish, vegetables, and grains. Scientists speculate that the Asian diet is one of the reasons for their reduced cancer rates. This raises an important question: What's in their food that's so protective?

Dietary research gives us the answer. Asian diets include less fat, more fiber, and an abundance of plant-derived compounds called phytoestrogens. On the other hand, Western populations, such as in the United States, typically eat a diet high in fat and low in fiber and phytoestrogens. Westerners also have higher incidences of breast and prostate cancer. In fact, the correlation between the typical American diet and these health problems has led some writers to refer to breast and prostate cancer as "the Western diseases."

Scientists currently speculate that a high intake of phytoestrogens may play a role in protecting Asian populations from breast, prostate, and other "hormone-sensitive" cancers. The growth of these cancers are stimulated by the hormone estrogen and, in the case of prostate cancer, possibly by male hormones called androgens. Scientists theorize that phytoestrogens consumed in food may help reduce cancer risk by hogging the landing sites on breast and other cells where "real" human hormones normally hang out. As a result, the cancer-stimulating hormones produced by our bodies have no place to go, and our cells receive less exposure to them.

What, you might be asking, does this have to do with flax? Simple: Flax is abundant in these phytoestrogens. In fact, it is a veritable gold mine of the substance! And, in particular, flax is extraordinarily rich in one special type of phytoestrogen called *lignans*.

Loads of Lignans

Flax contains anywhere from 75 to 800 times the amount of lignans as any tested plant food, depending on the variety of flax you choose. And it's lignans that have scientists so fired-up about flax, inspiring more than ten independent studies designed to look at flax's effects on cancer.

Why? Let's just look at the research record. H. Adlercreutz, in his article "Phytoestrogens: epidemiology and a possible role in cancer protection" (*Environmental Health Perspectives*, 1995), was so impressed with the data that he suggested that lignans are *natural cancer-protective compounds*.

Lignans first entered the limelight about two decades ago, when researchers detected their presence in the urine, blood, bile, and feces of humans. After some preliminary lab investigations, researchers proposed that these compounds may be natural anti-cancer agents in the diet. Interestingly, they also discovered that not all lignans appear to have been created equal: although several thousand lignans have been identified in the plant kingdom, very few of them are positively correlated with "chemoprotection or chemoprevention" against cancers. The lignans in flax, however, are among the happy group that *are!*

Cancer, Chemoprotection, and You

The principal lignan found in flaxseed is a mouthful of a scientific moniker: *secoisolariciresinol diglycoside*, or SDG, for short. Scientists spotted this chemical 'critter' back in 1956. About three decades later researchers discovered that mammals, including humans, also produce lignans. The two mammalian lignans are called *enterodiol* and *enterolactone*. And guess where we get the materials used by our bodies to make them? You guessed it! From flax and other lignan-containing plant foods.

Once nutrition researchers got hot on the trail of a food that appeared to protect against cancer, they began to look at how it gets the job done. They wanted to know just how it worked, and how much of it you need to get that health-giving effect. But that means figuring out how many lignans you're getting and whether or not the particular *type* of lignan in your food is the best for the health effect you desire.

Unfortunately, the issue isn't all that easy to resolve. Sure, it would be great if you could find out how many milligrams of lignans are contained in each tablespoon of flaxseed. But scientists cannot measure lignans as exactly as they can measure the amount of vitamin C per serving of orange juice. This is because flaxseed and other lignan-bearing foods contain more than one type of lignan, and scientists have yet to establish a single, standard laboratory procedure for extracting and identifying specific lignans for accurate measurement. Until such a procedure has been established, the best we can say is that flax is the richest known source of plant lignans, followed by cereal grains, many oilseeds, legumes, seaweeds, fruits, and vegetables.

A Lignan Primer

Before we go any further, however, lets cut down some of the confusion about different types of lignans in flaxseed, and how they're converted to mammalian lignans once they're consumed. Here is the basic breakdown:

Plant Lignans The main plant lignans in flaxseed are *secoisolariciresinol diglycoside* (SDG) and *matairesinol*. These plant lignans, when they've been eaten by mammals, are converted by the body into the mammalian lignans described below.

Mammalian Lignans Plant lignans consumed by mammals eventually travel into the colon, where bacteria convert them into more usable forms. In humans, SDG is changed into enterodiol (ED), while matairesinol becomes enterolactone (EL). ED may also undergo a process called oxidation and convert to EL. Once these new, human types of lignans are formed, they get processed by the body and excreted in the urine or the feces.

What's key to know is that, once they've been synthesized by the intestinal bacteria, the mammalian lignans are carried to the liver and secreted in the bile. It's at this point that they seem to do their cancer-fighting magic.

The ALA Factor

In addition to lignans, there is a fatty acid in flaxseed—alpha linolenic acid (ALA)—that may also play a role in cancer protection. In *Flaxseed in Human Nutrition* (edited by S. C. Cunnane and L. U. Thompson, 1995), University of Illinois researcher Patricia V. Johnston reviewed the performance of alpha-linolenic acid as a cancer-fighting agent. Although the evidence is very limited, Johnston concluded that, in animal studies at least, dietary ALA appears to retard tumor growth.

Johnston's findings, although not yet tested on human populations, offer tantalizing possibilities. More research needs to be done in this challenging field before we can conclude that ALA will reduce or cure cancer, but we do know that there is probably some retardant effect. Future research is needed before we can identify all the factors that may be involved in retarding tumor growth. For example, it appears that fatty acids affect the way that ALA is metabolized both in tumorous and in healthy tissue. Flaxseed oil contains several different fatty acids, including omega-3s, and their effect on the utility of ALA still needs to be studied.

Breast Cancer

Breast cancer is the Number One cancer threatening the health of women ages 40–59 in the United States. No wonder, then, that it is a hot topic in the media and in research labs throughout the country. Early scientific studies were comparative, assessing the incidence of breast cancer in the United States with its occurrence in the rest of the world. When it was discovered that people from some parts of the world had lower rates of breast cancer than others, researchers started looking at cultural factors that might explain the difference. One of the cultural factors they looked at was diet.

Here's where the story gets really interesting. Scientists discovered that the typical Western-type diet elevates plasma levels of estrogen and decreases the concentration of globulin, a substance that binds with estrogen. Lignans are known to increase this globulin, thus decreasing available estrogen. Studies show that the typical Western diet reduces the amount of mammalian lignans and isoflavonoid phytoestrogens that are produced by intestinal bacteria, as compared to the volume produced in the bodies of people accustomed to a different diet and who enjoy a lower incidence of breast cancer. This led researchers to believe that these two substances—lignans and isoflavonoid phytoestrogens—have an important role to play in fighting breast cancer.

Scientists have also begun to look at the role of dietary fats—the fats you consume from food—in promoting or inhibiting the incidence of breast cancer. There is a general consensus of opinion that a high-fat diet generally leads to obesity, which has been associated with an increased risk of several types of cancers, including postmenopausal breast cancer, endometrium and renal cancers, and possibly cancers of the colorectum, pancreas, and prostate. But, like lignans, not all dietary fats are created equal. Current studies suggest that a high intake of omega-6s plays a role in increasing the risk of cancer of the breast, colon, and possibly the prostate. On the other hand, omega-3s and monounsaturated fatty acids such as oleic acid, an omega-9 fatty acid, appear to serve a protective function.

All of this research has implications for flax. Flaxseed oil is very high in alpha-linolenic acid, one of the "protective" omega-3s. Two studies have explored the theory that alpha-linolenic acid inhibits the development of breast cancer. The first, published in the August 1994 *British Journal of Cancer*, studied 121 French women with breast cancer. When these women came in for their initial diagnosis or surgery, samples of their breast tissue were taken and examined for its fatty acid content. Later on, it was found that cancer had spread in 21 out of the 121 patients followed in the study. When the researchers checked their breast-tissue samples, they discovered that the women who developed metastases also showed lower levels of alpha-linolenic acid than their metastasis-free counterparts.

A second study, published in the February 2000 issue of the *European Journal of Cancer*, followed 123 French women with breast cancer and 59 French women with benign lumps in their breasts. Once again, breast tissue samples were taken during the first diagnostic visit, and the samples were analyzed to determine their fatty-acid content. In this study, too, women with low levels of alpha-linolenic acid had a higher breast cancer risk than the other women in the study, but none of the other fatty acids in the breast samples (saturated, monounsaturated, and polyunsaturated) showed this same relationship. These two studies most definitely suggest that a high intake of alpha-linolenic acid, alone among the fatty acids, is associated with a reduced risk of breast cancer.

Prevention

Given the exciting possibilities of lignans and alpha-linolenic acid—both found in abundance in flax—it's no wonder that researchers are investigating this humble plant's potential to prevent cancer. While no research directly addressing the prevention question has been done on humans, at least two studies of the cancer-preventative benefits of flax have been done in rats. The results so far are encouraging.

The first study, published in 1991 in *Cancer Letters*, was reported by M. Serraino and L. Thompson. Their article, "The Effect of Flaxseed Supplementation on Early Risk Markers for Mammary Carcinogenesis" documented the results of research in which several groups of rats were compared. One group was fed a basic, control diet. A second group got that basic diet, plus a 5 percent supplement of ground flaxseed. A third was fed the control diet supplemented by 10 percent ground flaxseed, and two other groups got defatted flaxseed meal, one at 5 percent and one at 10 percent. After 4 weeks, half of the rats were injected with a carcinogen that mimics breast cancer. Twenty-four hours later, the rats' cells were examined to see if any of them had changed from their normal structure or if they grew more rapidly than normal. The results of the experiment were dramatic: rats who got the flaxseed supplements showed a reduction in cell growth of between 39 and 55 percent, and a reduction in cell-structure changes of from 59 to 66 percent! The group that showed the greatest reductions was the one that received 5 percent ground flaxseed.

The researchers concluded that the reduction in cell growth rate seemed to make cells less susceptible to damage from carcinogens. Another study, by the same researchers, which was published in 1992 in the journal *Nutrition and Cancer*, was done to confirm these results. Here, too, the group of rats receiving 5 percent ground flaxseed showed the greatest reduction in cell growth rate and cell-structure changes.

Both studies also looked at the amount of lignans excreted by the rats. What researchers discovered was that these excretions significantly increased for rats who received flaxseed in their diet— and, once again, the 5 percent ground flaxseed group showed the most dramatic increase. This made researchers wonder what components of flax made the biggest differences—lignans or alpha-linolenic acid. Or are *both* equally important?

Help for breast cancer's early stages

The flaxseed component that is currently thought to be the biggest cancer-fighter is SDG, and several animal studies have been undertaken to confirm this theory. Once again, Serraino and Thompson had some interesting information to report. In their article for *Nutrition and Cancer*, mentioned earlier, they reported that cancerous rats who were fed flaxseed for 22 weeks showed a 57 percent decrease in the size of their tumors. In a similar study done four years later, L. Thompson, M. Seidl, S. Rickard, and others tried a different research approach. Their 1996 report, again carried by the

Nutrition and Cancer journal, explains that instead of feeding ground flaxseed to the rats, the researchers gave them pure SDG. In this experiment, the *size* of the rats' tumors didn't show a change, but—incredibly—the *number* did! SDG-eating rats had 47 percent *fewer* tumors than their counterparts in the control group!

The results of both experiments were encouraging—but they left the researchers scratching their heads. What could explain the difference in effects between flaxseed supplements and pure SDG? A 1999 study by S. E. Rickard, Y. V. Yuan, J. Chen, and L. Thompson, published in *Nutrition and Cancer*, was supposed to help clarify the different results. Three groups of rats were compared: a control group, a group fed flaxseed, and a group fed pure SDG. Both the flaxseed and SDG groups seemed to show a delay in the progression of tumors, but there was still no conclusive explanation for the disparity in performance between flaxseed and pure SDG. Researchers theorize that the discrepancies among all of these studies may be caused by differences in the laboratory procedures followed—the experiments did not all use the same dosage and type of carcinogen to stimulate cancer in the test animals, and each research team adopted a different design for their experiments. Nonetheless, the implication of the research is clear: SDG is a powerful anti-cancer agent.

So far, all that we have discussed are animal studies. Well, for the first time, preliminary results from human breast cancer patients were shared at the December 2000 San Antonio Breast Cancer Symposium. Professors Lillian Thompson from the University of Toronto and Paul Goss from Princess Margaret Hospital in Toronto stated "for the first time, it has been shown that flaxseed has considerable potential in reducing tumor growth in humans with breast cancer comparable to the effects seen with preoperative tamoxifen." Each day, some women with newly diagnosed breast cancer consumed 25 grams of flaxseed (about 2-1/2 tablespoons full) in a muffin, while others ate a control muffin containing no flaxseed. After 34 days, the tumors in the flaxseed group grew about 30 percent slower than the control group. These changes were comparable to those women who have used tamoxifen in similar study protocol. Thompson and Goss emphasize strongly that more research in this area must be done to confirm their results. They also noted that these results came from breast cancer patients who were not taking anticancer drugs, so flaxseed's effect when eaten in combination with cancer medication remains unknown. Therefore, caution is recommended until more studies have been done.

Flax and late-stage breast cancer

The news about flaxseed's cancer-preventive potential is very encouraging, but what can it do for people who've already been living with cancer for a while? A well designed 1996 study by leading researchers, including L. Thompson, S. Rickard, L. Orcheson, and M. Seidl, was conducted specifically to address this question. In this experiment, rats were injected with a carcinogen. After 13 weeks they had all developed a similar number of tumors of comparable size. They were then divided up into five groups, and each group received a special diet. One group got normal rat food, one received a 2.5 percent flaxseed supplement, the third got 5 percent flaxseed, the fourth got a supplement of 1.82 percent flaxseed oil, and the fifth got a 1.5 milligram supplement of pure SDG—the same amount of SDG contained in the 5 percent flaxseed supplement.

Seven weeks later, the rats' tumors were checked, and the researchers reported that all the test groups that received flaxseed supplements showed a 50 percent reduction in tumor growth when compared with the control group. What's more, the number and volume of new tumors were significantly lower in the group that was fed SDG. And the flaxseed- and SDG-eating rats seemed to have smaller tumors than the rats that were given flaxseed oil. It appears that the reduced tumor growth from flaxseed is partially due to lignans—and from SDG in particular. While no other studies have yet been done to confirm these results, it seems reasonable to conclude that flaxseed is a very powerful anti-cancer agent at *any* stage of breast cancer.

Colon Cancer

Epidemiological studies suggest that diet may play a major role in increasing the risk of colon cancer. In particular, research has shown convincingly that increasing the amount of fiber in your diet reduces your colon-cancer risk. Once again, flaxseed looks like a winner: rich in both soluble and insoluble fiber, it stands to reason that flaxseed can aid in the fight against the formation of colon cancer.

But flaxseed's high-fiber content isn't its only beneficial quality in this regard. Research also suggests that a diet low in animal fat and protein and abundant in vegetables containing vitamin A and lignans may protect against colon cancer as well.

Why lignans? To answer this question, researchers began by recognizing that mammals produce their lignans in the colon. It therefore seemed logical to conclude that the colon is where lignans have their greatest effect in the body. Studies of mammalian lignans show that they are carried from the colon to the liver, where they bond with either sulfates or glucuronic acid before they are sent back into the colon through the bile duct. Once back in the colon they encounter an enzyme (*B-glucuronidase*), which helps them to release their burden. Their work done, the lignans are reabsorbed by the body.

This helper enzyme, *B-glucuronidase*, intrigued colon-cancer researchers because it is involved in the activation and circulation of carcinogens and toxins. In the April 1992 issue of *Cancer Letters*, researchers noted that rats fed flaxseed meal or flour in a short-term study had 41 to 57 percent fewer tumors in the descending colon. While this was heartening news, four years would pass before another study was published confirming these results. This second, long-term study, reported by Mazda Jenab and Lilian Thompson in the June 1996 issue of *Carcinogenesis* also indicated that flaxseed has a colon cancer protective effect.

In this experiment, rats were injected with a colon carcinogen and, a week later, were separated into five groups, much like the experiments described earlier. Each group received a different diet composed of flaxseed or an SDG supplement in varying percentages. After 100 days, all groups showed a significant reduction in the size and number of tumors compared to the control group.

This 1996 research also noted that both the SDG-eating group and the groups that were fed flaxseed had similar results, which verified the hypothesis that it was this lignan that was responsible for the cancer protective effect of flaxseed. In addition, researchers noticed an increase in the activity of *B-glucuronidase* for the groups that ate either type of flaxseed. This last finding caused some confusion because, as noted earlier, *B-glucuronidase* is involved in the transportation of cancer and toxins throughout the body. If flaxseed protects against cancer, it would be expected that the enzyme would show less activity, not more.

To clear up this confusion, Jenab and associates conducted another experiment, which they reported in the 1999 issue of *Nutrition and Cancer*. This study showed that levels of SDG and flaxseed had a significant relationship with the activity level of *B-glucuronidase*. In other words, high levels of SDG were accompanied by increased enzyme activity, as well as by high levels of lignans excreted in the urine. The tentative conclusion reached by the researchers was that the beneficial effect of *B-glucuronidase* may come from its role in circulating more lignans throughout the body.

Other Cancers

The evidence of flaxseed's usefulness as an anticancer agent for breast and colon cancer is mounting, but these aren't the only cancer types that flaxseed appears to help fight against. Research has begun to focus on two other common cancers that appear to respond well to the nutrients found in flax: skin cancer and prostate cancer.

- *Skin cancer*: One study has investigated flaxseed's effect on the spread of melanoma cells (skin cancer) in mice. Flaxseed supplements in the diet were linked to fewer and smaller tumors.

- *Prostate Cancer*: Suggestive data in cross-cultural cancer research have shown that Asian men from China, Japan, and Thailand seem to have a much lower incidence of prostate cancer, compared to men from the Europe and North America. Vegetarian men also have a lower incidence of prostate cancer than men who include meat in their diet. A low-fat, high-fiber diet that provides a rich supply of weak dietary phytoestrogens (isoflavonoids, flavonoids, and lignans) seems to be the key. It also appears that omega-3 fatty acids may slow down prostate cancer. Total calories and saturated fats in the diet have also been marked as possible risk factors for prostate cancer.

Only one clinical study has been done specifically focusing on flaxseed's relationship to prostate cancer. Researchers at the Duke University Medical Center and the Durham V.A. Medical Center had a group of newly diagnosed prostate cancer patients follow a fat-restricted (20 percent or less) diet that included 30 grams of flaxseed per day (that's about 3 tablespoons worth). Before prostate surgery, 25 men followed this diet for an average of 34 days. The list of researchers involved in this study reads like a *Who's Who* of flax-based science: Wendy Demark-Wahnefried, David Price, Thomas Polascik, Cary Robertson, E. Everett Anderson, David Paulson, Philip Walther, Melissa Gannon, and Robin Vollmer. Their report, published in the journal *Urology* in 2001, shows that the flaxseed diet had favorable effects on the patients' hormonal levels and slowed down the growth of cancer cells. These are promising results, but more research is needed to verify them.

Some Anecdotal Evidence

Personal stories don't qualify as scientific evidence, but they sure can provide food for thought. Here are some that may intrigue you:

- Cyndi T. was diagnosed with colon cancer in December 1997, and was told she had only a few months to live. She and her husband, Thom, immediately started reading everything they could find about cancer and the immune system. On the basis of what they learned, they began making changes in their diets, adding all sorts of dietary supplements. I first met them in June 1998, at a lecture I gave on nutrition and cancer. They asked me to help them work out their present and future nutrition regimens, so I made a few suggestions. A little later, Cyndi reported that she had begun including flax in her diet, hoping that its high omega-3 content would help strengthen her immune system. Perhaps it helped: Cyndi was with all of us much longer than anticipated. Sadly, however, she eventually lost her battle in November of 1999.

- By 1995 Diana D. had had *three* diagnoses of cancer, two of them being breast cancer. She decided to make some nutrition and lifestyle changes to optimize her chances for long term recovery. Diana first heard about flax in an article she read in the September 1995 issue of *Prevention Magazine*, and she started exploring the topic further in the medical and nutritional literature. She ultimately decided to include flaxseed in her diet, starting out by adding a tablespoon of ground seeds to her specially-formulated morning shakes (see Chapter 7 for recipes). Later on, she started adding ground flax seeds to many other dishes, such as veggies, muffins, and pancakes, and she sprinkled ground flaxseed on top of yogurt and fruit. Today, Diana remains cancer-free and considers flaxseed to have been a key element in her cancer-fighting success.

- Mary Bell was also diagnosed with breast cancer, and her oncologist advised her that she ran a high risk of recurrence. Although she received conventional medical treatment, she wanted to do more, so she set out in search of alternative therapies. Her search eventually took her onto the Internet, where she found a breast-cancer's survivors group. There she met a woman who had a worse prognosis than she did—stage IV breast cancer—but who had been successfully using diet and supplements, including flax, for the previous nine years. Inspired by her Internet friend's example, Mary Bell began adding ground flax in her soy shakes and cottage cheese. Although she had to start out slowly (flax has a laxative effect, so she needed to develop a tolerance to it), she reports that she feels better today than ever before and remains cancer-free.

How Much Should I Take?

As of now, there are no definite guidelines established by science that tell us exactly how much flax it takes to help protect against cancer. However, research seems to indicate the following:

Whole or ground flaxseed: 2 tablespoons, daily

Cancer isn't the only serious medical condition that flaxseed can help you fight. Researchers are also excited by its possible uses in coping with heart disease. In the next chapter, you'll get a peek into the labs and scientific studies to find out just how much help flax can provide in keeping your heart healthy.

A Quick Review

- Scientists have long recognized a relationship between nutrition and the incidence of cancer.

- Flaxseed is high in lignans—particularly SDG—that are believed to play a role in fighting cancer.

- Alpha linolenic acid (ALA) appears to have a powerful cancer-protective effect, potentially capable of retarding tumor growth.

- The anti-cancer effects of SDG have been noted for a broad range of cancer types, from breast to prostate and even skin cancers.

Flax Fights Heart Disease

3

The Number One killer in America, heart disease, affects us all. Every one of us has family or friends who battle this disease. It's no wonder, then, that the scientific community is spending a lot of time and money looking for new weapons to help fight this deadly disease. And it's no wonder that they're looking closely at flax as they search for solutions: flaxseed contains some powerful substances that can ward off heart disease.

Heart-Healthy Substances

As you already know from earlier chapters, flaxseed is particularly rich in fiber and the omega-3 fatty acid, alpha-linolenic acid (ALA). Both of these are known to have important beneficial properties in fighting heart disease. But don't just take my word for it. Look at how the research bears this claim out!

Let's Ask the Nurses

One of the earliest indications of flax's potential role in the prevention and treatment of cardiovascular disease came as a result of epidemiological studies of the health-giving properties of alpha-linolenic acid. One study in particular, known as "the Nurse's Health Study," conducted by researchers in Harvard's School of Public Health, had some intriguing results. In this study, 76,283 female nurses noted their dietary choices in food diaries for a period of 10 years. It was discovered that the participants who consumed foods higher in ALA, mostly in the form of oil-and-vinegar salad dressing, showed a reduced incidence of fatal ischemic heart disease—that is, heart attack caused by an obstruction of the major arteries—when compared with the experience of participants who had low ALA intakes.

Another study was conducted by researchers at the Veterans Affairs Medical Center in San Francisco, California. Using data from an earlier research program called MRFIT (short for Multiple Risk Factor Intervention Trial), this study focused on factors contributing to or reducing the risk of strokes in men. Researchers discovered that middle-aged men who had elevated levels of ALA in their blood enjoyed a 37 percent reduction in the incidence of strokes. Once again, flax, with its high ALA content, looks like a good candidate for reducing your risk of heart problems.

Even more interesting is the "Lyon Diet Heart Study," which focused on people living in the Mediterranean region and was first reported in the journal *Circulation* in 1994. The researchers were struck by the fact that the death rate from cardiovascular disease is very low in the countries that border the Mediterranean area, compared to other countries. The first report showed that people who consumed a Mediterranean-type diet that is rich in fruits and vegetables, low in saturated fat, and rich in monounsaturated fat (from olive oil) had nearly 70 percent fewer myocardial infarctions (MI) and cardiac deaths, even though there was no corresponding reduction in blood cholesterol and triglycerides.

A follow-up report was published in 1999, confirming the original research results. Clearly, a diet rich in ALA had a significant influence upon the risk of heart attack and cardiac-related deaths.

Oil or Seed?

One thing that increases your risk of heart disease is the amount of fats in your blood. The lower your blood-fat level, the lower your risk for heart disease. Foods that reduce your blood-fat levels seem a logical choice if you are looking to make your diet more heart healthy. We already know that omega-3 fatty acids help lower blood-fat levels, which is why foods high in omega-3s—like salmon—are recommended for people at risk of heart disease. Since flax oil is a very rich source of omega-3 fatty acid, in the form of ALA, then it seems only reasonable to assume that flax oil may provide similar benefits to what you get from fish oils. This is where the surprise came in.

In *Flaxseed in Human Nutrition*, edited by S. C. Cunnane and L. U. Thompson, and published in 1995, two researchers reported their findings on the effect of dietary ALA on blood fats and lipoproteins in humans. The authors of the article, Gary Nelson and Jack Chamberlain, found that flax oil appears to have little effect on blood-fat levels as measured by total cholesterol, LDL cholesterol, and HDL cholesterol levels. At high dosages, flax oil seems to lead to a small reduction in serum triglycerides, another blood-fat level indicating heart disease risk.

Since Nelson and Chamberlain's 1995 review, there have been several further studies of the effects of flax oil on human blood-fat levels, and these have all supported the original results. That would appear to be disappointing to flax-for-heart-health proponents, but read on: the research suggests that even though blood-fat changes are not very significant, other heart-health properties may lurk in our friend, flax.

For example, flax oil seems to be helpful in improving blood circulation, which lowers your cardiovascular risk. The key to improving blood circulation is to keep your arteries and veins in good order, and that's where flax comes in. An Australian study reported in the August 1998 issue of the *British Journal of Nutrition* looked at the effects of flax oil supplements on the arteries of 15 obesity sufferers. The research concluded that after 4 weeks of a low-fat diet supplemented with 2 tablespoons of flax oil, the study subjects' arteries were more elastic and pliable.

And that's not the only benefit from flax oil. Another Australian study, done at the University of Sydney, looked at the effect of flax oil on blood clotting. In this study, 29 young males consumed approximately 3 tablespoons of either flax or safflower oil for 23 days. Safflower oil is rich in the omega-6 fatty acid known as linoleic acid, while flax is, as you will recall, rich in ALA (alpha-linolenic acid). The researchers found that the test subjects who consumed flax oil showed more than double the amount of a substance called EPA in the blood. EPA is derived from ALA and helps inhibit blood clots from forming. The implication of the research is great news for flax: since it's rich in ALA, flax oil may be an effective ally in the fight against cardiovascular disease because it helps cut down on the number of clots that may form.

And flax oil may help prevent another heart ailment: arrhythmia. Arrhythmia is sometimes caused by blockage in the arteries around the heart. A few researchers have begun investigating the possibility that omega-3 fatty acids can help in this area, too. While no human studies have been done as yet, scientists at Ohio State University conducted an animal study, reported in *Circulation* in May of 1999, that produced some very interesting results. Pure concentrations of either flax oil or fish oils were given intravenously to a small group of dogs, while another group got soybean oil instead. Both groups of dogs were then subjected to mechanical stimulation of their hearts in order to induce ventricular fibrillation—an irregularity in the rhythm of the heartbeat. Such irregular rhythms, at the intensity induced by the researchers, should have been fatal—as, indeed, they were for many of the dogs that were given soybean oil. The majority of the dogs that had been given flax or fish oils survived, however, leading researchers to conclude that the omega-3 fatty acids from these substances provided the dogs with some protection.

Flaxseed Findings

Like flax oil, flaxseed seems to show great promise in the fight against heart disease. Two studies, presented at the 54th Flax Institute of the United States, held in 1992, showed a glimmer of flax's potential for use in the prevention and treatment of heart disease. The first study was done by Holly A. Dieken of the Food and Nutrition Department at North Dakota State University. Test subjects were separated into two groups, one group consisting of individuals who showed normal levels of blood fats, the other consisting of people who had high levels of cholesterol. In both groups, the individuals consumed two muffins per day, getting a total of 45 grams (approximately 5 ½ tablespoons) of ground flaxseed. The "normal" subjects showed no marked changes in their blood, but the high-cholesterol individuals showed some pretty dramatic improvements. Their blood-serum triglycerides dropped by 17 percent! That is a strong suggestion that the omega-3s and fiber in the muffins were conferring a real heart-healthy benefit!

A second study shows how flax can be used in conjunction with other foods to increase its beneficial effects. In this study, conducted by Faustina Aryee-Bohannon and Mary L. Gengler through the Agricultural Experiment Station at South Dakota State University, researchers worked with a group of test subjects who showed moderately high cholesterol levels in their blood. The subjects were divided into three groups. One group was told to incorporate 50 grams (approximately 6 tablespoons) of ground flaxseed into their diet each day, the second was told to use the same amount of oat bran instead, and the third group was given a combination of flaxseed and oat bran.

The results of the study were very encouraging. Blood cholesterol levels went down 4 percent for the groups that added flax or oat bran alone, but the group that ate a combination of the two did even better: their blood cholesterol levels dropped a full seven percent. In addition, both the flax-eaters and the combination group showed a great improvement in their blood triglyceride levels: these went down 40 percent for both groups! And the group that ate both flax and oat bran showed one other great improvement: their HDL (good cholesterol) levels went up 17 percent, while their LDL (bad cholesterol) levels dropped by the same amount!

The encouraging results of these early studies have inspired other scientists to look more closely at the benefits of flax. In 1993, researchers at the University of Toronto asked a number of female subjects to consume 50 grams (approximately 6 tablespoons) of ground flaxseed each day for 4 weeks. One group got their flaxseed in supplement form; the other ate it baked into bread. Regardless of the form in which they got their flax, at the end of the study both groups showed similar improvements. Their blood cholesterol levels dropped a total of 9 percent, while their levels of LDL cholesterol decreased a whopping 18 percent.

In the same year, the *Journal of the American College of Nutrition* published a study of its own. Researchers here selected a group of human test subjects who had high levels of cholesterol or blood fats. For the first three months of the study, subjects took 800 IU's of vitamin E each day. During the next 3 months subjects continued taking their daily dose of vitamin E, but now they also added 15 grams (approximately 2 tablespoons) of ground flaxseed. After the first 3 months on vitamin E supplements alone, the test subjects showed no significant changes in their blood-fat levels. At the end of the six months, however, the picture was very different. The test subjects showed a 7 percent drop in their total cholesterol levels and a 10 percent drop in their levels of LDL cholesterol! In addition, their triglycerides went down 12 percent!

Back up at the University of Toronto, another team of researchers recently examined flaxseed from a whole new perspective, reporting their results in the 1999 *American Journal of Clinical Nutrition*. All previous flaxseed studies looked only at the full-fat version of the seed, whereas these researchers decided to use a partially defatted version. Their study subjects were put on a low-cholesterol diet, to which they were instructed to add either flaxseed or wheat-bran muffins. Regardless of whether a subject went with flaxseed or wheat-bran, everyone showed a reduction in total cholesterol of 6 percent. LDL levels showed an even greater reduction: 10 percent.

What is the significance of this study? Clearly, the study's findings suggest that flax may be offering a lot more than the obvious beneficial substances like alpha-linolenic acids. After all, partially defatted flaxseed has less ALA than flaxseed that has not been defatted, yet the subjects who ate defatted flaxseed got almost as good results in lowering total blood cholesterol (down 6 percent) and LDL (down 10 percent) as did their counterparts in other studies where non-defatted flaxseed was used.

Loosen Up Those Arteries!

We've been concentrating on flaxseed's utility in reducing blood cholesterol levels, but there's evidence that there are more heart-healthy benefits to be gained as well. At the University of Saskatchewan, researchers led by K. Prasad tested the effects of flaxseed on rabbits. In the July 1997 volume of the journal *Atherosclerosis*, Prasad and his colleagues reported that flaxseed appears to be at least partly responsible for a 46 percent reduction in the clogging of the main aortic artery. A year later, Prasad and his team published a second study in that same journal, reporting that their rabbits showed a 69 percent reduction in the development of atherosclerosis (what we commonly call "hardening of the arteries"). For this study, the researchers used flaxseed that had been processed to contain extremely low alpha-linolenic acid content, so we know that it's not the ALA in flaxseed that got these great results. It is to be hoped that future researchers will look into the as yet unidentified health-giving components of flaxseed.

Prasad and his team followed these first two studies with an investigation of flaxseed's lignans. Once again using rabbits, they isolated the SDG lignan from flaxseed and incorporated it into their rabbit food. After 4 weeks they tested their rabbits' blood and found that total cholesterol had been lowered 33 percent, LDL cholesterol had dropped 35 percent, and atherosclerosis was reduced by an amazing 73 percent. At the same time, HDL cholesterol levels rose by an incredible 140 percent! Clearly, there's enough encouraging news here to warrant future studies—studies that will target the specific components within flaxseed that play a beneficial role in the prevention and treatment of heart disease.

More Anecdotal Evidence

Here are some more intriguing personal stories of individual experiences with flax and health.

- Millie W. first came to me for help in losing weight and became a regular monthly client. She also attended one of my flaxseed classes at Greatest Grains because she was looking for natural alternatives to help lower her cholesterol. After the class, she started adding 2 tablespoons of flaxseed daily to her diet, drinking it in a shake. Interestingly, she made no other dietary changes at the time. Still, within a year her total cholesterol went down 5 percent, and her LDL went down 8 percent.

- Jerome T. was plagued with a genetic predisposition toward high blood lipids, and his father had died of heart disease at an early age. This made him very determined to make some lifestyle changes to improve his heart health. I suggested adding soy foods and flax seed to his diet, and he began eating flax bread and oatmeal with flaxseed sprinkled on top every day. After 6 months, Jerome's total cholesterol went down 3 percent and his triglycerides went down 23 percent.

- I met Roy S.'s wife June at my first flaxseed class. Roy had high blood lipids as well as a high prostate count, indicating prostate cancer. June and Roy were looking for natural alternatives, for they did not want to begin any medications without trying natural methods first. So Roy started using 1 tablespoon of flax oil on his vegetables and ate 1 tablespoon ground flaxseed every day. Results after 6 months were amazing: total cholesterol went down 31 percent, triglycerides went down at least 20 percent, and LDL cholesterol went down at least 10 percent!

How Much Should I Take?

As of now, there are no definite guidelines established by science that tell us exactly how much flax it takes to help protect against heart disease. However, research seems to indicate the following:

Whole or ground flaxseed: 3 tablespoons, daily

A Quick Review

- Flaxseed is high in alpha-linolenic acid (ALA) and fiber, both important in fighting heart disease.

- Flax oil has shown little effect on blood-fat levels, yet may be effective in cutting down blood clots.

- Clinical studies consistently show flaxseed helping with the battle against heart disease, by lowering blood-fats, such as total cholesterol, LDL cholesterol, and triglycerides.

From Diabetes to Menopause

4

Heart disease and cancer aren't the only health problems that flax may help fight. The high-quality nutrients of this humble seed may play an important role in combating a great many other conditions and chronic diseases that plague millions of Americans, including diabetes, arthritis and other inflammatory ailments, kidney disease, and even menopause! In this chapter we'll take a look at just what scientists are beginning to discover.

Flax Fights Diabetes

It has been discovered that the omega-3 fat and high fiber content in flax may play a role in the fight against diabetes. How? These substances help to control the level of blood sugar, cholesterol, and triglycerides in your body. Here's the lowdown on how this works.

Blood sugar regulation

Diabetes comes in two forms: Type I, or childhood diabetes; and Type II, otherwise known as adult-onset diabetes. In both forms of the disease, the treatment goal is to bring high levels of blood sugar under control. Flax may help in reaching this treatment goal. In a 1993 study conducted by researchers of the University of Toronto, test subjects—healthy, non-diabetic people—were given one of two types of bread at breakfast. The first group got bread made with a total of about five tablespoons of ground flaxseed, while the second group got bread made with white wheat flour. The findings clearly showed that flax had an immediate impact on blood sugar levels: when tested an hour after breakfast, the blood sugar levels of subjects getting flaxseed-based bread fell 28 percent compared with their counterparts.

Two years later, the same researchers replicated their results in a somewhat longer (four weeks) trial. This time, test subjects ate either flaxseed muffins or muffins made of regular wheat-flour at breakfast. Once again, blood sugar levels in the flaxseed group were lower after breakfast.

While the researchers have clearly demonstrated that flax had a significant effect on blood sugar levels, they are still not sure just what is causing this benefit. They are beginning to suspect, however, that the water-soluble fibers in flax may play a key role. One of these fiber types, called *mucilage*, is contained in the outer part of the seed. When scientists take concentrated mucilage and add it to sugar water, they have found that the percentage of the sugar in the water decreases by about 27 percent! What's happening? The high viscosity of the mucilage appears to entrap the sugar, keeping it from spreading freely throughout the water. In your body, this same effect slows the absorption of sugar, slowing its passage into the blood.

While flax certainly seems to help manage blood sugar levels for diabetics, not all forms of flax currently on the market are likely to provide the same benefit. Flax oil, for example, lacks the fibers of the flax seed, and it appears to have no effect on blood sugar levels. So far there's not a product that isolates the fiber from flax, and I somehow doubt that murky mucilage or drinks based on soluble flax fiber will appeal to the designer-beverage crowd. The most palatable way to go is simply to add—you guessed it—flaxseed to your diet.

Fighting blood fats

In addition to high blood sugar, diabetics tend to have higher than normal levels of blood fats or lipids: cholesterol and triglycerides. Compounding the problem, these substances also raise the risk of heart disease, so there's twice the reason to try to get them under control. And here, too, flax can help.

As you've already learned, ground flaxseed appears to have phenomenal powers to lower cholesterol and triglyceride-levels. That would appear to make flaxseed just what the doctor ordered for diabetics. On the other hand, flaxseed oil, once again, seems to be far less useful than ground flaxseed. In two University of Alberta, Canada, studies published in 1996 and 1997, diabetics supplemented their diets with either a flaxseed oil or fish oil supplement for three months. Neither of the supplements had any effect on cholesterol levels, and only the fish oil lowered triglycerides. This suggests that you're best advised to use the more complete flaxseed variant rather than relying on the limited nutrients found in the oil.

Flax and insulin

Insulin is your body's most important ally when it comes to regulating blood sugar. Insulin acts like an "usher," escorting sugar from the blood into the body's cells, where it can be used for energy. People with Type I diabetes, however, produce little or none of this helpful hormone. Sugar therefore builds up in the blood, and the cells don't get the fuel they need.

In Type II diabetes, the body produces insulin, but some cells simply refuse to interact with it. When the hormone tries to transport sugar from the blood to the cells where it belongs, the cells refuse to recognize it and won't let the sugar pass through their walls. In this case, once again, the blood sugar doesn't get into the cells and remains in the bloodstream.

Research on animals suggest that flax is helpful in this second scenario. A South Dakota State University study, presented at the 55th Conference of the Flax Institute of the United States in 1994, found that the addition of flaxseed to a rat's diet appears to re-sensitize "insulin resistant" receptors in the animal's cells. This is great news for diabetics, because the more insulin receptors you have available, the better control you have over your blood sugar levels. Still, this research is only preliminary. More studies need to be done to confirm such important findings.

Babies and Beyond

Once I got into researching the beneficial effects of flaxseed, it seemed as if everybody had something new to tell me that related to my studies. Even my 4-year-old son's speech pathologist, Sharon, got into the act. She had run across a brochure at her local health food store that claimed that flax oil could help children with attention deficit disorder (ADD). This is a subject close to my heart, since my own son is a special needs child. I decided to follow up and check out this claim.

What I discovered was inconclusive, but intriguing. Studies seem to indicate that there is a link between low blood levels of the essential fats—particularly the omega-3s—and childhood learning and behavioral problems. One such study, carried out at Purdue University and reported in the April/May 1996 issue of *Physiology and Behavior*, specifically found that children who had a greater amount of behavioral, learning, and health problems also had lower total omega-3 fat levels.

The research on this subject is still in its infancy, so we can't simply assume that increasing a child's omega-3 dietary intake will make learning and behavioral problems disappear. Still, it appears to be a good idea to include foods with high omega-3 content—foods like flaxseed—in your child's diet.

Just a Regular Guy . . .

The American Dietetic Association recommends that adults need to consume about 20 to 35 grams of fiber per day. According to the latest USDA surveys, most people get only half the fiber they need. Too little insoluble fiber in the diet leads to constipation. Here, again, flax is a great dietary resource: a single tablespoon contains 2 to 3 grams of *both* soluble and insoluble fiber.

The generous dose of insoluble fiber contained in flax can help relieve constipation, while the soluble fiber helps to lower your cholesterol. In a study published in the January 1995 issue of the *American Journal of Clinical Nutrition*, researchers from the Department of Nutrition Science at the University of Toronto reported that a diet including flaxseed supplements of about 50 grams (about 5 tablespoons) of flaxseed per day—that's just a couple of muffins—increased bowel movements by 30 percent.

Of course, you want to phase in any increased intake in fiber, so that your body has a chance to get used to your new dietary regimen. Otherwise, you may find yourself running to the bathroom a little too frequently! And any increase in dietary fiber should always be accompanied with an increase in water consumption. You want to get six or more glasses of water a day to help the fiber pass through the intestines. Believe it or not, without enough liquids, fiber can actually *cause* constipation.

Easing Inflammation

It's a fact: omega-6 fats may actually increase inflammation problems. But omega-3s are known to help *reduce* them. That's why even such health experts as former Surgeon General C. Everett Koop suggest eating foods high in omega-3s for people suffering from rheumatoid arthritis. Could flaxseed help with this and other inflammatory conditions, like multiple sclerosis, psoriasis, colitis, and kidney problems? Let's examine the evidence.

Rheumatoid arthritis

My mother-in-law, Rita, has been dealing with rheumatoid arthritis for more than 20 years. An antique collector and folk artist, Rita was finding it difficult to finish her projects, due to the stiffness and pain in her joints. She describes what it feels like: "You're in constant pain, and you feel like you just can't do *anything*. It's no picnic, I'll tell you. The worst part is dealing with the lumps and bumps on my hands, knees, and elbows." When I told her about my research into flaxseed and it's possible use in easing arthritis, she really wanted to hear more.

My first encounter with the connection between flax and rheumatoid arthritis was while I was teaching a flax class at Greatest Grains, a local health food store. It's the old story of the teacher learning from her students. A few class participants were chatting among themselves about a shared problem with arthritis pain and mentioned that flax and fish-oil pills gave them some relief. Could it be that here, again, flax has something to offer? At home, after class, I logged on to my computer to check out the research on the subject.

I discovered that my students were absolutely correct: research strongly suggests that omega-3 fats really do fight inflammation— and it's the inflammation within joints that contributes to joint pain and immobility. There is consistent evidence that one type of omega-3 fats, derived from fish oils, reduces tenderness in the joints and eases the morning stiffness that accompanies rheumatoid arthritis. For example, in January 2000, researchers from the Division of Rheumatology at Albany Medical College in New York reported that rheumatoid arthritis patients who consumed fish oil supplements not only obtained moderate pain relief, they were also able to reduce or even discontinue their regularly prescribed anti-inflammatory drugs!

But while there's been a lot of research on the utility of omega-3s from fish oil, only a few studies have been done to determine if the same results could be achieved using flaxseed oil. Still, the studies I found were encouraging. For example, researchers affiliated with the rheumatology unit of the Royal Adelaide Hospital in Australia reported in the January 1996 issue of the *American Journal of Clinical Nutrition* the results of their four-week, healthy-human-subject study of flax oil in the diet. They found that flax oil supplements definitely reduced inflammatory substances by as much as 30 percent. While flaxseed oil didn't perform quite as well as fish-oil supplements, the effect was still impressive—so much so that the researchers returned to the *Journal* four years later to recommend that flaxseed oil be used as an adjunct to conventional anti-inflammatory drugs in the treatment of rheumatoid arthritis pain.

Flax and kidney disease

I got into my research on flax convinced that this was a potentially useful food, but never in my wildest dreams did I imagine just *how* many ways flax in the diet could help to deal with serious medical problems. I first learned about the potential for help with kidney ailments almost by accident. I got a call from my dear friend Ginny, who's 78 years young but troubled with a kidney condition. She knew I was looking into "unconventional" foods and wanted my advice. Her doctor had recommended that she start adding flax to her diet to help improve her kidney function.

What great timing! I had just begun to dig into the research on flax's role in combating disease, and particularly it's potential for dealing with inflammation, thanks to all those helpful omega-3s in the oil. Since kidney disease has an inflammatory factor, it was right up my research alley, so to speak.

At the outset, I ran into a few problems in finding research that dealt specifically with flax—most studies concentrate on the omega-3s in fish oil. Studies on lab animals have consistently shown that fish-oil supplements do, indeed, help slow down the progression of kidney disease, and that the substance responsible for this is—you guessed it, the omega-3s.

In recent years, flax's wealth of omega-3 fats and lignans have sent Canadian researchers from two Ontario hospitals into the lab. Their results, presented at the 55th Conference of the Flax Institute of the U.S. (1994), are definitely encouraging. They've discovered that by giving flax to animals with kidney disease they could slow down the progression of the disease—and, as an added bonus, the healthy parts of the kidney were energized enough to run at top speed. Once again, flaxseed itself was found to be more effective than extracted flaxseed oil.

Since animal research was so promising, the Canadian researchers took their investigation a step further to examine the effects of flaxseed on humans. Two studies to date have been done on patients with lupus nephritis, an inflammation of the kidneys that is caused by lupus, which strikes mostly young women between the ages of 15 and 35. While not all lupus sufferers contract lupus nephritis, about half of them do, and the disease manifests itself in an inflammation of the renal blood vessels, leading ultimately to kidney failure in many cases.

The first study, done in 1996 and reported at the 56th Conference of the Flax Institute of the U.S., had the support of the Kidney Foundation of Canada and the Victoria Hospital Research Institute. It was designed simply to test the waters: it was short term (approximately four months) and involved only a limited number of subjects (nine in all). Study participants were given a variety of levels of ground flaxseed in their diet: some got as few as 15 grams per day, some as much as 45. Interestingly, even at the lowest supplement level there were clear signs that the progression of the disease was slowed! Because participants found it difficult to eat 45 grams of flaxseed every single day, and because beneficial effects were clearly seen even at lower levels of consumption, researchers struck a happy medium, recommending a daily supplement of 30 grams flaxseed, or about three tablespoons.

Spurred on by the success of this first study, the researchers decided to set up a longer-term, two-year study to see if the beneficial effects of flaxseed could be maintained over time. In the new study, participants during the first year were given two 15-gram (about 3 tablespoons) servings of flaxseed daily, mixed in cereal or added to juice. During the second year they got no flaxseed supplement. The results, reported by W. F. Clark, C. Kortas, A. P. Heidenheim, J. Garland, E. Spanner, and A. Parbtani in the April 2001 issue of the Journal of the American College of Nutrition, were not as phenomenal as those achieved in the first study, but there was some good news—renal function improved dramatically in patients who ate flaxseed. Unfortunately, some of the participants simply couldn't keep up with the 30-gram-per-day regimen.

Clearly, flaxseed was offering significant health improvements. It was just that participants had trouble incorporating adequate amounts into their diets. So the next step was to identify the specific substances within flaxseed that were providing the benefits. That way, maybe, the daily volume required could be reduced. Back in the research lab, the hunt was on: the researchers began trying to isolate flaxseed's individual components to find the ones that got the best results.

The scientists discovered that one particular component was providing the most benefit: our old friend SDG, the main flaxseed lignan. In a report published in the journal *Lupus* in 2000, researchers W. F. Clark, A. D. Muir, N. D. Westcott, and A. Parbtani showed that SDG alone delayed the progression of kidney disease and preserved the healthy parts of the kidney just as well as the whole flaxseed did, and at much lower volumes. Unfortunately, SDG cannot be purchased in isolated form just yet, so if you want the health-giving effect, you're going to have to go with ground flaxseed.

Now, back to my friend Ginny. Wanting to act on her doctor's recommendations, but unsure how to make flax a regular part of her diet, she asked me what to do. I told her that flax oil alone wasn't going to do the trick. Instead, I suggested that she start keeping ground flax handy to add to her food as a cereal topping, in sauces and soups, in juices—just sprinkle a tablespoon into just about anything she's eating or drinking at the time. Those tablespoons-full add up over the course of the day!

Well, Ginny took my advice, and she reports that it was pretty easy to get into the habit. And the results have been great! She used to have to go to the kidney center for treatment every 3 months, but now she only has to go every 6 months. Sure, some of this progress may be due to her medication, but chances are that the flax supplements to her diet have helped a lot, too—just ask those Canadian researchers!

Making It Through Menopause

Two of my older sisters, hearing about my flax research, came to me with a question that I'm sure many of you may be asking right about now: can flaxseed help deal with the symptoms of menopause—the hot flashes, the night sweats, the moodiness, and the irritability? We've all heard that certain foods like tofu and other soy products can help minimize these symptoms. How about flax?

We know that many of the symptoms of menopause are the result of fluctuations in a woman's hormone levels, especially estrogen. Research over the past several years has taught us that phytoestrogens—estrogen-like substances found in plants—can act as a kind of natural hormone therapy, stabilizing the body's hormonal levels and counteracting the physical manifestations of menopause.

Cross-cultural research shows that women whose traditional diet features a high intake of soy and flax have, on average, a milder menopausal experience. This conclusion is supported by scientific studies. Take, for example, the research of D. M. Tham, C. D. Gardner, and W. L. Haskell of the Stanford Center for Research in Disease Prevention at Stanford University Medical School. These scientists drew upon experiments in molecular and cellular biology, animal studies, and some human clinical trials. Their conclusions, published in the July 1998 issue of the *Journal of Clinical Endocrinological Metabolism* concluded that "phytoestrogens may potentially confer health benefits related to . . . menopausal symptoms."

A systematic review of the research, conducted by M. M. Seidl and D. E. Stewart of the Toronto Hospital and published in the June

1998 issue of the *Canadian Family Physician,* makes this point even more emphatically: "In available controlled studies, the strongest data support phytoestrogens for their role in diminishing menopausal symptoms related to estrogen deficiency. . . ." It would be nice to think that phytoestrogens would help *all* women get rid of those nasty night sweats and moodiness, but that doesn't seem likely. However, as many as two-thirds of menopausal women may benefit from a diet containing high levels of these substances.

That's where flax comes in. Like soy, flax has very high levels of phytoestrogens. In fact, flax's phytoestrogen levels are even *higher* than soy, which has long been touted as a great boon to menopausal women. Let's take a peek at the science that underlies flax's claim to fame in relieving the symptoms of menopause.

Here's a hot (news) flash

Perhaps the most familiar of all the menopausal symptoms is the hot flash (and its bedtime cousin, night sweats). There have been claims that soy and flaxseed can help with these, but the scientific data simply aren't available yet. Still, I've heard lots of first-hand stories among the women in my flax classes suggesting that regular consumption of flaxseed seems to help ease the frequency and severity of these symptoms. It certainly can't hurt, and you just might start noticing some improvement.

Overcoming osteoporosis

With the onset of menopause, women are also at increased risk of developing osteoporosis, a condition in which the bones become brittle and thus more susceptible to breakage. Once again, the sex hormone estrogen is an important factor. As women's natural production of human estrogen declines, phytoestrogen supplements can be very helpful. Researchers from Oklahoma State University and the University of Illinois conducted a 12-week study of the effects of flaxseed on bone metabolism in postmenopausal women and reported their results in the *Conference Proceedings of the 57th Flax Institute of the United States* (1998).

In this study, postmenopausal women who were not using traditional hormone replacement therapy were divided into two groups. The women in one group supplemented their daily diet with 38 grams (about 4 Tbsp) of flaxseed; the other group got the same amount of sunflower seed that had been baked into breads and muffins. Bone formation and bone loss measurements were taken at the end of the clinical trial. The women who ate flaxseed showed greater bone formation and less bone loss than those who ate sunflower seeds. Once again, more research is needed, but the powerful results of this study surely warrant more investigation.

Questionable Claims

It's only to be expected, unfortunately: whenever a new food—even one with proven health benefits—reaches public awareness, there's always somebody out there ready to tout it as some kind of miracle cure. Sadly, inflated claims have a tendency to make even the best dietary addition start to look a little dubious. In the interest of full disclosure, I'm presenting here a few less-than-proven claims you just might run into when you're checking out the fliers and handouts at your local health food store.

The heartbreak of psoriasis?

Given my chosen line of work, it's not surprising that I'm on the mailing lists of lots of companies that promote dietary supplements. One day I found an advertising with the following headlined claim: "After only *7 days* you will have smoother skin with less flaking and scaling, a virtual cure-all for all your psoriasis problems." This brochure, put out by a flax-supplement manufacturer, virtually promised that flax was a miracle cure for skin problems. Well, I'm a big fan of flax, but I'm also a professional dietitian, so promises of miraculous cures always raise a red flag for me. No way was I going to take this claim without a pretty hefty grain of salt.

Back at my computer, I did some research to see if there's any science to back up the brochure's claims. The idea behind the claims seems to be that an improper balance of fats in the body (too many omega-6s, not enough omega-3s) may contribute to psoriasis. If that's true, it might be reasonable to think that flaxseed, rich in omega-3s, would help, right? But the research doesn't bear this out. There are *no* studies focusing specifically on flax and psoriasis, and the handful of studies on omega-3's in general—derived from fish oil—are *not* encouraging. Results have been contradictory at best, and an article in the June 1993 issue of *New England Journal of Medicine* flatly stated that there was simply no correlation between omega-3 supplements (from fish oil) and improvements in the condition of psoriasis patients.

Inflammatory bowel diseases

You may run into some claims that flaxseed will help with inflammatory bowel diseases (IBDs), which include ulcerative colitis and Crohn's disease. These are inflammations of the intestines and colon that can cause fatigue, cramping, weight loss, diarrhea and fever. Doctors still do not know exactly what causes IBDs—but cross-cultural studies show that Eskimos rarely get them. One distinctive factor in the Eskimo diet, compared to the Western diet, is the high amount of omega-3 fats they consume, since they eat a great deal of fish. Could there be a possible link?

Maybe. But, once again, we are far from having proof. As with psoriasis research, the few studies done have not tested flaxseed or flax oil, and the results of tests using fish-oils have been contradictory. Data from several studies on the effect of fish oils is inconclusive. While adding flaxseed to your diet won't hurt, there's just no scientific basis for claims that it will help in this instance.

Multiple Sclerosis

Recently, I ran across an astonishing claim for flaxseed, one that touted its efficacy as a miracle treatment for multiple sclerosis (MS). This claim has almost no scientific support. There's been a little research on the relation between fatty acids and MS, but the findings are contradictory. For example, in 1989 researchers at the University of Newcastle upon Tyne commenced a long-term study of 312 MS patients, in which the effectiveness of omega-6s and omega-3s were evaluated. Two years into the five year study, the scientists reported no significant effect. A year later, however, they reported that results from a second experimental group, when compared with ongoing results from the first one, indicated that there may be a mild reduction in the severity and frequency of relapses.

That second study seemed promising, but in 1992 an Italian study found no such linkage after all, suggesting that the improvements that had been noted previously were probably the result of faulty research design. Still another study, done in 1997 by scientists at the Hospital General Gregorio Maranon in Madrid, seems to indicate that maybe there *is* a linkage, but they stop short of making any definitive claims. They content themselves with calling for "rigorous evaluation" and further research.

Vaginal dryness

This is another symptom where the research has yet to bear out the claim that flaxseed can help. Only one study, published in the October 1990 issue of the *British Medical Journal*, has directly addressed this question. In this study, which focused on postmenopausal women averaging 59 years of age, a daily dietary supplement of about six tablespoons of soy flour was given to one group, while the other was given about two tablespoons of flaxseed. After six weeks, the flaxseed group showed an improvement in their vaginal secretions similar to that achieved by the soy group. After the supplements were removed from the daily diet, vaginal secretions in both groups returned to their more typically post-menopausal levels. The data were not conclusive, however, and results have not been replicated in follow-up studies. Still, you've got nothing to lose by trying, and the effectiveness of flax for other menopausally related symptoms makes it worth your while to give it a try.

A Quick Review

- The components of flaxseed that seems most useful across a wide range of physical ailments are the lignans and alpha-linolenic acid (ALA), the omega-3 fatty acid.

- Other components, such as fiber, have also been demonstrated to be helpful in maintaining optimal health.

- The phytoestrogens (lignans) in flaxseed seem particularly helpful in easing symptoms of menopause and in relieving inflammation.

- Not all claims made in behalf of flaxseed have been clinically tested. Consumers should carefully check before assuming that flax will help with their particular complaints.

Flaxseed Basics

5

As flaxseed gains in popularity, it is becoming increasingly available in a variety of forms. From whole seeds to ground seeds to oils and even pills, there are many different ways to incorporate the benefits of flax into your diet. Now that we've learned all the wonderful things that flax can do for you, it is time to take a closer look at the wide range of flax options available.

Whole and Wholesome

Whole flaxseeds are available for purchase in bulk form or in convenient packages through health food stores, some supermarkets, or direct from the manufacturers. Of course, savvy consumers know that buying in bulk is the most cost-effective way to go, but many people prefer the convenience of pre-packaged foods—they're easier to store and easier to handle. Still, the relatively long shelf-life of whole flaxseed (up to a year) makes bulk-buying a cost-conscious option that you just may want to consider.

For the esthetically minded, you get a choice of colors: the most commonly seen seeds are reddish brown in color, but a second variety is yellow or golden. In the U.S. and Canada, the color makes little difference when it comes to taste or nutritional value: both offer similar levels of the nutrients that make flax such a great addition to your daily diet. But, do take note: there is another yellow seed in Canada that looks like flax, but is not. It is solin seed, a crop developed from flax. Solin seeds do *not* provide the same nutritional benefits, for it contains less than one-tenth of the ALA found in flaxseeds. Luckily for consumers, solin is not directly available in the standard stores and outlets that sell flaxseed. All in all, as long as you're getting the real thing, color doesn't matter much: availability and personal preference are really the only deciding factors when choosing the variety you'll use at home.

Whole flaxseed has a hard hull that is difficult for the digestive system to break down. For those of you who are blessed with strong teeth, the seeds make a tasty snack and add a change-of-pace texture when sprinkled on top of other foods, like salads. To get the maximum benefit from the whole seeds, just chew well to shred the seed coat.

However, some people have difficulty with whole seeds—and not just flaxseeds. If you have a condition called *diverticulosis*, for example, you may find yourself sharing in a problem reported by a few of the students in my flaxseed classes. These students reported that seeds sometimes became lodged in small pouches that are located in the intestine—this can cause pain and discomfort. If you've had trouble digesting other small seeds, therefore, you might want to consider using ground flaxseed rather than the whole ones.

Getting into the Grind

Ground flaxseed offers you a major advantage that makes this the form you will probably want to use most of the time: the grinding process helps release all the nutrients more effectively than is possible simply by chewing the whole seeds. You get far more of the omega-3 fatty acids and lignans, and thus more of the great health benefits that flax can offer.

The terminology of flaxseed marketing can be confusing. Ground flaxseed is sometimes marketed as "flax flour" or as "milled flaxseed" for example, and sometimes the packaging won't specify any treatment at all. In addition, there's flaxseed meal, which is somewhat different. Flaxseed meal has been processed so that most of the oil has been removed, leaving it with about 12–15 percent oil content. This form may be used in prepared foods and mixes, but most flax meal is used in animal feed.

Flax, enhanced

First-time flaxseed users may find it most convenient to buy the product already ground—and since convenience is an important factor in whether or not you actually use the product, this is no small consideration. In addition, many companies enhance the nutritional value of their ground flaxseed by adding extra vitamin and mineral supplements. This is done to address some concerns that flaxseed might inhibit the absorption of certain nutrients, notably vitamin B6 and zinc. While these concerns have not yet been confirmed by research, many manufacturers have decided to take the cautious route and add these nutrients in during the grinding process.

In addition, some ground flaxseed providers have come up with a way to address another problem: long-term storage. Because of the oil content of flaxseed, it can spoil quickly if the manufacturer doesn't have some way to counteract the process. The problem is how to achieve this without having to drastically reduce the oil content of the product. Rather than convert the ground flaxseed to meal, some manufacturers have supplemented it with antioxidents such as vitamins C and E, thus prolonging the shelf-life of the product. Certainly, it's not a bad thing to supplement ground flaxseed with additional nutrients. However, extra processing has an impact on the price of the product.

Grinding Your Own

Of course, you can always buy whole flaxseeds and grind them up at home, just like you can grind your own coffee beans—and you can even use your coffee grinder to do the job. The benefit, of course, is that you don't have to worry about freshness: if you grind up only as much as you need for your recipe, you're optimizing both the flavor *and* the nutritional value of the seeds, and whole seeds can be stored longer than the ready-ground version. I personally like to grind about a week's worth of seed at a time, but you can make life a little more convenient by grinding as much as three or four months' worth. Ground flaxseed is shelf-stable for up to four months stored in tightly lidded container. Refrigeration extends its shelf life and keeps it fresh longer.

A Word About Oil

As you've already learned, flax oil is a wonderful source of alpha-linolenic acid. However, when you buy flax in this form, this is *all* you're getting! In other words, flax oil is lacking in all the other important nutrients that provide so much benefit, particularly fiber, lignans, and protein.

Right now, the only place you can get flax oil is by ordering directly through a manufacturer or in the refrigerator section of your local health food store. It comes in two different forms: regular and high-lignan oil. This latter variety struck me as odd when I first began researching flax and flax-based products, since the oil is, by definition, lacking in lignans. I did some investigating, contacting several companies that produce the "high-lignan" version to check out just what process they use in its manufacture. Unfortunately, I could not verify that lignans are somehow added back in to the oil. Therefore, I suggest you be wary when confronting such claims.

And here is one last *caveat* about flaxseed oil. Because of its chemical composition, flax oil must be kept refrigerated *at all times*. Even refrigerated, it's got a pretty short shelf-life—you have to use it within six to eight weeks after opening the bottle—after that it goes rancid. How do you know if your flax oil has gone bad? You'll get a bitter taste or even a burning sensation on your tongue, and it will start to smell like paint thinner! Unrefrigerated, it spoils much faster, as I discovered during an experiment I did on my own. I left a bottle of flax oil out on my kitchen counter, checking it daily. After just a few days, the odor it gave off had changed dramatically! Not a flavor I wanted to add to *my* meals, that's for sure!

Keep in mind that flax oil is expensive. Since it spoils relatively quickly, and since the research shows that whole or ground flaxseed has far more beneficial properties, it seems wiser to skip the oil and go straight for the seeds.

Pill Popping

Isn't it amazing how, as soon as we discover that a nutrient is good for you, there are always a few companies that quickly figure out a way to turn it into a pill or capsule? That's already happened with flax! These days, you can get your flax in two different types of pill form. One contains only the oil, the other contains ground flaxseed. The oil-based pills have all the drawbacks of regular flaxseed oil: it only contains the fat, lacking the lignans, proteins, and fiber; and you have to keep it tightly sealed and refrigerated. The ground flaxseed pills keep longer and contain more of the nutrients associated with ground flaxseed.

So keep in mind that, while getting your flax via pills sounds convenient, there are lots of drawbacks. For instance:

- To obtain a beneficial amount of ground flax or flax oil through pills, you have to take several each day. For example, one brand of ground flax pills recommends a daily dosage of 8 pills! And for all those pills, you're only getting the equivalent of just one-half a teaspoon of ground flaxseed. To get the benefits of a *single tablespoon* of flaxseed, you'd have to take 53 pills a day! Similarly, to get the benefit of a single tablespoon of flax oil, you'd have to eat 14 flax-oil pills daily! And these pills aren't cheap!

- The pill form does not reduce the calories of your flax! Many people are under the impression that pill-style supplements are a calorie-free way to get the nutrients they need. This is just not true. If you are using the pill form as a way to cut calories, you're only fooling yourself: flax oil pills contain all fat!

- Pill supplements present only a select set of the many substances found in the actual flaxseed. Since flax research is still in its infancy, however, scientists have not yet identified all the potentially health-promoting substances contained in flax. You may therefore be missing some important, but as yet unrecognized, nutritional benefit if you restrict your flax intake to pills.

And here is one final point about taking your flax in pill form. The Food and Drug Administration does not monitor food supplements as strictly as it regulates drugs, so there's no real oversight of the industry. The only organization that sets standards for supplements marketed in the U.S. is the United States Pharmacopeia (USP). Unfortunately, USP standards are not mandatory, so it is up to the individual manufacture to comply with them. These standards are meant to ensure the following:

- The tablet will disintegrate into small pieces in the stomach and gut so that your system can absorb it.

- When the expiration date rolls around, the product will still contain at least 90 percent of the nutrient level listed on the label.

- The ingredients are pure, with a minimum of contaminants.

If all manufacturers adhered to these standards, you'd have little to worry about. But while the some do, others may not, so check your labels! If you're committed to taking your flax in pill form, at least make sure the label specifically notes that the product complies with USP standards.

Putting It to Good Use

So, okay . . . you're ready to take the plunge and start adding flax to your diet. The question now is to decide how to manage this change. After all, to make this a regular component of your meals, you'll want to do more than just scarf down a handful of seeds, right?

The good news is that both whole and ground flaxseed are very stable, capable of standing up to use in baking and stove-top cooking. The nutrients remain intact, even after you've incorporated the flaxseed in your recipes! Still, it helps to have a little guidance on how to use this product. In the final chapters of this book I'll be giving you some full-scale recipes to follow, and in no time at all you'll be cooking with flax like a pro. For now, however, here are some fast, simple ways to use whole or ground flaxseed that you can put into practice right away!

As a sprinkled topping or garnish for:

- oatmeal

- cream of wheat

- cold cereal

- soups

- salads

- yogurt, frozen yogurt, pudding, or ice cream

- cottage cheese

When baking, you can add flaxseed into the batter or dough for lots of foods, including:

- meatloaf

- casseroles

- lasagna

- muffins

- cookies

- breads

- pizza crust

Flaxseed mixes in with foods cooked on the stove top, too. Try adding a little the next time you make:

- spaghetti sauce

- stew

- scrambled eggs

- rice dishes

- pancakes

- waffles

- burgers (beef, turkey, or soy)

Sounds easy, doesn't it! And it really is as easy as it sounds. But even these lists don't exhaust the possibilities. For example, you can boost the nutritional value of your favorite beverages just by stirring or blending some ground flaxseed into your juice or smoothie. And how's this for an idea: before baking, brush the top of your bread dough with skim milk or egg white, then sprinkle on some whole flaxseed. It makes a great addition to whole-grain bread!

Let's Get Creative

If you're feeling adventurous, you can take a cue from Emeril Lagasse and "bump it up a notch" by experimenting with adding flax to some of your family's favorite recipes.

Recipe substitution isn't too hard to do, as long as you keep in mind what flaxseed is made of: protein, fiber, and fat (oil). This knowledge gives you clues as to the best way to alter your recipes. For example, the high oil content of flaxseed makes it a reasonable substitute for shortening or conventional cooking oils. In my experience, a 3:1 substitution ratio works well: three tablespoons of ground flaxseed replaces one tablespoon of oil or shortening. Similarly, the protein content of flaxseed makes it a great egg substitute if you mix it with water. One tablespoon of ground flaxseed mixed with 3 tablespoons of water, then left to sit for a minute or two, handily replaces a single egg.

A Quick Review

- Flaxseed comes in a variety of forms, from whole to ground to oils and even pills.

- Pre-ground flaxseed is often enriched with substances, like antioxidents, that help prevent spoilage and add to the overall nutritional value.

- Flaxseed oil, although rich in the omega-3 fatty acid, alpha-linolenic acid (ALA), lacks many of the beneficial substances of flax, and is very expensive.

- Pills limit the number of nutrients in your flax intake, and you have to take an awful lot of them to get the benefits in much smaller portions of the ground version.

- Flaxseed is easily incorporated into a broad range of conventional foods, as a "sprinkle-on" addition or as a substitution in many standard recipes.

Finding Flaxseed Products

6

On the ride home after visiting Natural Ovens of Manitowoc, Wisconsin, a food manufacturer that makes products with flax, I caught my husband munching down a handful of their Granola mix. Caught in the act of eating "fast food," he felt obliged to explain himself this way: "I don't care *how* healthy flax is—if I can't get it in something that's ready-made, I'll never fit it into my diet."

My husband spoke for most of us, whether he knew it or not. We *all* know we're supposed to eat foods that are good for us, but if they aren't easy to prepare *and* tasty, we usually skip them for something that's less healthy but more convenient. It's simple human nature.

Well, I'm no fool—I know that there's little point in extolling the great virtues of flax if I can't talk people into eating it. So I started looking into the ready-made flax-based (or, at least, flax-containing) options available.

Head on Down to the Health Food Store

By this time I'd already become pretty savvy about flaxseed, but even *I* was amazed by the number of choices in flaxseed products were available at my local health food store. Sure, I knew about some cereals and even a line of ready-made waffles—but when I started putting together a list of all the options available, well . . . just look what I came up with!

Buying the basics

If you're looking for flax in its generic condition—whole or ground seeds—you can probably find it in most health food stores easily enough. In fact, now that more and more people are tuning into the potential benefits of flax in the diet, even some of the larger supermarket chains are beginning to carry flaxseed and some flax-based products. If your favorite store doesn't carry them yet, here are some suppliers' names you can pass along to the manager. And even if the stores in your area don't carry flaxseed, you can order it directly from these companies or off the internet.

- Bob's Red Mill Natural Foods, Inc

- Omega-Life, Inc.

- Heintzman Farms

- Nunweiler's Flour Co.

- Pizzey's Milling and Baking Co.

- Arrowhead Mills, Inc.

- North American Nutrition

Most of the companies listed here also put out a line of ready-made products, which we'll discuss in greater detail in the next few pages. Check the lists that follow for contact information for these manufacturers. North American Nutrition, however, specializes in whole and ground flax. You can write to them at 121 Elm Drive, Warroad, Minnesota 56763, or call them at (800) 387-5516. You can also reach them on-line at www.goldenflax.com.

But don't stop there! There's a whole world of flaxseed choices out there. From breads to granola-like toppings, you've got all sorts of choices available.

A bakery bonanza

Not surprisingly, flax works really well in baked goods—the tiny seeds and their oil make a natural addition to the grains and flours used in breads, buns, and muffins. Here is a basic list of products and their manufacturers:

Product Name	Manufacturer
Flaxseed Rye Bread 100% Organic Rye Bread with Flaxseed	Dimpflmeier Bakery, Ltd. 32 Advance Road Toronto, Ontario Canada M8Z 2T4 Tel: (800) 723-8823 Fax: (905) 945-1128 www.dimpflbreadex.com

Northwest Grain Country Five Seed Bread Innkeepers 8 Grain Bread Oregon Western Hazelnut Bread Oregon Stoneground Whole Wheat Bread Hazelnut Bread Safeway Select Organic Seeds & Grains Bread	Bread.com 6024 Jean Road Suite C150 Lake Oswego, OR 97035 Tel: (877)-4BREADS www.bread.com
Original Round Top Bread Original Sandwich Bread Original Hamburger Buns Original Hot Dog Buns English Muffins Split Top with Oat Bran Bread Honey Wheatberry Bread Seven Grain Bread Sun Grain Bread Twelve Grain Bread	Roman Meal Company P.O. Box 11126 Tacoma, WA 98411 Tel: (800) 922-0017 Fax: (253) 475-1906 www.romanmeal.com
Glorious Cinnamon Raisin Bread 7-Grain Herb Bread Health Max Bread Hunger Filler Bread Nutty Natural Wheat Bread Multigrain Stay Trim Bread Happiness Bread 100% Whole Grain Bread Sunny Millet Bread Right Wheat Bread Cracked Wheat Bread Soft Hearth Bread Mild Rye Bread Whole Grain Bagels Brainy Bagels Cinnamon & Raisin Bagels Blueberry Bagels Sundried Tomato Basil Bagels Better Wheat Buns Frankly Better Wheat Buns (long) Gourmet Dinner Rolls Raisin Bran Muffins Blueberry Muffins Carrot Muffins	Natural Ovens of Manitowoc Wisconsin 4300 County Trunk CR P.O. Box 730 Manitowoc, WI 54221 Tel: (800) 558-3535 Fax: (920) 758-2594 www.naturalovens.com

A cereal cornucopia

Flaxseed products can make a natural appearance in your breakfast routine, too. A wide array of cereal products containing flax is available, for example. And for those of you who like to start your day with something a little more filling, how about ready-made waffles, hot from the toaster? Here's a list:

Product Name	Manufacturer
5-Grain Rolled Cereal 7-Grain Cereal Apple, Cinnamon, Grains Cereal 8-Grain Wheatless Cereal 10-Grain Cereal Right Stuff Hot Cereal	Bob's Red Mill Natural Foods, Inc. 5209 S. E. International Way Milwaukie, OR 97222 Tel: (800) 349-2173 Fax: (503) 653-1339 www.bobsredmill.com
Paul's Oat Cereal	Natural Ovens of Manitowoc Wisconsin 4300 County Trunk CR P.O. Box 730 Manitowoc, WI 54221 Tel: (800) 558-3535 Fax: (920) 758-2594 www.naturalovens.com
Hearty Apple Cinnamon Hot Cereal Original Cereal	Roman Meal Company P.O. Box 11126 Tacoma, WA 98411 Tel: (800) 922-0017 Fax: (253) 475-1906 www.romanmeal.com
Flax Plus Cereal	Lifestream 7453 Progress Way Delta, British Columbia Canada V4G 1E8 Tel: (604) 940-0505 Fax: (604) 940-0522 www.naturespath.com

Mesa Sunrise Cereal Flax 'n Oats (hot cereal bowl) Optimum Power Breakfast Cereal	Nature's Path Foods, Inc. 7453 Progress Way Delta, British Columbia Canada V4G 1E8 Tel: (604) 940-0505 Fax: (604) 940-0522 www.naturespath.com
4 Grain Plus Flax Cereal Perfect Harvest Multigrain Cereal	Arrowhead Mills, Inc. 110 South Lawton Street P.O. Box 2059 Hereford, TX 79045 Tel: (800) 749-0730 Fax: (806) 364-9322

Red River Hot Cereal-Original
Red River Hot Cereal-Ready to
    Serve (in Original and Maple
    & Brown Sugar flavors)
	Robin Hood
	60 Columbia Way
	Markham, Ontario
	Canada L3R 0C9
	Tel: (800) 268-3232
	www.redrivercereal.com

Organic Golden Flax Cereal	Health Valley Company 16100 Foothill Boulevard Irwindale, CA 91706 Tel: (800) 423-4846 Fax: (626) 969-3687 www.Hain-Celestrial.com
Organic Hot Cereal (U.S.) Sunny Boy Quick Cooking Hot Cereal (Canada)	Prairie Sun Grains 4601 51st Avenue P.O. Box 1570 Camrose, Alberta Canada T4V 1X4 Tel: (800) 556-6807 www.Prairiesungrains.com
Uncle Sam Cereal New Morning Bran Flakes New Morning Corn Flakes New Morning Honey Frosted Flakes New Morning Raisin Bran	U.S. Mills, Inc. 200 Reservoir Street Needham, MA 02494 Tel: (781) 444-0440 Fax: (781) 444-3411

8 Grain Sesame Toaster Waffles Flax Plus Toaster Waffles Mesa Sunrise Toaster Waffles Hemp Plus Toaster Waffles	Lifestream 7453 Progress Way Delta, British Columbia Canada V4G 1E8 Tel: (604) 940-0505 Fax: (604) 940-0522 www.naturespath.com

Crackers 'n snacks

Another way to add flax to your everyday diet is in munchies and snacks. Quick and convenient for a mid-morning or mid-afternoon pick-me-up, snack items like these are a healthy alternative to the high-sugar and high-salt conventional snack options. Here are a few for you to try out:

Product Name	Manufacturer
Sesame and Flaxseed Crackers Cracker Classic Crackers	Venus Wafers, Inc. 70 Research Road Hingham, MA 02043 Tel: (800) 545-4538 Fax: (781) 749-7195 www.venuswafers.com
SBG Square Meal Bars	Cell Tech 565 Century Court Klamath Falls, OR 97601 Tel: (800) 800-1300 www.celltech.com
Organic Energy Bar, Original W/ Almond Organic Energy Bar, Chocolate over Chai Organic Energy Bar, Lushus Lemon Organic Energy Bar, Original Organic Energy Bar, Chocolate Crisp	Bumble Bar 20211 Vashon Highway, SW Vashon, WA 98070 Tel: (206) 463-2088 www.bumblebar.com

Omega Bar	Omega Life, Inc. P.O. Box 208 Brookfield, WI 53008 Tel: (800) 328-3529 Fax: (414) 786-6566
Bite Me Golden Flaxseed Bar	Heintzman Farms R.R. 2 Box 265 Onaka, SD 57466 Tel: (800) 333-5813 Fax: (605) 447-5855 www.heintzmanfarms.com
Earthy Square (In Original, Strawberry-Banana, and Orange-Pineapple flavors)	Earthy Foods, Inc. 3000 Giant Road San Pablo, CA 94806 Tel: (800) 299-0979 Fax: (510) 231-5880 www.earthyfoods.com
Carmel Soy-Flax Chews	Mai's Foods/Margaret's Kitchen 329 Stow Road Boxborough, MA 01719 Tel/Fax: (978) 263-6465 www.maisfoods.com
Great Granola Chip Mate Cookies Oatmeal Raisin Cookies	Natural Ovens of Manitowoc Wisconsin 4300 County Trunk CR P.O. Box 730 Manitowoc, WI 54221 Tel: (800) 558-3535 Fax: (920) 758-2594 www.naturalovens.com
Hemp Plus Granola	Nature's Path Foods, Inc. 7453 Progress Way Delta, British Columbia Canada V4G 1E8 Tel: (604) 940-0505 Fax: (604) 940-0522 www.naturespath.com

Flax & Soy Granola (in cranberries, currants and almond oats flavors) Flax and Soy Bars (in chocolate and apple crisp flavors)	Zoe Foods 49 Winchester Street Newton, MA 02461 Tel: (617) 244-3635 Fax: (617) 244-3676 www.zoefoods.com

Mixing it up

Ah, the aroma of home-made muffins filling your kitchen. Or how about a high-energy drink, fortified with flax and other healthy nutrients—wouldn't that taste great? But who's got time to experiment with from-scratch recipes? Well, help is at hand. Here's a list of some of the many mixes available that incorporate flax. (Items marked with an * are for bread machines.)

Product Name	Manufacturer
Flax Muffin Mix Flax Pancake and Waffle Mix	Pizzey's Milling and Baking Co. P.O. Box 132 Angusville, Manitoba Canada R0J O4O Tel: (800) 804-6433 Fax: (204) 773-2317 www.pizzeys.com
*100% Whole Wheat Bread Mix 10-Grain Pancake and Waffle Mix 10-Grain Flour	Bob's Red Mill Natural Foods, Inc. 5209 S. E. International Way Milwaukie, OR 97222 Tel: (800) 349-2173 Fax: (503) 653-1339 www.bobsredmill.com
Indian Multi-grain Bread	Timberline Farms 165 North 1330 West Suite B4 Orem, UT 84057 Tel: (888) 327-9649 Fax: (801) 434-4563 www.tpfoods.com

Wheat 'n Flax Pancake Mix	Nunweiler's Flour Co. #106-1219 Commercial Way Penticton, British Columbia Canada V2A 3H4 Tel: (888) 726-2253 Fax: (888) 688-2288 www.pancakemix.com

Barbara Stitt's Pancake and
    Waffle Mix
Zesty Energy Mix (drink mix)
Ultra Omega Balance
    (drink mix)
	Natural Ovens of
	    Manitowoc Wisconsin
	4300 County Trunk CR
	P.O. Box 730
	Manitowoc, Wisconsin
	54221
	Tel: (800) 558-3535
	Fax: (920) 758-2594
	www.naturalovens.com

Power Pack Energy Drink Mix	Omega-Life, Inc. P.O. Box 208 Brookfield, WI 53008 Tel: (800) 328-3529 Fax: (414) 786-6566
*Multigrain Bread Mix	Arrowhead Mills, Inc. 110 South Lawton Street P.O. Box 2059 Hereford, TX 79045 Tel: (800) 749-0730 Fax: (806) 364-9322
*Nine Grain Bread Mix	Hodgson Mill, Inc. 1203 Niccum Avenue Effingham, IL 62401 Tel: (800) 525-0177 Fax: (217) 347-0198 www.hodgsonmill.com

To top it all off

Of course, when it comes to adding flax to your diet, there's a really simple way. You can do what bran-lovers have been doing for years: use flaxseed products as a simple topping or garnish on conventional foods. Here, too, you've got help at hand right on the shelves of your local stores. Zoe Foods, for example, puts out granola containing flax that can be used as a topping.

Spread the Word!

Of course, not every community is fortunate enough to support a well-stocked health-food store. However, most local grocers and supermarket managers are happy to take suggestions from their customers about the foods they stock on their shelves. After all, it is in their best interests to keep their customers satisfied?

So, if you're interested in adding flax-based products to your pantry or refrigerator shelves, but you can't find them in your community just yet, why not take matters into your own hands? It is easy to do: just let your local grocer know that you're a ready-made market for these products—and pass along to him or her the contact information for their manufacturers. It's a good way to increase your choices in the market, and at the same time you will be helping to raise local awareness of the health benefits of flax.

A Quick Review

- A wide variety of ready-made foods incorporate flaxseed.

- If you don't live near a health food store, you can order flaxseed products directly from most manufacturers or off the internet.

- Contact the manager of your conventional market—many of them are willing to stock unusual products, like flaxseed-based ones—if their customers express an interest!

Flax In the Kitchen: The Recipes

7

Beautiful Breads
>   Hearty oatmeal bread
>   Flax whole-wheat bread

Marvelous Muffins
>   Confetti muffins
>   Orange-cranberry flax muffins

Cookies and Cakes
>   Crispy shortbread cookies
>   Jane's flaxseed cookies
>   Rosemary's flaxseed coffee cake

Assorted Other Snacks
>   T.J.'s flax bars
>   Pam's dessert bars
>   Homemade granola
>   Peanut butter balls

Flax Makes the Meal
>   Bob's porridge
>   Pizza bread
>   Turkey meatloaf

Some Final Thoughts

Well, now that you know about all the potential health benefits of adding flax to your diet, are you ready to take the plunge? For this chapter, I've collected a batch of recipes that use flaxseed in tasty, tempting ways. With these, you'll have no trouble at all in getting a healthy helping of flaxseed into your daily meals and snacks. But before we really get into the recipes, let's whip up a refreshing beverage and drink a toast to your commitment to better health:

Diana's Super Soy and Phytochemical Shake

This recipe comes from Diana Dyer, MS, RD, and is reprinted with her permission from her book "A Dietitian's Cancer Story: Information and Inspiration for Recovery and Healing." For more information, check out her website at www.CancerRD.com.

2-1/2 oz. Soft or silken tofu (1/6 of a1 lb. Block)	3/4 cup calcium fortified soy milk
1 large carrot or 6 to 8 baby carrots	3/4 cup calcium-fortified orange juice
3/4 cup fresh or frozen unsweetended fruit	1 tablespoon wheat bran
1 tablespoon wheat germ	1 tablespoon ground flax seed

Put all the ingredients into a blender. Begin with blender set at low speed, then increase it to high and run for 1 to 3 minutes to fully blend the mixture. Blenders vary in power, so time may vary to get full blending. **Makes 3 cups, containing one full tablespoon flaxseed.**

Nutritional Information Per Serving:	
Calories: 450	Carbohydrates: 65 g
Total Fat: 10 g	Protein: 25 g
Saturated Fat: 1.1 g	Cholesterol: 0 mg
Monounsaturated Fat: 1.7 g	Fiber: 14 g
Polyunsaturated Fat: 5.2 g	

Beautiful Breads

What beats the smell of fresh-baked breads? And what more tempting way to incorporate some flax into the foods you eat! Here are a couple of great recipes to try:

Hearty oatmeal bread

1 can (1 pound) pear halves in juice, undrained	1-1/2 cups whole wheat pastry flour
1/2 cup quick-cooking oats	1/2 cup dark brown sugar
1/4 cup ground flaxseed	2 tsp. baking powder
3/4 tsp. baking soda	1 tsp. vanilla extract
1/2 cup chopped dried apricots, prunes, or dark raisins	1/3 cup chopped walnuts or toasted pecans

Preheat oven to 325 degrees F.

Drain the pears, reserving the juice. Place the pears in a a blender and process until smooth. Pour the pureed pears into a 2 cup measure and add enough of the reserved juice to bring the volume up to 1-1/2 cups. Set aside.

Place the flour, oats, brown sugar, and ground flaxseed in a large bowl and mix well. Use the back of a spoon to press out any lumps in the brown sugar. Add the baking powder and baking soda and mix well. Then add the pears and vanilla extract to the flour mixture, sitrring just until the dry ingredients are moistened. Fold in the apricots, prunes, or raisins and the walnuts or pecans.

Coat an 8x4 inch loaf pan with nonstick cooking spray, then spread the mixture evenly in the pan. Bake at 325 degrees F for about 45 minutes, or just until a wooden toothpick insterted in the center of the loaf comes out clean. Be careful not to overbake.

Remove the loaf from the oven, and let sit for 10 minutes. Invert the loaf onto a wire rack, turn right side up, and cool to room temperature. Wrap the loaf in plastic wrap or aluminum foil and allow to sit for 8 hours or overnight before slicing and serving. (Overnight storage will give the loaf a softer, moister crust.) Refrigerate any leftovers not eaten within 24 hours. **Makes 16 servings. Each serving contains about 1/4th tablespoon of flaxseed.**

Nutritional Information Per Serving:	
Calories: 103	Carbohydrates: 20 g

Total Fat: 1.9 g	Protein: 2.9 g
Saturated Fat: 0.2 g	Cholesterol: 0 mg
Monounsaturated Fat: 0.3 g	Fiber: 2.8 g
Polyunsaturated Fat: 1.3 g	

This recipe comes from from *Secrets of Cooking for Long Life* by Sandra Woodruff, RD, Avery Publishing, 1999.

Flax whole-wheat bread

1-1/4 cups water	1 tablespoon honey
1-3/4 cup bread flour	3/4 cup ground flaxseed
1-1/2 tsp salt	1 tablespoon brown sugar
2 tablespoons dry skim milk powder	2 tablespoons margarine
2 tsp. Fast rising instant yeast	1-3/4 cups whole wheat flour

Place measured ingredients in bread machine pan in the order recommended by machine manufacturer. Select Whole-Wheat Rapid Cycle. When cycle is completed, remove baked bread from pan and let cool on wire rack. **Makes 16 servings. Each serving contains 3/4ths tablespoons of flaxseed.**

Nutritional Information Per Serving:	
Calories: 152	Carbohydrates: 25 g
Total Fat: 3.8 g	Protein: 5.2 g
Saturated Fat: .6 g	Cholesterol: 0 mg
Monounsaturated Fat: 1.0 g	Fiber: 3.1 g
Polyunsaturated Fat: 1.8 g	

Used with permission from the Flax Council of Canada

Marvelous Muffins

As a snack or with breakfast, muffins are always a welcome treat. They're also easy to make with flaxseed, as the following recipes show:

Confetti muffins

3/4 cup all purpose flour	3/4 cup milled flax seed
3/4 cup oat bran	1 cup brown sugar
2 tsp. baking soda	1 tsp. baking powder
3/4 cup whole wheat flour	2 tsp. cinnamon
1-1/2 cups carrots, finely shredded	2 apples, peeled, shredded
3/4 cup skim milk	3/4 cup raisins
1 tsp. vanilla	2 Tbsp. canola oil
2 beaten eggs	

Preheat oven to 350 degrees F.

Mix together flours, milled flax seed, oat bran, brown sugar, baking soda, baking powder, and cinnamon in a large bowl. Stir in carrots, apples, and raisins. In a separate bowl, combine milk, beaten eggs, vanilla, and oil. Pour liquid ingredients into dry ingredients. Stir until ingredients are moistened. Do not over mix. Fill muffin cups 3/4 full. Bake at 350 degrees F for 15-20 minutes. **Makes 17 muffins. Each muffin contains 3/4ths tablespoon flaxseed.**

Nutritional Information Per Serving:	
Calories: 186	Carbohydrates: 34.7 g
Total Fat: 4.7 g	Protein: 4.7 g
Saturated Fat: 0.6 g	Cholesterol: 25 mg
Monounsaturated Fat: 1.7 g	Fiber: 4.2 g
Polyunsaturated Fat: 2.1 g	

Orange-cranberry flax muffins

1 cup cranberries, coarsely chopped	1/4 cup sugar
1/4 cup orange juice	2-3/4 cups all purpose flour
1/2 cup milled flax seed	1/2 cup sugar
2 tsp. baking powder	1 tsp. baking soda
1/2 tsp. salt	1 tsp. orange peel, grated
1 beaten egg	1/4 cup canola oil
1-1/4 cups orange juice	

Preheat oven to 375 degrees F.

Blend together cranberries, sugar, and a little orange juice to moisten. Set aside. In a separate, larger bowl, mix the flour, milled flaxseed, sugar, baking powder, baking soda, salt, and orange peel. Combine the beaten egg and oil to the remaining orange juice, then pour these liquid ingredients into dry ingredients. Stir until ingredients are moistened. Do not over mix. Fold in cranberry mixture with a few strokes. Fill muffin cups 3/4 full. Bake at 375 degrees F for 30 to 35 minutes. **Makes 12 servings. Each serving contains 3/4ths tablespoons of flaxseed.**

Nutritional Information Per Serving:	
Calories: 248	Carbohydrates: 41 g
Total Fat: 7.2 g	Protein: 5.3 g
Saturated Fat: 0.7 g	Cholesterol: 17 mg
Monounsaturated Fat: 3.2 g	Fiber: 3.2 g
Polyunsaturated Fat: 2.8 g	

Used with permission from the Flax Council of Canada

Cookies and Cakes

Here's a helping of sweet dessert ideas that I know you and your family will love:

Crispy shortbread cookies

1 cup white sugar	1 cup brown sugar, packed
1 cup margarine	1 egg
2 tsp. vanilla	1/3 cup unsweetened applesauce
3-1/2 cups unbleached flour	1 tsp. baking soda
1/2 tsp. baking powder	1 tsp. salt
1 tsp. cream of tartar	1/2 cup walnuts or pecans
1 cup flaxseed	1 cup quick oats
1 cup rice krispies	

Preheat oven to 350 degrees F.

Beat together the white sugar, brown sugar, margarine, egg, vanilla, and applesauce in a large bowl. Set aside. In another bowl, sift together the flour, baking soda, baking powder, salt, and cream of tartar. Set this bowl aside too.

Grind 1/2 cup walnuts or pecans in coffee grinder, then grind 1 cup flaxseed.

Combine all the set aside mixtures with the nuts and flaxseed, then add in the quick oats and rice krispies. Drop by rounded heaping teaspoon on ungreased cookie sheets. Bake at 350 degrees F for 10 to 12 minutes. **Makes 50 cookies. Each cookie contains 1/3 tablespoon flaxseed.**

Nutritional Information Per Serving:	
Calories: 123	Carbohydrates: 17.7 g
Total Fat: 5.3 g	Protein: 1.9 g
Saturated Fat: 0.9 g	Cholesterol: 4.3 mg
Monounsaturated Fat: 2.1 g	Fiber: 1.3 g

Jane's flaxseed cookies

1 cup margarine	1 cup sugar
1 cup brown sugar	2 eggs
1 tsp. vanilla	1-1/2 cups all purpose flour
3/4 cup soy flour	1 cup oatmeal
1/2 cup ground flaxseed	1/2 tsp. salt
1 tsp. baking powder	1 tsp. baking soda
1/2 cup chopped almonds	1/2 cup chocolate chips

Preheat oven to 350 degrees F.

Cream margarine and sugars until mixture is light and fluffy. Add eggs and vanilla and beat well. In a separate bowl, mix together flour, oatmeal, ground flax seed, salt, baking powder, and baking soda. Stir into creamed mixture. Add almonds and chocolate chips. Mix until blended. Drop by heaping teaspoon on a greased cookie sheet, leaving about 2 inches between cookies. Bake at 350 F for 8 to 10 minutes. **Makes 50 cookies. Each cookie contains 1/2 teaspoon flaxseed.**

Nutritional Information	
Calories: 113	Carbohydrates: 14.7 g
Total Fat: 5.3 g	Protein: 2.1 g

Saturated Fat: 1.2 g	Cholesterol: 8.5 mg
Monounsaturated Fat: 2.4 g	Fiber: 1.1 g
Polyunsaturated Fat: 1.5 g	

Rosemary's flaxseed coffee cake

1/4 cup flaxseed, ground	1/2 cup sugar
1 cup skim milk	1 egg
1 cup all-purpose flour	1/2 cup whole wheat flour
1 tsp. baking powder	1/2 tsp. baking soda
2 tsp. cinnamon	1 tsp. nutmeg
1/4 tsp. salt	1/2 cup raisins
1 Tbsp. molasses	3/4 cup oats

Preheat oven to 350 degrees F.

Combine the flaxseed, sugar, milk, egg, all-purpose flour, whole wheat flour, baking powder, baking soda, cinnamon, nutmeg, and salt in a large mixing bowl. Mix, until well blended. Add in the raisins. Spread the batter into a greased (sprayed w/nonstick spray) 8×8 inch baking pan. Mix the molasses and oats in a small bowl, until uniformly crumbly. Sprinkle the crumb mixture evenly over the batter. Bake at 350 degrees F for about 30 minutes, until a toothpick inserted in the center of the cake comes out clean. Cut into 2-inch squares. **Makes 16 servings. Each serving contains 1/4th tablespoon of flaxseed.**

Nutritional Information Per Serving:	
Calories: 118	Carbohydrates: 24 g
Total Fat: 1.3 g	Protein: 3.4 g
Saturated Fat: .3 g	Cholesterol: 13.6 mg
Monounsaturated Fat: .3 g	Fiber: 2.2 g
Polyunsaturated Fat: .6 g	

Recipe provided by Rosemary Caspary, RD.

Assorted Other Snacks

Whether its a quick mid-morning pick-me-up or a munchie to nibble on while you're watching a movie, flaxseed works well in all sorts of snacks. Here are just a few more ideas:

T.J.'s flax bars

1 cup creamy peanut butter	1 cup corn syrup
1 cup brown sugar	1 cup ground flaxseed
1 teaspoon vanilla	5 cups Rice Krispies

In a microwave-safe bowl, mix together the peanut butter, corn syrup, and brown sugar. Microwave for about 3 minutes on HIGH. Stir in the ground flaxseed and vanilla, then pour the mixture over Rice Krispies and mix well. Coat a 9×13 inch baking pan with nonstick cooking spray, then spread the mixture into the pan and press down to form a dense sheet. Let the mixture sit for 5 to 10 minutes, until firmly set, then cut into bars. **Makes about 28 bars. Each bar contains approximately 2/3 tbsp. of flaxseed.**

Nutritional Information Per Serving:	
Calories: 144	Carbohydrates: 21 g
Total Fat: 6.3 g	Protein: 3.3 g
Saturated Fat: 1.1 g	Cholesterol: 0 mg
Monounsaturated Fat: 2.6 g	Fiber: 1.9 g
Polyunsaturated Fat: 2.3g	

Pam's dessert bars

1/2 cup margarine	1/2 cup brown sugar
1/4 cup freshly ground flax seed	1/4 cup flour
1-1/2 cups oatmeal	6 to 8 oz. fruit jam

Preheat oven to 375 degrees F.

Cream margarine and brown sugar. Add oatmeal, flour and flaxseed. Reserve 1 cup of mixture for topping. Coat a 9×9 inch pan with nonstick cooking spray. Press mixture into pan. Spread jam to within 1/2 inch of side of pan. Sprinkle reserved mixture evenly over top of jam. Bake 25-30 minutes in 375 degrees F. By the way, you can use any flavor jam you like, but Pam recommends blueberries because they are wonderful antioxidants. **Makes 16 servings. Each serving contains 1/4th tablespoon flaxseed.**

Nutritional Information Per Serving:	
Calories: 155	Carbohydrates: 23 g
Total Fat: 6.7 g	Protein: 1.7 g
Saturated Fat: 1.1 g	Cholesterol: 0 mg
Monounsaturated Fat: 2.2 g	Fiber: 2.1 g
Polyunsaturated Fat: 3.1 g	

Recipe provided by Pamela M., who has added flax to her diet in order to help cope with arthritis pain and for its potential as a breast-cancer fighting agent.

Homemade granola

6 cups dry oatmeal	1/2 cup sunflower seeds
1 cup soy nuts	1/2 cup sesame seeds
1 cup ground flaxseed	1/2 cup wheat germ
1 cup raisins	1-1/2 cups honey
1/2 cup canola oil	

Preheat oven to 350 degrees F.

Mix all the dry ingredients together in a large bowl. In a separate bowl, combine all the wet ingredients. Add the wet to the dry mixture. Spray a cookie sheet with non-stick spray. Pour mixture out on the cookie sheet. Bake in a 350 degrees F. for 12-15 minutes. Remove from oven, stir, then bake 5 minutes more. Repeat once more. After final baking, remove from oven and continue to stir every 10 minutes, until the mixture begins to cool down, then transfer mixture to a large bowl and stir every 10 minutes to break up clumps as they form. Store in a cool, dry place or refrigerate. **Makes about 30 servings. Each serving contains 1/2 tablespoon flaxseed.**

Nutritional Information Per Serving:	
Calories: 233	Carbohydrates: 34.6 g
Total Fat: 9.4 g	Protein: 6.6 g
Saturated Fat: 1.0 g	Cholesterol: 0 mg

Monounsaturated Fat: 3.5 g	Fiber: 4.6 g
Polyunsaturated Fat: 4.4 g	

Peanut butter balls

1/2 cup creamy peanut butter	1/2 cup honey
3/4 cup nonfat milk powder	1/3 cup chocolate chips
1/2 cup ground flaxseed	

Combine all ingredients in a bowl. Roll mixture into small balls and place on waxed paper. Chill in refrigerator for at least 1 hour before serving. **Makes 16 peanut butter balls. Each ball contains about 1/2 tablespoon flaxseed.**

Nutritional Information Per Serving:	
Calories: 139	Carbohydrates: 17 g
Total Fat: 6.5 g	Protein: 5.0 g
Saturated Fat: 1.6 g	Cholesterol: 1.1 mg
Monounsaturated Fat: 2.5 g	Fiber: 1.8 g
Polyunsaturated Fat: 2.1 g	

Flax Makes the Meal

While it's great to use flax in snacks, shakes, or desserts, it's equally easy to incorporate flaxseed in your regular meal recipes, too. From breakfast to the last meal of your day, you can make flax an integral part of your regular foods, as the following recipes show:

Bob's porridge

1/2 cup dry oatmeal	1 cup water
2 Tablespoons ground flaxseed	1/2 cup blueberries

Mix oatmeal, water, and flaxseed in an oversized bowl. Microwave on HIGH for approximately 2 to 3 minutes. Add blueberries and enjoy! **Makes a single serving. Serving contains 2 tablespoons flaxseed.**

Nutritional Information Per Serving:	
Calories: 251	Carbohydrates: 45 g

Total Fat: 6.6 g	Protein: 8.1 g
Saturated Fat: .7 g	Cholesterol: 0 mg
Monounsaturated Fat: 1.3 g	Fiber: 11.1 g
Polyunsaturated Fat: 4.1 g	

Recipe provided by Robert A. Flowers, M.D.

Pizza bread

1/2 cup sun-dried tomatoes	2-1/4 cups all-purpose flour
1/2 cup light parmesan cheese	1 tablespoon white sugar
1/2 cup ground flaxseed	1 tablespoon baking powder
2 tsp. oregano leaves	1/2 tsp. salt
1/4 tsp. black pepper	1-1/4 cups skim milk
2 tablespoons canola oil	1 egg
1 small tomato, diced	1/4 cup diced green pepper
1/3 cup shredded mozzarella cheese	

Preheat oven to 350 degrees F.

Cover sun-dried tomatoes with boiling water. Let stand for 10 minutes or until softened. Drain and dice. In a bowl, combine sun-dried tomatoes, flour, parmesan cheese, sugar, ground flax, baking powder, oregano, salt, and pepper. In a separate bowl, whisk together milk, oil, and egg. Pour liquid into dry ingredients. Stir just until dry ingredients are moistened. Pour into a well greased 8×4 load pan. Sprinkle tomatoes, green pepper and mozzarella cheese on top of batter. Bake 55 to 60 minutes or until wooden pick inserted in center comes out clean. **Makes 20 servings. Each serving contains 1/2 tablespoon flaxseed.**

Nutritional Information per Serving:	
Calories: 119	Carbohydrates: 16.8 g
Total Fat: 3.9 g	Protein: 4.9 g
Saturated Fat: .7 g	Cholesterol: 13.9 mg
Monounsaturated Fat: 1.1 g	Fiber: 1.6 g
Polyunsaturated Fat: 1.9 g	

Used with permission from the Flax Council of Canada

Turkey meatloaf

1/4 cup oatmeal	1/4 cup ground flaxseed
1 Tablespoon dry onion	1/2 cup catsup
1/2 tsp. salt	1 tsp. worcestershire sauce
1 egg	1 pound ground turkey
2 tablespoons whole flaxseed	

Preheat oven to 375 degrees F.

Mix all the ingredients in a large bowl. Coat a loaf pan with nonstick cooking spray. Put mixture in loaf pan, topping with a light coating of catsup and whole flaxseeds. Cover with aluminum foil. Bake for 1 hour covered, then remove cover and continue baking for another 10 minutes. Let stand for 5 to 10 minutes before serving. **Makes 12 servings. Each serving contains 2/3 tablespoons of flaxseed.**

Nutritional Information Per Serving:	
Calories: 102	Carbohydrates: 5.7 g
Total Fat: 5.2 g	Protein: 8.4 g
Saturated Fat: 1.1 g	Cholesterol: 48 mg
Monounsaturated Fat: 1.7 g	Fiber: 1.6 g
Polyunsaturated Fat: 1.9 g	

Some Final Thoughts

So there you have it: recipes that will help you make flax a regular part of your daily diet. And now that you've seen how easy it is to incorporate flax into familiar recipes, maybe you'll feel inspired to come up with a few inventive recipes of your own! Don't be surprised to find that some of these will quickly become family favorites!

Index

Further Resources

Flax Council of Canada
465-167 Lombard Avenue
Winnipeg, Manitoba
Canada R3B 0T6
204-982-2115 phone
204-942-1841 fax
www.flaxcouncil.ca

AmeriFlax
3015 Highway 25
Mandan, North Dakota 58554
701-663-9799 phone
701-663-6574 fax
www.ameriflax.com

Books and Articles

Allman, M. A., M. M. Pena, and D. Pang. "Supplementation with flaxseed oil versus sunflower seed oil in healthy young men consuming a low fat diet: effects on platelet composition and function." *European Journal of Clinical Nutrition* 49, no. 3 (1995): 169–178.

Bhatty, R. S. "Nutrient Composition of Whole Flaxseed and Flaxseed Meal." In *Flaxseed in Human Nutrition*, Cunnane and Thompson, eds., 1995.

Bierenbaum, M. L., R. Reichstein, and T. R. Watkins. "Reducing atherogenic risk in hyperlipemic humans with flaxseed supplementation: a preliminary report." *Journal of American College of Nutrition* 12, no. 5 (1993): 501–504.

Canadian Grain Commission of Winnipeg. *Nutritional Analysis*. Flax Council of Canada, 2001.

Chen, Z-Y., W. M. N. Ratnayake, and S. C. Cunnane. "Oxidative stability of flaxseed lipids during baking." *Journal of American Oil Chemists Society* 71 (1994): 629–632.

Clark, W. F., C. Kortas, A. Heidenheim, J. Garland, E. Spanner, and A. Parbtani. "Flaxseed in Lupus nephritis." *Journal of American College of Nutrition*, 2000.

Clark, W. F., A. D. Muir, N. D. Westcott, and A. Parbtani. "A novel treatment for lupus nephritis: lignan precursor derived from flax." *Lupus* 9, no. 6 (2000): 429–436.

Cunnane, S. C., M. J. Hamadeh, A. C. Liede, L. U. Thompson, T. M. Wolever, and D. J. Jenkins. "Nutritional attributes of traditional flaxseed in healthy young adults." *American Journal of Clinical Nutrition* 61 (1995): 62–68.

Cunnane, S. C., S. Ganuli, C. Menard, A. C. Liede, M. J. Hamadeh, Z-Y. Chen, T. M. Wolever, and D. J. Jenkins. "High alpha-linolenic acid flaxseed: some nutritional properties in humans." *British Jounal of Nutrition* 69, no. 2 (1993): 443–453.

Cunnane, S. C., and L. U. Thompson, eds. *Flaxseed in Human Nutrition*. AOCS Press, 1995.

de Lorgeril, M., P. Salen, J. L. Martin, I. Monjaud, J. Delaye, and N. Mamelle. "Mediterranean diet, traditional risk factors, and the rate of cardiovascular complication after myocardial infarction: final report of the Lyon Diet Heart Study." *Circulation* 99, no. 6 (1999): 779–785.

Goh, Y. K., J. A. Jumpsen, E. A. Ryan, and M. T. Clandinin. "Effect of omega-three fatty acid on plasma lipids, cholesterol and lipoprotein fatty acid content in NIDDM patients." *Diabetologia* 40, no. 1 (1997): 45–52.

Haggans, C. J., A. M. Hutchins, B. A. Olson, W. Thomas, M. C. Martini, and J. L. Slavin. "Effect of flaxseed consumption on urinary estrogen metabolites in postmenopausal women." *Nutrition and Cancer* 33, no. 2 (1999): 188–195.

Hu, F. B., M. J. Stampfer, J. E. Manson, E. B. Rimm, A. Wolk, G. A. Colditz, C. H. Hennekens, and W. C. Willett. "Dietary intake of alpha-linolenic acid and risk of fatal ischemic heart disease among women." *American Journal of Clinical Nutrition* 69, no. 5 (1999): 890–897.

James, M. J., R. A. Gibson, and L. G. Cleland. "Dietary polyunsaturated fatty acids and inflammatory mediator production." *American Journal of Clinical Nutrition* 71 (2000): 343S–348S.

Jenab, M., S. Rickard, L. Orcheson, and Thompson L. "Flaxseed and Lignans Increase Cecal B-Glucuronidase Activity in Rats." *Nutrition and Cancer* 33, no. 2 (1999): 154–158.

Jenkins, D. J., C. W. Kendall, E. Vidgen, S. Agarwal, A. V. Rao, R. S. Rosenberg, E. P. Diamandis, R. Novokmet, C. C. Mehling, T. Perera, L. C. Griffin, and S. C. Cunnane. "Health aspects of partially defatted flaxseed, including effects on serum lipids, oxidative measures, and ex vivo androgen and progestin activity: a controlled crossover trial." *American Journal of Clinical Nutrition* 69, no. 3 (1999): 395–402.

Judd, A. "Flax: Some Historical Considerations." In *Flaxseed in Human Nutrition*, Cunnane and Thompson, eds., 1995.

Kremer, J. M. "Omega-three fatty acid supplements in rheumatoid arthritis." *American Journal of Clinical Nutrition* 71 (2000) 349S–51S.

McManus, R. M., J. Jumpson, D. T. Finegood, M. T. Clandinin, and E. A. Ryan. "A comparison of the effects of omega-three fatty acids from linseed oil and fish oil in well-controlled type II diabetes." *Diabetes Care* 19, no. 5 (1996): 463–467.

Malcolmson, L. J., R. Przybylski, and J. K. Daun. "Storage stability of milled flaxseed." Proceedings of the 57th Flax Institute of the United States, (1998): 75–80.

Morris, D. H. "Essential Fatty Acids, Flaxseed and Prostate Cancer." Paper prepared for Flax Council of Canada, 1999.

Pang, D., M. A. Allman-Farinelli, T. Wong, R. Barnes, K. M. Kingham. "Replacement of linoleic acid with alpha-linolenic acid does not alter blood lipids in normolipidaemic men." *British Journal of Nutrition* 80, no. 2 (1998): 163–167.

Parbtani, A., and W. F. Clark. "Flaxseed and Its Components in Renal Disease." In *Flaxseed in Human Nutrition*, Cunnane and Thompson, eds., 1995.

Ratnayake, W. M. N., W. A. Behrens, P. W. F. Fischer, M. R. L'Abbe, R. Mongeau, and J. L. Beare-Rogers. "Chemical and nutritional studies of flaxseed in rats." *Journal of Nutritional Biochemistry* 3 (1992): 232–240.

Rickard, S. E., Y. V. Yuan, J. Chen, and L. U. Thompson. "Dose effects of flaxseed and its lignan on N-methyl-N-nitrosourea-induced mammary tumorigenesis in rats." *Nutrition and Cancer* 35, no. 1 (1999): 50–57.

Simon, J. A., J. Fong, J. T. Bernert Jr, and W. S. Browner. "Serum fatty acids and the risk of stroke." *Stroke* 26, no. 5 (1995): 778–782.

Stevens, L. J., S. S. Zentall, J. L. Deck, M. L. Abate, B. A. Watkins, S. R. Lipp, and J. R. Burgess. "Essential fatty acid metablism in boys with attention-deficit hyperactivity disorder." *American Journal of Clinical Nutrition* 62, no. 4 (1995): 761–768.

Stitt, P. *History of Flax: 9000 years ago to 1986.* Proceeding of the 55th Flax Institute of the United States, 1994. Pp. 152–153.

Thompson, L. U. "Experimental Studies on lignans and cancer." *Bailliere's Clinical Endocrinology and Metabolism* 12, no. 4 (1998): 691–705.

Thompson, L. U., T. Li, J. Chen, and P. E. Goss. "Biological effects of dietary flaxseed in patients with breast cancer." *Breast Cancer Research Treatment* 64, no. 1 (December 2000): 50.

Tou, J. C., and L. U. Thompson. "Exposure to flaxseed or its lignan component during different developmental stages influences rat mammary gland structures." *Carcinogenesis* 20, no. 9 (1999): 1831–1835.

Vaisey-Genser, Marion, Msc., RD, and Diane H. Morris, Ph.D., RD. *Flaxseed: Health, Nutrition and Functionality.* Flax Council of Canada, 1997

Wolever T. "Flaxseed and glucose metabolism." In *Flaxseed in Human Nutrition*, Cunnane and Thompson, eds, 1995.

About the Author

Jane Reinhardt-Martin, known to her clients and TV audiences as "Dietitian Jane," received her B.S. degree in Dietetics and Food Service Management from the University of Wisconsin at Madison in 1986. In that same year she was accredited as a Registered Dietitian by the American Dietetic Association and is a Licensed Dietitian in the states of Iowa and Illinois. She is a member of both the American Dietetic Association and the Mississippi Valley Dietetic Association. She has also been a certified Jazzercise instructor.

She has devoted her career to promoting health and fitness, and to improving public awareness about these issues. She has been published in such professional journals as *Nutrition Forum* and the *American Journal of Clinical Nutrition,* and a regular contributor for *Parenting Magazine.* She has appeared as a food commentator on the Paula Sands Live Show, on KWQC-TV6, an NBC affiliate out of Davenport Iowa, and has even produced a video, *Exploring Vegetarianism: A Healthy Alternative* in 1999. In addition, she serves as consultant for area hospitals, head start agencies, and physician offices.

ORDER FORM

Flax Your Way to Better Health. . . .

$12.95 plus $1.50 Shipping and Handling. Illinois residents, add $.92 sales tax.

You can order this book directly using your credit card, through our website: **www.Flaxrd.com**. Or you can use the handy order form below. Just fill it out and send it with your check or money order to: Jane Reinhardt-Martin, 3711 23d Avenue, PMB 158, Moline, IL 61265.

NAME: _____

ADDRESS: _____

ADDRESS: _____

CITY: _____STATE: _____ZIP: _____

E-Mail Address: _____

PLEASE SEND ME _____ copies of *Flax Your Way to Better Health.*

Amount Enclosed: _____

The Buddha and His Teachings

The Buddha and
His Teachings

Edited by
Samuel Bercholz *and*
Sherab Chödzin Kohn

SHAMBHALA
Boulder
2003

Shambhala Publications, Inc.
4720 Walnut Street
Boulder, Colorado 80301
www.shambhala.com

13 12 11 10 9 8

Printed in the United States of America
∞ This edition is printed on acid-free paper that meets
the American National Standards Institute z39.48 Standard.

♻ This book is printed on 30% postconsumer recycled paper.
For more information please visit www.shambhala.com.

Distributed in the United States by Penguin Random House LLC
and in Canada by Random House of Canada Ltd

Author photo credits: Chögyam Trungpa: Karen Schulenberg.
Pema Chödrön: Lynn Davis, Dainin Katagiri; Richard Bend © 1985.
Ajahn Chah: Jim Roy.

Library of Congress Cataloging-in-Publication Data

The Buddha and his teachings/edited by Samuel Bercholz
and Sherab Chödzin Kohn.
p. cm.
Includes bibliographical references.
ISBN 978-1-57062-960-0
1. Gautama Buddha—Teachings. 2. Buddhism—Doctrines.
I. Bercholz, Samuel. II. Chödzin, Sherab.
BQ4132 .B83 2003 294.3—DC21
2002026876

CONTENTS

LIST OF ILLUSTRATIONS

A C K N O W L E D G M E N T S

THE EDITORS would like to thank the following people for
their efforts in making the publication of this book possible:
Bernardo Bertolucci, Jeremy Thomas, and Rudy Wurlitzer, respectively director, producer, and screenwriter of the film *Little
Buddha*, for being the catalysts for the creation of this book;
Laura Kaufman, for her excellent work in researching the art
for this volume and writing the captions; Debra Kelvin, for
gathering the permissions for both the art and the written material; Hiromitsu Washizuka of the Agency for Cultural Affairs,
Tokyo, for arranging the use of various works of art from Japanese museum collections; Anne MacQuarrie, for sharing her
"beginner's mind" in reviewing various chapters; Larry Mer-
melstein and Peter Turner of Shambhala Publications, for their
suggestions and contacts; and Emily Hilburn Sell and Kendra
Crossen of Shambhala Publications, for their suggestions and
for preparing the manuscript for publication.

"BUDDHISM" is a relatively modern Western term. The body of spiritual doctrine and practice to which it refers has generally been known on its own ground, in countries across Asia, as the Buddha Dharma, which is perhaps best translated "way of the Buddha." This teaching came from one young man who "woke up" from life's melodrama more than twenty-five hundred years ago and was thereafter called the Buddha, "the awakened one."

Now it turned out that this enlightenment of the Buddha's was profound and brilliant, accurate and powerful, and also warm and compassionate. It was like the sun behind the clouds. Anyone who has taken off in an airplane on a grim and gloomy day knows that beyond the cloud cover the sun is always shining. Even at night the sun is shining, but then we can't see it because the earth is in the way, and probably our pillow also. The Buddha explained that behind the cloud cover of thoughts—including very heavy clouds of emotionally charged thoughts backed up by entrenched habitual patterns—there is continual warm, bright, loving intelligence constantly shining. And even though in the midst of thoughts, emotions, and habitual patterns, intelligence may become dulled and confused, it is still this intelligence in the midst of the thoughts and emotions and habits that makes them so very captivating, so resourceful and various, so inexhaustible. This cloudy world of thoughts and emotions backed by habits continually churns out what I referred to above as life's melodrama, which from the Buddha's point of view is sleep. According to the Buddha

Dharma, everyone can wake up from this sleep. Everyone is capable of becoming Buddha.

When we go to the movies, many of us don't only like to see nice, pleasant, lovable movies. Just as much, or perhaps even more, we like to see sad, tragic, painful, or aggressive movies, even horror movies. The positive and the negative both draw us under their spell. In the same way, the Buddha recognized, we keep our own personal melodramas (made up of thoughts once removed) juicy and entertaining with these same very effective, sometimes positive but often negative elements. According to the Buddha Dharma, the personal melodrama that we keep going in one form or another over the years is known as ego.

Basically, of course, we know that even ego, or the sense of self, is made up of that warm basic intelligence fully discovered by the Buddha, because there simply isn't anything else clever enough to produce and maintain ego. But some kind of confusion has arisen, like a storm blowing up out of a cloudless sky. It's a very pervasive and stubbornly persistent storm. It contains all our hopes and fears relating to the processes of birth, growing up, being in our prime, aging, sickness, and death—a lot of pleasure and pain. But since the Buddha himself had awakened from all that hope and fear, he knew awakening from it was possible. He taught people how to go about awakening from it. With some people he just showed them his profound, brilliant wakefulness directly, and they too woke up on the spot, just like shaking off a dream.

So that is what Buddha Dharma is about—recognizing our psychological condition and working with it so we can wake up from the confused aspect of it. Buddhists follow the way that the Buddha taught for waking up from ego's confusion. Of course, occasionally one or another Buddhist wakes up before completing all the steps recommended by the Buddha. There are always a few rascals around like that. But most Buddhists patiently continue following the Buddha's path.

The main method the Buddha taught to help people awaken from confusion is meditation. Meditating in the Buddhist way is not like praying. It is not trying to believe in anything or making utterances in your mind about your beliefs, longings, or intentions. It is more like relaxing and just letting things be as they are—without cranking anything up. We spend a lot of time in our lives trying to crank something up. In meditating, Buddhists take the approach of letting go of all that struggle and resting in the way things really are, which is however they happen to be.

Various techniques for taming attention, which tends to be wild and jump around erratically when people first begin to meditate, were taught by the Buddha. These techniques help to bring about natural composure in mind and body. This in turn helps us to relinquish ego's ongoing struggle. As we learn to relax from that, the turbulent and captivating ego world of thoughts and emotions begins to become transparent, and our basic profound, brilliant, and loving intelligence begins to shine through.

You might think that if you let go of your ego world, you might become passive and defenseless like some kind of crash dummy, and people will take advantage of you. Or that you might wander around aimlessly in the street without an agenda. If this were the case, as one contemporary Buddhist master pointed out, it would be necessary to have enlightenment wards in hospitals to take care of bruised or socially inoperative buddhas. But this is not the case. Rather than being inmate types, people who have become enlightened to any degree are builders of hospitals for other people. Their intelligence and compassion are relatively unobstructed, and they tend to become quite active and effective citizens.

Even though the Buddha Dharma is based on direct experience and encourages its practitioners to relate to naked experience with bare attention, there are aspects of the teaching, which help to form a background for the practitioner's effort, that seem like they are speculative thoughts at least one step removed from direct experience. For example, we have the notions of karma and rebirth. These sound like the usual kind of religious doctrines requiring belief or faith. But let us look for a moment at these two teachings.

Karma is a Sanskrit word meaning "action." The teaching about karma is that the actions we take now will have consequences later. For the most part, this is the everyday idea of cause-and-effect that most people take for granted. If you kick a ball it goes. If you lose your airline ticket, you have hassles. This is karma, action and its action, or effect.

But according to the Buddha, action's action sometimes happens on a more subtle level. Sometimes the conditions necessary for action's effect to happen are not present. Let's say you murdered somebody in the woods. There was no one else around and no evidence. Nobody suspected you at all. Yet there was a horrible moment of raw aggression, unforgettably vivid. Does that just go away? Of course we have the memory of it. But what is memory anyway?

According to the Buddha, action's action does not tend to dissipate. The effect will tend to happen some time, whenever suitable conditions are present. That moment of horrible aggression is likely to have its backlash some time. But will that backlash happen to you?

This question connects the idea of karma to that of rebirth, or reincarnation. In the India of the Buddha's time, in the first millennium BCE (as to a great extent in the India of today), the notion of rebirth was taken for granted by almost everybody. According to the popular Indian idea of reincarnation, you get reborn again and again in different forms, sometimes as a human, sometimes as an animal, sometimes as a god, sometimes in hell—in all kinds of better or worse circumstances. What you do now, it is thought, will effect your future rebirth. If you're greedy and mean, you might be reborn as a dung beetle. If you're a splendid person, you might be reborn as a god or a king or queen. A murderer will suffer a hideous situation somewhere along in the series of his rebirths. Other karma might come to fruition first, but some time or other the backlash of his aggression will strike him—with a corresponding force and character, of course, because it is the action of his earlier action.

The Buddha's teaching about karma and rebirth resembles this picture in some ways but differs from it essentially. How? One of the fundamental teachings of the Buddha is egolessness, the fundamental unreality of the self. If there is no self that gets reborn, what does rebirth mean? And can you just die and get away with murder?

According to one Buddhist text, the *Kalachakra Tantra*, the karma of sentient beings is so powerful that it brings worlds into existence in order to reach fulfillment. Between the existences of worlds—at the right moment, when the necessary conditions have gathered—karma, the incompleted action of the previous action of sentient beings, begins to activate the basic particles of space. The particles come into motion generating a vast karmic wind that stirs up the other cosmic elements—fire, water, and earth—and a world or worlds are formed.

It can also be said that individual sentient beings, like worlds, come into existence through the coming together of the force of karma and other necessary conditions. Causally related karmic elements tend to hang together in the transmigratory history of sentient beings. In that way, memory itself seems to be an expression of karmic continuity. But in most cases there are no coherent conscious memories of the relationships that related the karmic elements that are the threads of our everyday lives.

But according to the Buddha, karma is not all-pervasive and all-determining. The wind of karma only blows in the cloudy weather systems of thoughts related to passion, aggression, and willful ignorance. In the endless brilliance of the cloudless sunlit sky, there is nothing for it to blow. In open, unobstructed space of sentient beings' basic intelligence, karma becomes inoperative. The awakened one is victorious over karma.

Understandings such as this, which may seem abstract, are part of the Buddha Dharma, because they were included in the vastness of the unobstructed direct experience of the Buddha and other enlightened masters of the Buddha Dharma. They have been handed down through unbroken lineages of enlightened teachers stemming from the Buddha himself as part of the support system provided to help people wake up. But they are not required articles of belief. The Buddha discouraged people from taking his teachings on blind faith. He invited anyone wishing to follow his path to verify all his teachings personally and to maintain a healthy skepticism until realization clears up doubts. So all the Buddhist teachings are provided for the practitioner's examination and concrete testing. It is always helpful to remember that the Buddha himself was not a Buddhist.

The editors of this book have chosen a variety of texts from the centuries' store of Dharma writing to give readers convenient access to the essential teachings of the Buddha. The selection begins with a brief life of the Buddha and a quick factual survey of Buddhist history. Then follow texts expressing the thought and practice of the three main divisions of the Buddha Dharma, the Hinayana, Mahayana, and Vajrayana. The works of great Buddhist masters of the past and present have been included.

An introduction to meditation practice will be found, as well as chapters to help answer common questions about karma and rebirth. Thus interested readers will find what they need to acquire a comprehensive impression of the Buddha Dharma that has both depth and breadth.

Not all the selections in this book make easy reading. A passage may be difficult because it runs against the current of our habitual thinking. Sometimes meaning may be elusive because the subject matter is subtle and profound. Also, specialized terms have been developed over the centuries, and they have been translated into English in different ways. (To standardize foreign terms and lessen confusion, we have changed most Pali terminology in the selections to Sanskrit. A glossary is also provided, of which the reader is encouraged to make liberal use.) Still, with a little perseverance, the reader will be able to gain insights that may bring helpful new perspectives to everyday life. Trying meditation might be helpful. It is the way par excellence of discovering the great truths in one's own experience.

Traditionally it is said that when a person catches a glimpse of ego's confusion and connects this with an aspiration to awaken, he or she begins to enter the stream of Dharma. When you find you are trusting yourself in all kinds of new and fresh ways you never imagined before, you are really getting your feet wet. These days more and more Westerners seem to be doing this.

PART ONE

The Life
of the Buddha
and the Spread of
Buddhism

The Life of the Buddha   1

SHERAB CHÖDZIN KOHN

 THE BUDDHA SHAKYAMUNI'S enlightenment and his forty-five years of teaching following it are the source of the Buddha Dharma. The Buddha's whole life is an inspiring model for Buddhist practitioners. A key point is the Buddha's insuperable longing for the truth, which led to his great renunciation—when he left the life of a royal householder with its wealth, power, pleasures. Though it is not necessary to quit one's worldly station, this renunciation is something every practitioner must replicate on some level. On the basis of the same kind of longing for the truth, practitioners will find a way of releasing themselves at least to some degree from attachment to gain or loss, fame or disgrace, praise or blame, pleasure or pain—in order to make their minds free to perceive the truth. Like the Buddha, practitioners must diligently apply the means to personal realization of the truth, meditation. Buddhists have an advantage over the Buddha—the directions of the old wayfarer himself on how to travel the path. Then, like the Buddha, they may become enlightened and teach others. Since the Buddha transmitted the awakened state of mind, together with the methodology for attaining it, to hundreds of his disciples, countless women and men down through the centuries have

also attained enlightenment and conveyed it to others, fresh and new in each generation. The following piece, abridged from a longer work, gives the essence of the Buddha's story.

SHAKYAMUNI BUDDHA, THE AWAKENED ONE, RECOUNTED HIS own story to his close disciple Ananda.

Through countless lives, he was a bodhisattva, one who is on the path of awakening, who labored and sacrificed for the benefit of other beings. In a past age of the world, as a forest-dwelling ascetic named Sumedha, he threw himself at the feet of an earlier buddha, Dipankara, and resolved to become a buddha himself. Dipankara looked down and saw the bodhisattva lying in the mud before him, offering his body as a plank to be walked upon so that the Buddha would not have to soil his feet. He paused in his progress and prophesied to the multitude that accompanied him everywhere that after many eons this young ascetic would indeed also become a buddha. Through many subsequent lives, the bodhisattva practiced the ten transcendental virtues that prepare the way to buddhahood, complete enlightenment. Finally, when he had neared perfection of compassion and understanding, he took birth as a god in the fourth heaven of the desire realm, Tushita, the Heaven of the Contented. There, as Bearer of the White Banner, Shvetaketu, he shone as the teacher and king of a hundred thousand long-lived gods. That life in the Heaven of the Contented had already gone on for many thousands of years when the bodhisattva heard a tumultuous sound resounding through the entire universe, the uproar caused by all the gods of the three thousand world systems telling each other that at last the time had come for the bodhisattva to attain buddhahood. On three kinds of occasions is such an uproar heard: when a world age is to end in destruction, when a universal monarch is to be born, and when a buddha is to be born. Now all the gods gathered in the Heaven of the Contented and implored Bearer of the White Banner not to let the moment pass, but to be born on earth and become a buddha for the sake of all sentient beings.

When he had decided that the time had come to be born, the bodhisattva went to the Nandana Grove in the capital of the Heaven of the Contented, and there, mindfully and fully aware, he died. At the same moment, fully mindful and aware, he entered his earthly mother's womb.

It was in the middle of the first millennium BCE that the bodhisattva took his final birth, on Jambudvipa, the southern continent of this world system, in the country of the Shakyas, which lay in the foothills of the Himalayas in present-day southern Nepal. His father, Shuddhodana, was the king of the Shakyas. As befitted a king, he was of the kshatriya, or warrior, caste, and his clan lineage, that of the Gautamas, was ancient and pure. The bodhisattva's mother was Mahamaya, the daughter of Suprabuddha, a powerful Shakyan noble. Since the bodhisattva was born a prince of the Shakyas, after his enlightenment he was known as the sage of the Shakyas, Shakyamuni. Since his clan name was Gautama, he was later also called Gautama Buddha.

One night during the midsummer festival in Kapilavastu, Queen Mahamaya dreamed that she ascended a height, and a large and beautiful white elephant with six tusks entered her womb through her right side. Then a great multitude bowed down to her. When she awoke, she had a feeling of great well-being and knew she was with child.

When she told the king of this, he called his brahmin wise men, who were versed in astrology and the interpretation of dreams. The brahmins told the king that a son would be born to him who would have the thirty-two major marks and the eighty minor marks of a great being. If he remained in the palace and pursued a worldly life, he would become a chakravartin, a universal monarch. However, if he renounced his home, wealth, and position and wandered forth as a holy man, he would become a completely enlightened buddha, and satisfy all beings with the elixir of deathlessness. The king was very pleased with these predictions. He gave the brahmins rich gifts and distributed food and gifts to the people.

Mahamaya's pregnancy lasted ten months. It was springtime when she began to feel the imminence of the birth. She asked to be taken to Lumbini, a pleasure grove belonging to her family that she had loved as a girl. Shuddhodana gave orders, and a great train of nobles, courtiers, and servants issued from the city to accompany her there. Colorful tents housing comfortable living quarters were set up, and all preparations were made for the birth.

In the middle of the month, on the full-moon day, Queen Mahamaya was walking in the grove when suddenly she felt heavy and raised her right arm to take hold of a tree branch for support. Just then, as she stood grasping the branch, the bodhisattva was born into the world, instantly and painlessly. A light shone through the worlds and the earth shook. Then the bodhisattva, who already had the form of a small child, took seven firm steps, looked into the four directions, and said, "I am the leader of the world, the guide of the world. This is my final birth." Two spouts of water, one warm and one cool, issued from the air above the bodhisattva's head and poured their pure and soothing waters over him. Thus washed, he was placed on a couch covered with silk brocades, and a white parasol was raised above his head.

On the fifth day after the bodhisattva's birth, Shuddhodana called for the traditional naming ceremony to be performed. Nobles, courtiers, and brahmins were invited in large numbers. Food and drink were plentiful, and generous gifts were made to all. The boy was given the name Siddhartha, which means "accomplishment of the goal."

Seven days after the Buddha's birth, Queen Mahamaya died. Her sister Mahaprajapati Gautami, who was also married to King Shuddhodana, was chosen to nurse and raise the child. Mahaprajapati was full of love for her sister's son and raised him like her own favorite.

For King Shuddhodana, all the wondrous events surrounding his son's arrival had been a source of gladness, but they had also been uncanny and had cast a shadow of awe and uncertainty. Queen Mahamaya's death again touched this darker side. In his moment of loss, his mind came to rest on the equivocal predictions of the brahmins. His son would be either a universal monarch or a buddha. True, greatness and glory lay with either, but it was now the former possibility that became enshrined in the king's heart. If his son succeeded him and became a great ruler, all the king's wishes would be fulfilled. But if the prince abandoned royal palace and position, Shuddhodana would be without an heir—his house would be empty. This possibility now became a menace to be warded off. Thus he set about doing everything in his power to make matters take the desired turn. He carefully sheltered the prince from the world and surrounded him with luxury and pleasures. If the prince found nothing more to wish for, the king thought, the notion of abandoning the palace would never occur to him.

As Siddhartha grew older, the king surrounded him with scores of unblemished beauties who were skilled in singing, dancing, and playing musical instruments. Beautiful women, in constantly changing variety, accompanied the prince always, seeking in every way to divert and entertain him and provide him with pleasure. Beautiful rooms with rich furnishings and lushly planted roof gardens with gorgeous silken canopies were the prince's daily haunts. Much of the time he did not even descend to the lower stories of the palace.

When Siddhartha reached the age of sixteen, a suitable bride was chosen for him. She was Yashodhara, a dignified and beautiful young woman, the daughter of a Shakyan noble family. A royal wedding was held, and the young woman came to share Siddhartha's life in the palace.

For the next dozen years little changed in the conditions of Siddhartha's life. The prince was bound not only by this carefree life of pleasure, but also by strong ties of family and position. Nonetheless in the course of time the spell of the palace wore thin. When the sorrows and limitations of ordinary life finally began to beat in upon the prince, they struck him almost as an insult, an insolent intrusion. And they made an extremely strong impression on him.

Tradition tells us of four encounters that finally shattered the bodhisattva's contentment with his life of pleasure.

The prince had a charioteer named Chandaka whom he used to have take him on occasional outings. These outings were well orchestrated by those whom Shuddhodana had placed in charge of the prince's service. Care was always taken to clear and decorate the way, and especially to remove anything ugly or unpleasant that might disturb the prince's mood.

One day, when the prince was already in his late twenties, he commanded Chandaka to take him to a particular garden to spend the afternoon. On the way, alongside the road they encountered a man bent over with age. His hair was gray and sparse, his face wizened, his eyes red. His hands shook and his gait was unsteady as he walked feebly, leaning on a stick. The prince asked Chandaka, "Who is that man? The hairs of his head do not seem to resemble those of other people. His eyes also are strange, and he walks so oddly."

Chandaka replied, "Lord, that is an old man. He is that way because of the effect time has on everyone who is born. What that man has are the afflictions of old age that await all of us. The skin dries and wrinkles, the hair loses its color and falls out, the veins and arteries stiffen, the flesh loses its suppleness and shapelessly sags. We are beset with pains. Our eyes skin over and get red. The rest of our senses grow feeble. In fact, as time goes on, our whole body winds up with little strength left in it, hardly enough to move along, as you see with that old fellow there."

When the prince heard this explanation, he became frightened and upset. Instead of continuing on to the garden as he had intended, he ordered Chandaka to turn around and return to the palace.

On another outing in his chariot, by the side of the road Siddhartha saw a man suffering from disease. He was emaciated and pale. Parts of his body were swollen and other parts were covered with sores. He was leaning on another man for support and occasionally emitted piteous cries of pain. When Chandaka explained to Siddhartha what disease was, rather than continue with his outing, the prince returned to the palace deeply troubled.

On a third occasion driving in his chariot, the prince encountered a funeral procession. He saw a corpse being borne on a litter followed by bereaved relatives wailing, tearing their clothes, and covering themselves with ashes. He asked Chandaka to explain this horrifying spectacle.

"My prince, do you not know? This man lying on the litter is dead. His life has come to an end. His senses and feelings and consciousness have departed forever. He has become just like a log or a bundle of hay. Those relatives of his who have cared for him and cherished him through his life will never see him again. Without exception, everything that is born must die."

In deep distress, the prince commanded Chandaka to return to the palace.

On a fourth occasion when the bodhisattva was out driving in his chariot with Chandaka, he encountered a mendicant with upright bearing and a serene and radiant countenance. Siddhartha was impressed by this sight and questioned Chandaka about the man. Chandaka replied, "This is a holy man who has renounced worldly life and entered upon a life of homelessness. Such homeless mendicants devote themselves to spiritual pursuits such as meditation or practicing austerities. They have no possessions but wander from place to place, begging their daily food."

In deep thought, the prince had himself driven back to the palace.

To divert his son from his preoccupations, the king decided to send him on a visit to a nearby farming village. He hoped that Siddhartha would take an interest in the methods of the farmers. But when he got there, the delicate youth saw the toiling workers, dirty and half-clad, streaming with sweat as they struggled in the heat of the sun. The oxen were laden with heavy yokes that rubbed the hide from their shoulders. The plows they pulled bruised the earth and destroyed worms and insects in their progress. To force the beasts to work, the farmers had to prod them with iron goads that made their straining flanks run with blood. Slaver and foam dripped from their mouths as they were forced to drag the heavy plows over long distances. Thick clouds of gnats and stinging flies never ceased to torment them.

The prince was overcome with revulsion. When he learned that the laborers were his father's slaves, he freed them on the spot, telling them, "From today, you will no longer be slaves. You are free to go wherever you like and live in happiness." He also released the oxen, saying to them, "Go. From now on be free and eat the sweetest grass and drink the purest water and be fanned by cool breezes from every direction."

The bodhisattva had reached his twenty-ninth year, and his wife, Yashodhara, was with child. But he was now thinking in earnest of leaving home. Old age, sickness, and death, and the suffering that seemed to be everywhere, cast restrictions on existence that he could not accept as final. Somehow he had to triumph over these enemies of happiness. Yet he could not hope to do so by whiling away his life in the palace. His encounter with the mendicant seemed to show the path he must follow to come to grips with these profound vexations.

One night in the women's quarters, after an evening of entertainment, the prince woke up, and in the still-flickering lamplight saw the beautiful women lying about him, asleep in various positions of abandon. One young woman, who still held her lute, lay drooling from one side of her open mouth and snoring loudly. Other women lay propped against the walls or against pieces of furniture. Some had wine stains on their clothing. Others with their rich costumes thrown open lay in ungainly postures with their bodies exposed. In the stupor of sleep, they looked like randomly heaped corpses. The seductive vision of their beauty, which had so long captivated the prince, was shattered.

That same night, Yashodhara had a dream that Siddhartha had left her. She awoke and told him the dream. Then she said, "Lord, wherever you go, please take me with you." And knowing that he was going to a place beyond suffering and death, he agreed, and told her, "Where I go, you may go too."

It was a night not too long after the birth of his son, Rahula, that the bodhisattva chose to quit the palace forever and enter the path of homelessness. He decided to have a last look at Rahula before leaving. He found him asleep next to Yashodhara, with her hand resting lightly on his head. He knew that if he picked the baby up, he would wake his wife and leaving would become difficult. He turned on the spot, vowing to see his son again after he had attained enlightenment. All the palace women and all the guards and their captains, even those on watch, seemed to be sleeping soundly, for no one emerged to hinder his departure. The bodhisattva woke the charioteer Chandaka, commanded him to saddle his favorite horse, Kanthaka, and to accompany him on foot.

It was the full-moon night of the summer month of Ashadha when the bodhisattva, astride Kanthaka and with Chandaka at his heels, left Kapalivastu and struck out south through the forest.

Reaching the top of a hill outside Kapilavastu, the bodhisattva considered turning to have a last look in the light of the moon at the city where he had spent his life. He had just firmly resolved to continue without looking back, when Mara, the embodiment of self-deception, appeared suspended in the air before him.

"Do not go," cried Mara, "for in seven days the golden wheel of universal sovereignty will appear, and you will become ruler over the whole world with its four great continents and myriads of islands."

"Mara! I know you!" exclaimed the bodhisattva. "And well I know that what you have said is true. But rulership over this world is not what I seek, but to become a buddha in order to heal its suffering."

Having been seen for what he was, Mara disappeared, but from that time on he clung to the bodhisattva like a shadow, waiting for the moment when weakness might appear.

The bodhisattva continued riding through the night and put a great distance between himself and Kapilavastu. In the morning he crossed a small river and dismounted on the far bank.

"Chandaka," he said, "I am entering the life of homelessness in order to seek truth for the sake of all. It is time for you to take Kanthaka and go back to Kapilavastu and my father." He removed his gold and jewel ornaments, including the royal diadem from his head, and gave them also to Chandaka to bring back.

Although Chandaka pleaded with the prince to give up his plan and return to the palace, Siddhartha was firm. He took Chandaka's sword and cut off his long hair, which was gathered on top of his head in a princely coif. Then his attention fell on his robe of fine embroidered silk, and he thought how ill-suited it was for a wandering mendicant. He was puzzling over what alternative might be possible when a deer hunter stepped out of the forest wearing a simple saffron-dyed robe much like those worn by wandering mendicants. The bodhisattva greeted the hunter and offered to exchange clothing with him. The man was well pleased and soon departed in the prince's rich robe, while the bodhisattva, equally pleased, remained behind in the plain one. There was nothing to distinguish him now from an ordinary mendicant other than his lordly bearing and beauty of face and limb. Only a seer or a rare brahmin might have recognized the thirty-two major and eighty minor marks he bore upon him.

"Now go back and tell the king what you have seen," the bodhisattva told Chandaka.

The bodhisattva had gone from prince to beggar in an instant. He had won the life he had contemplated with longing. Freedom was his; all worldly bonds had been severed. He resolved never to turn back until he had accomplished this victory, and he began his wandering.

Day by day he learned to beg food. At first, accustomed as he was to only the finest dishes, he was nearly unable to put the leftovers of crude fare he collected in his alms bowl to his lips. But gradually he became used to this coarse food and to sleeping on the ground with no shelter but trees or rocks.

The mendicant made his way south by stages across the Ganges to the country of the Magadhans. As the bodhisattva wandered, it began to dawn on him that he would eventually have to find a teacher. And so, after a time, having heard of a highly reputed master, he traveled back north across the Ganges to the hermitage of the renowned sage Arada of the Kalama clan, not far from the city of Vaishali. When he got there he found that Arada had a large community of followers living round about him in the forest. Without hesitation, Gautama asked to see the teacher. One of the disciples conducted him into Master Arada's presence.

"Sir," said Gautama, "I wish to lead a holy life under your guidance. Please allow me to remain here and teach me your doctrine and practice."

Arada was impressed by the bodhisattva and agreed to teach him his metaphysical views about an eternal principle lying beyond the world of the senses. Gautama quickly learned Arada's doctrine in detail. When he was able to recite it flawlessly and answer questions about it correctly, Arada gave him the instructions he needed to attain successive levels of meditative absorption. So quickly did Gautama accomplish the levels of meditation taught by the teacher that Arada said to him, "I am very fortunate to have encountered a disciple as gifted as you. In a short time you have learned and directly realized everything I know myself. I have no more to teach you. Why not remain here with us, and you and I together will lead this community?"

But Gautama still felt himself far from total liberation. The goal of enlightenment still lay before him. So he thanked Arada Kalama for all that he had taught him, and courteously took his leave.

Gautama then sought the teaching of another well-known forest master, Rudraka Ramaputra, whose community was not far away. Rudraka's doctrine was more elaborate than Arada's but similar. The meditative practice also was along the same lines, but Rudraka had mastered one further level of meditation.

In a short time Gautama attained this final level, but he recognized that complete liberation still eluded him. Thus, although Rudraka, in recognition of Gautama's level of realization, requested him to stay and take over sole leadership of the community, Gautama declined and again resumed his wandering. He felt now that there was no more he could learn from teachers. He was determined to spare no exertion to attain enlightenment, his final goal.

Gautama began traveling southeast and again crossed the Ganges. Then he moved by short stages through the country of the Magadhans. At last he came to the region of Uruvilva on the Nairanjana River, not far from the little town of Gaya, a place where he decided to settle down and work on his task in earnest.

Since he had entered homelessness, all about him he had seen holy men performing ascetic practices such as retaining the breath, fasting, or meditating under the midday sun within a circle of fire. These practices meant subjecting oneself to tremendous hardship and pain, which seemed to be a way to conquer the desires and attachments that made one get caught up again and again in the transient world of birth, old age, sickness, and death. Since Gautama had failed to attain enlightenment through the methods he had tried so far, he now felt he must try asceticism.

In time, word of Gautama's activities spread through the country among the mendicant seekers. They told one another how the former prince had quickly equaled Arada and Rudraka but then declined leadership of their communities. Especially they told of how he had now given himself over to the most relentless extremes of asceticism imaginable and must soon attain liberation or die. Kaundinya, the young brahmin who had predicted at the time of his birth that he would become a buddha and who had long since entered homelessness himself, heard of these things, and he came to find Gautama. He brought with him four fellow seekers named Ashvajit, Vashpa, Mahanaman, and Bhadrika. These five became Gautama's followers, and they served him. They brought him his tiny pittances of food. When he was too weak to drink, they helped him drink. When he was too weak to wash himself, they helped him wash. When he was too weak to stand, they helped him stand. And they awaited the day when he would attain enlightenment and be able to guide them also to the goal.

After nearly six years had passed in this way, Gautama was close to death. Yet with all his austerities, he had not succeeded in lifting himself beyond the ordinary human state. Supreme knowledge and vision still remained beyond his grasp. Might there be another way of attaining enlightenment?

Over the next days, Gautama resumed taking one meager meal per day. His followers thought he had given up the struggle and was indulging himself, and they left him. Since he was still too weak to gather alms himself, young women from the village, who felt both pity and awe for him, brought him a little food each day. His strength and his fine radiant color began to return.

On the morning of the full-moon day of the spring month of Vaishekha, thirty-five years to the day after he was born, the bodhisattva made his way to the nearby Nairanjana River to bathe. Afterward he climbed out on the bank and sat down in a grove of trees. He was still a little weak but he was full of confidence. As he was sitting there, a beautiful young woman in a dress of dark blue cloth approached. She was Sujata, the daughter of the chief cowherder of the village. Sujata bowed to him and shyly asked him to accept her special food offering of rice boiled in cream and sweetened with wild honey. Gautama smiled and ate the delicious rice, the best food he had had since leaving the palace. It made him feel strong and good. Then he rested in the grove until the heat of the day had passed.

Toward evening he was pervaded by a strong sense of purpose. He was sure that the time had come for the accomplishment of his task. He got up and crossed the river. On the other side, he met a grass-cutter who gave him some tufts of soft ku-

1. Liang K'ai, SHAKYAMUNI DESCENDING FROM
THE MOUNTAINS. China, thirteenth century, ink and
color on silk. Tokyo National Museum.

Siddhartha, the future Buddha Shakyamuni, is shown here
as he leaves the wilderness where he practiced austerities. It
is a great turning point, for he has renounced both the life
of a householder and the life of an ascetic, and is now alone
on his spiritual journey. The artist, Liang K'ai, uses a som-
ber wintry landscape to convey the mood of Siddhartha's
open state.

2. THE BUDDHA IN MEDITATION. Sri Lanka, Anuradhapura, third or fourth century. Photo by Ananda K. Coomaraswamy.

After Siddhartha left the wilderness, he wandered to Gaya. He sat beneath a tree and resolved to remain in meditation until his own insight had shown him the true nature of things. This large stone statue portrays the Buddha in his meditation, with legs crossed and hands folded in his lap. The heroic, deeply human treatment is characteristic of the art of Sri Lanka.

3. Mahabodhi Temple, Bodh Gaya, India. Photo by John C. Huntington.

As Siddhartha meditated, he saw with penetrating clarity all beings' lack of enduring essence, the patterns by which they perpetuate suffering, and the means to end suffering. The site at Bodh Gaya where he attained enlightenment is the preeminent holy place of Buddhism. The stone tower of the Mahabodhi Temple rises beside a venerable tree reportedly descended from the one under which the Buddha sat. Today the Buddhist pilgrims who visit Bodh Gaya come from all over the world.

4. THE BUDDHA PREACHING THE FIRST SERMON. India, fifth century, stone. Ar-cheological Museum, Sarnath. Photo by John C. Huntington.

Shakyamuni Buddha set in motion the "wheel of the teachings" when he delivered his first sermon at the Deer Park in Sarnath. This statue of the teaching Buddha was carved at Sarnath about a thousand years after the event. The Buddha makes the hand gesture of "turning the wheel." Beneath his seat is the audience of the first sermon—his former ascetic companions. The statue is renowned for its refined detail and perfected proportions. Its idealization suggests the transcendent nature of Buddhahood.

5. THE PARINIRVANA OF THE BUDDHA. Sri Lanka, twelfth century, living rock. Gal Vihara, Polonnaruwa. Photo by John C. Huntington.

The Buddha passed into *parinirvana* at Kushinagara. There is a widespread tradition of portraying the event in sculpture of colossal scale. This powerful work, carved from a great outcropping of rock, is almost fifty feet long. As in scriptural accounts, the Buddha is represented in death lying on his right side with his hand under his head.

6. The "Two Houses Caves," Vulture Peak Mountain. Bihar State, India. Photo by John C. Huntington.

The Buddha traveled and preached throughout northeastern India for about fifty years. At Vulture Peak Mountain, located outside the ancient city of Rajagriha, one may still see the caves formed by natural rock outcroppings where the Buddha and his disciples are believed to have stayed. Many scriptures are said to be records of teachings that the Buddha delivered at Vulture Peak Mountain.

sha grass. He walked on until he came to a place that felt suitable, and there he made a seat with the kusha grass on the east side of a pipal tree. Then Gautama swore a resolute oath not to stir from that seat until he had attained enlightenment, even at the cost of his life.

As Gautama settled firmly into the cross-legged meditation posture, Mara too realized that the crucial moment had come, and he trembled. He knew that once the bodhisattva had attained enlightenment, he would be forever beyond his power. Mara first sought to intimidate the bodhisattva. "Rise up, Siddhartha, warrior prince afraid of death," he cried. "How dare you seat yourself in my seat. You have ventured where you surely do not belong! You overstep yourself, little man. Follow your proper path and give up the way of liberation. Look after your abandoned family and kingdom!"

The bodhisattva remained composed and paid Mara no heed.

Then Mara approached the bodhisattva in the guise of the god of love. He raised his bow of flowers strung with a line of humming bees and shot the bodhisattva with the arrow of desire. But the arrow hung in the air and fell harmlessly aside.

Then Mara mounted his war elephant and gathered his host. There were monsters and goblins of every description who screeched and howled, challenging the heavens with their din. Before this onslaught, the bodhisattva remained unmoved, unperturbed.

In desperation Mara demanded by what right the bodhisattva dared to occupy the seat that rightly belonged to himself. He launched a whirlwind at Gautama, but not even the hem of the bodhisattva's robe stirred. Mara sent a raging deluge, then blinding sheets of fire. The bodhisattva remained untouched and profoundly composed. Then he answered Mara's question. He declared that he had earned the right to that sacred seat through the merit of countless lives of practicing generosity and the rest of the ten transcendental virtues. "If you have any right to this seat," he challenged Mara, "then what witnesses do you have that you have practiced the ten virtues?"

Mara roared with laughter, and all of his misshapen creatures loudly bawled out their testimony. Then he turned on the bodhisattva, thinking that now he had him because he was utterly alone. "What witnesses do *you* have?" he lashed out.

The bodhisattva reached out and touched the earth with his

fingertips. "The earth is my witness," he said. Then from very deep down came an immense booming and rumbling from the shaking of the very essence of the earth element itself. All the earth shook and its thundering drowned out the terrified cries of Mara's minions. In a moment the entire host had fled. Then Mara himself, defeated, slunk away.

The air cleared and was still. The full moon rose in the sky and shone softly. The bodhisattva, unmoving, entered into the first level of meditation. The night was utterly silent, as even insects made no murmur. As the moon continued to rise, the bodhisattva's composure deepened, and one by one he mastered the levels of meditation until he reached the fourth. His concentration was bright and unblemished, full and balanced. Then through great confidence and trust, he relinquished the watcher, and his mind entered into an effortless, fathomless openness untroubled by content. Yet he did not become caught up in this. Rather, with utter clarity and tenderness, he turned his mind to untying the knot of birth, old age, sickness, and death.

He saw that the condition for old age, sickness, and death is birth. Once birth happens, the rest follows inevitably. He saw that the condition for birth lay in processes of becoming already set in motion; that the condition for this was grasping or craving; that the condition for this was desire; and the condition for desire, feelings of happiness, suffering, or indifference; and the condition for these, sensual contact; and the condition for sensual contact, the fields of the senses; the condition for sense fields, the arising of mind-body; the condition for mind-body, consciousness. He saw that mind-body and consciousness condition each other to make a rudimentary sense of self. He saw that the condition for consciousness was volitional impulses, and finally that the condition for volitional impulses was ignorance.

Thus he saw that the whole process ending in old age and death begins when basic intelligence slips into unawareness of its own nature. In this way all-pervading intelligence strays into the sense of a self.

After this, the clarity and openness of his mind increased yet further. Then in the first watch of the night, his inner vision became completely unobstructed. Then he turned his attention to the past, and he saw his and others' countless past lives stretching back over many eons and ages of the world.

In the second watch of the night, moved by compassion he opened his wisdom eye yet further and saw the spectacle of the whole universe as in a spotless mirror. He saw beings being born and passing away in accordance with karma, the laws of cause and effect. Seeing birth and death occurring in accordance with this chain of causality, the bodhisattva saw the cyclic paths of all beings. He saw the unfortunate, the exalted, and the lowly going their various ways. He saw how, ignorant and suffering, they were tossed on the stormy waves of birth, old age, sickness, and death.

In the third and last watch of the night, he applied himself to the task of rooting out this suffering once and for all. He had clearly understood the wheel of dependent arising in which each stage follows from a preceding cause, beginning with ignorance. And he saw how beings were driven on it by the powerful motive force of karma. Now his divine eye sought the means of liberation. He saw that through the cessation of birth, old age and death would not exist; through the cessation of becoming, there would be no birth; through the cessation of grasping, no becoming—and so back through the sequence of causation to ignorance. He saw suffering, the cause of suffering, the cessation of suffering, and at last also the path to cessation.

At the end of the third watch, at the first light of dawn the bodhisattva saw through the very last trace of ignorance in himself. Thus he attained complete and utter enlightenment and became the Buddha. The first words that came to him were these:

> Seeking but not finding the House Builder,
> I traveled through the round of countless births:
> O painful is birth ever and again.
> > House Builder, you have now been seen;
> > You shall not build the house again.
> > Your rafters have been broken down;
> > Your ridge pole is demolished too.
> > My mind has now attained the unformed nirvana
> > And reached the end of every kind of craving.

Then he thought: "I have attained the unborn. My liberation is unassailable. This is my last birth. There will now be no renewal of becoming."

Following the moment of enlightenment, the Buddha continued to meditate at the Bodhi (Enlightenment) Tree and subsequently at various other places in its vicinity. After a time he considered whether he should teach the Dharma to others. "It is too profound and too difficult to be taught," he thought. "It runs too much against the grain of stubborn and all-pervasive delusion. A world so totally caught up in attachment, so used to living in lust and aggression, has too much dust on its eyes ever to be able to perceive the truth that it hides from." Thus the Blessed One concluded he would not teach. He would remain silent.

Then the god Sahampati became aware of the Buddha's decision. He appeared before the Blessed One and with palms joined entreated him on behalf of all beings to "turn the wheel of Dharma." He pleaded that there were many who were genuine seekers of the truth with but little dust on their eyes. These would be able to perceive the Dharma in its subtlety and depth. "If you will only teach," he said, "you will liberate countless beings from the cycle of suffering."

Having been entreated in this manner, the Buddha was moved by compassion. He consented to the god's request by remaining silent, and when he knew he had been heard, Sahampati bowed and departed.

Having remained by the Bodhi Tree near Gaya in the region of Uruvilva for as long as he chose, the Blessed One started north for Varanasi.

After a few days, having crossed the Ganges, he arrived at the Deer Park not far from Varanasi. The group of his five former disciples who were sitting there saw him coming. At first, because they considered him a backslider from the true path, they did not show him any deference, and when he offered to teach them what he had realized, they declined. But at last, in the face of his unwavering insistence, they yielded and agreed to at least listen to his teaching.

In the first of his talks on the Dharma, the Buddha taught not only the Eightfold Path but also the Four Noble Truths. He said: "There is this Noble Truth of suffering: Birth is suffering, aging is suffering, sickness is suffering, death is suffering, sorrow and lamentation, pain, grief, and despair are suffering, association with the loathed is suffering, dissociation from the loved is suffering, not to get what one wants is suffering. . . .

"There is this Noble Truth of the origin of suffering: It is craving, which produces renewal of being, is accompanied by relish and lust, relishing this and that; in other words, craving for sensual desires, craving for being, craving for nonbeing.

"There is this Noble Truth of the cessation of suffering: It is the remainderless fading and ceasing, the giving up, relinquishing, letting go, and rejecting of that same craving.

"There is this Noble Truth of the way leading to the cessation of suffering: It is this Noble Eightfold Path, that is to say: right view, right intention, right speech, right action, right livelihood, right effort, right mindfulness, and right concentration."

He explained that the truth of suffering had to be penetrated by fully understanding suffering. As for the truth of the origin of suffering, one has to abandon that origin. The truth of the cessation of suffering means realizing that the cessation of suffering is really possible, and to achieve that cessation one has to cultivate the Eightfold Path. He explained that he had achieved enlightenment by fully realizing these Four Noble Truths.

As the Blessed One was explaining these things, Kaundinya's doubts vanished, and perfect confidence based on his own direct knowledge arose. He had acquired that kind of independent knowledge that no longer requires confirmation from someone else, no longer needs to be further tested.

Then Kaundinya asked the Buddha to accept him formally as his disciple. So the Buddha gave him ordination as a bhikshu, or monk, in the order of mendicants headed by himself. He did this simply by saying: "Come, bhikshu. The Dharma has been properly proclaimed. Live the holy life for the complete ending of suffering."

Then the Blessed One instructed the four others further, and after a short time, there arose in them also a pure vision of the Dharma. They too asked to be accepted into the Buddha's order, and the Buddha ordained them in the same way as he had ordained Kaundinya.

The morning after this first turning of the wheel of Dharma, the Buddha continued teaching in the Deer Park. Listening to him day after day, his first five disciples attained the four levels of realization and became *arhats,* "enemy destroyers," those who have destroyed within themselves all the obstacles to enlightenment.

There were many others in the Deer Park who were trying to understand how to lead the holy life, and many of them also began listening to the Buddha.

During this period, the Blessed One gave the teaching on nonself, or non-ego. The idea of an eternal self, an ego or soul, connected with an eternal divine principle in the universe and transmigrating from rebirth to rebirth, was a central tenet of Hinduism. The Buddha taught that there is no such self, but only the illusion of a self. If a real self did exist, he explained, it would only be a cause of suffering, and if it were eternal it would be a cause of suffering that could never be removed. That eternal self would enter again and again into the web of experience, into the cycle of rebirth. Then there would be no Third Noble Truth of the cessation of suffering and thus no enlightenment. As it is, he taught, there is only an illusion of a self, but even that is enough to function as the principal obstacle to liberation, to the cessation of suffering.

But the obstacle of an illusory self, taught the Tathagata—the Perfected One—who was fresh from victory, falls away when it is seen as it is. Rather than being a solid, eternal entity, it is merely a temporary composite of form, feeling, perception, conceptual formations, and consciousness, which are called the five skandhas, or aggregates. Rather than a definite self to cling to, and which in turn clings to other things, there is just an ever-shifting mosaic composed of those five aggregates. Once this is recognized, one becomes dispassionate toward what one formerly clung to. Desire fades away, and the heart is liberated. Nothing remains that is subject to the round of suffering and rebirth.

Not long after the Buddha had begun turning the wheel of
Dharma in the Deer Park, a rich merchant's son named
Yasha—who, much like the Buddha himself, had become disgusted with his life of luxury—fled his father's house. Wandering in the night, he came upon the Buddha pacing back and
forth in the open. He saw Yasha coming, and when the youth
was quite close, he heard him say, "This is terrifying, this is
horrid!" And the Buddha said, "Here there is nothing terrifying
or horrid, Yasha. Come have a seat, and I will teach you the
Dharma."

Yasha at once felt a sense of comfort and hope. He took off
his golden slippers, prostrated to the Tathagata, and sat down
to receive the teaching, and as he sat there, a clear and perfect
vision of the Dharma arose in him. Eventually not only Yasha
but also numerous friends of his who had heard of the Buddha's teaching and come to see him, all were liberated from
defilements and became arhats. Now there were sixty-one
monks who had entered arhatship under the Buddha.

The Buddha gathered all the arhats together, and said: "Bhikshus, I am free from all shackles, whether human or divine. You
are free from all shackles, whether human or divine. Go now
and wander for the welfare and happiness of many, out of compassion for the world, for the benefit, welfare, and happiness of
gods and men. Teach the Dharma that is good in the beginning,
good in the middle, and good in the end, both the words and
the meaning. Explain a holy life that is utterly perfect and pure.
There are beings with little dust on their eyes who will be lost
through not hearing the Dharma. Some will understand the
Dharma." And he also told them: "As for myself, I have decided
to go to Uruvilva in the Magadhan land to teach the Dharma."

By now, the bhikshus whom the Blessed One had sent out
had wandered in all directions and were beginning to bring in
men who wanted to enter homelessness and be fully ordained
as monks, members of the Sangha. It was becoming increasingly difficult to make arrangements for them all to come to the
Buddha for this purpose. So the Buddha convoked an assembly
of the bhikshus and authorized them all to grant both the entry
into homelessness and the ordination. And he formulated exactly how it should be done.

First the entrant's hair and beard were to be shaved. Then
the saffron-colored body cloth was to be put on and the upper

robe arranged over one shoulder. The entrant then was to prostrate at the bhikshu's feet; then, kneeling, with the palms of the
hands together, he was to repeat, "I take refuge in the Buddha,
I take refuge in the Dharma, I take refuge in the Sangha" three
times.

The Buddha also gave the assembled Sangha further teachings, in which he formulated doctrine and method more precisely than before and also gave some instructions for the organization of Sangha life.

In these times, when the Buddha was setting his Dharma and
Sangha on a firm foundation, Mara frequently appeared, to try
to shake his confidence—but always to no avail.

The Buddha spent the first rainy season after his enlightenment
in the Deer Park near Varanasi. When he had remained there
as long as he chose, he set off south for Uruvilva. In that region
at the time, there were three well-known holy men who wore
long, matted hair and invoked the power of certain deities
through a fire ritual. These three were called Kashyapa of Uruvilva, Kashyapa of the River, and Kashyapa of Gaya. Together
they were the principal spiritual influence over the kingdom of
Magadha at that time. But through the power of the Buddha's
teaching and the wonders that he performed, all three teachers
and their followers cut their hair, discarded their fire-ritual im-
plements, and joined the community of bhikshus.

After staying at Uruvilva as long as he chose, the Tathagata
went to Gayashirsha accompanied by the thousand bhikshus
who shortly before had been matted-hair ascetics. In Gayashirsha there is a hill with a great rock on its slope, shaped like an
elephant's head. The Blessed One with two or three attendants
climbed to the top of this and uttered the following discourse:

"Bhikshus, everything is burning. The eye is burning, the
nose is burning, the tongue is burning, the body is burning, the
mind is burning. The consciousness of all these is burning. Visible forms, sounds, odors, flavors, touchable things, and mental
objects are burning. Sense contact and mental contact is burning, and the feeling—pleasant, unpleasant, or indifferent—arising from sense and mental contact is burning. It is all burning
with the fire of passion, the fire of aggression, and the fire of

delusion. It is burning with birth, aging, and death. It is burning with sorrow, crying out, grief, pain, and despair.

"Seeing this, bhikshus, the noble disciple becomes dispassionate toward all that is burning, toward the senses and the mind, their consciousness, their objects, their contact, and the feeling arising from these. Becoming dispassionate, his passion fades away. Thus his heart is liberated, and with that comes the knowledge that it has been liberated. He realizes that birth has been exhausted and the holy life has been lived to completion. What had to be done has been done. There is no more still to come."

When the Blessed One had uttered this discourse, all the thousand former matted-hair ascetics were entirely liberated from their defilements through absence of clinging. Thus all of them became arhats.

After this, the Blessed One with his thousand arhat disciples continued on toward the city of Rajagriha. There, at the invitation of his devoted patron King Bimbisara, the Buddha and his thousand bhikshus made their way to the king's palace, where they were served a meal from the king's own hands. When the Blessed One had finished eating and put down his bowl, the king announced that he wanted to offer a gift of a piece of land outside the city known as the Venuvana, or Bamboo Grove. He felt it had suitable qualities for a monastic retreat, because it was a lovely place and far enough away from the city so that the monks would not be disturbed by urban activity and noise, but close enough so that they could come for alms. Then the king rose and presented the gift in a formal ceremony, reciting a formula of donation while pouring water over the Buddha's hands from a golden pitcher.

The Buddha accepted the gift. Then he roused and delighted the king with words of Dharma, and when he was ready, he rose from his seat and departed.

At this time there were two young brahmins named Shariputra and Maudgalyayana living near Rajagriha with a community of wandering ascetics. These two had mastered the brahmanical texts at a very early age, and had wandered from home together in search of the deathless. One morning Shariputra observed a young bhikshu named Ashvajit gathering alms in Rajagriha.

The young man had already gained mastery over his senses; thus he moved with grace and composure. His eyes were cast slightly downward, his gestures bespoke clarity and calm, and his attention did not wander. Shariputra was so touched by this evidence of spiritual attainment that he asked the young bhikshu who his teacher was. And so Ashvajit told him of the Awakened One, Shakyamuni, and described the essence of his teaching: "Of all things arising through a cause, the Tathagata has told the cause, and he has also shown their cessation. That is the teaching of the great monk."

Merely hearing these words was enough to make the pure vision of Dharma arise in Shariputra. He saw that all that arises also passes away. Up until this point he had been fixed on the idea of a permanent, uncaused self. This was a principal tenet of brahmanical doctrine. But when he heard Ashvajit's words, he suddenly realized that the sense of self, arisen from a cause, was also subject to cessation. This meant there was no obstacle to liberation.

Having experienced this clear vision on the spot, he went to tell his friend.

As soon as Maudgalyayana heard the words of Shariputra, he also experienced the same illumination. After a while the two friends gathered their few things and set out to find Shakyamuni.

When the Buddha saw Shariputra and Maudgalyayana coming in the distance, he said to the bhikshus around him, "That auspicious pair has already recognized the truth. Those two friends will be my chief disciples." The two young men declared their faith in his Dharma, and the Blessed One allowed them to enter homelessness and join the order. In the years that followed, Shariputra became foremost in the Sangha in wisdom and insight, and Maudgalyayana in the exercise of supernormal abilities.

While the Buddha was still staying near Vulture Peak Mountain, a brahmin from the Kashyapa clan, a young man of fine appearance and noble bearing named Pippali, showed up among the many seekers who daily came to hear the Buddha teach and called out from among the crowd to ask to be his disciple. The Buddha saw that the young man had great longing for ultimate knowledge, that his mind was pure, and that he had already exerted himself considerably to find the truth. So he accepted Pippali by saying, "Welcome."

Pippali, now relieved of his weariness and uncertainty, remained standing there, gazing at the Blessed One with rapt attention. The Buddha began speaking about the Dharma, but instead of giving progressive instruction as usual, he came to the essence of the teaching in only three or four sentences. Then, catching Pippali's eye, he held up a flower that lay by him, twirled it slightly in his hand, and smiled. At this gesture, the ultimate knowledge passed between the Buddha and Pippali. Outwardly, only a slight smile curved the young man's lips to indicate that he had understood. Afterward, because he had been able to attain the realization of an arhat with such sudden completeness, he was called Mahakashyapa, the Great Kashyapa. Years later, at the Buddha's death, Mahakashyapa would succeed him as the leader of the Sangha.

In Kapilavastu, King Shuddhodana had been doing his best to keep informed of his son's doings. The king had heard he was teaching as an awakened one, a buddha, and had already gathered thousands of disciples, many of whom had become arhats. Shuddhodana was getting old and wanted to see his son before he died. He thus sent one of his ministers, Kalodayin, who had also been one of Siddhartha's childhood companions, to request the Blessed One to visit Kapilavastu. And so it was that the Blessed One set out for the city he had left in the night nearly seven years ago.

When the Shakyans heard that he had arrived, the king and the nobles of the city came out to meet him, sending the children and younger people ahead with flowers. They conducted the Blessed One to the park, where he sat down on a seat that had been prepared for him. Although the young people prostrated to the Buddha, the elders felt no obligation to pay homage to him, for they regarded the Buddha as a younger brother. The Tathagata knew that with the solidity of the Shakyans' pride arrayed against him, it was not a fit situation for teaching. If they were lacking in veneration toward the teacher, their hearts would be closed against the Dharma. To remedy the problem, the Blessed One performed various wonders. He even performed the twin miracle of making water and fire shoot forth from his body at the same time. He also caused a shower of rain to fall out of a clear sky, raining on some of the Shakyans and not on others. This show of wonders brought about the desired result. The king and all the Shakyan nobles rose and prostrated to the Blessed One. After this an atmosphere of peace and well-being reigned over the assembly.

The next morning, when it was time for the alms round, the Blessed One entered Kapilavastu. No one was there to take his bowl or invite him to their house. So he reflected on whether the buddhas of the past, when entering the city of their own kin, had simply gone begging from house to house or had gone directly to the houses of their relatives. Perceiving that they had begged from house to house, the Blessed One began doing the same.

When the king learned that his son was begging from door to door, he felt shamed and confronted the Blessed One. The Buddha explained to his father about the buddhas and the holy life. He said there was little time to waste in adopting the holy life, for those who led it enjoyed bliss both in this life and in the next. As his father listened to the Tathagata speak, his mind was opened, and recognition of the truth of the Dharma dawned in him. He then took the Blessed One's bowl and led him and his retinue to the palace. There he served them excellent food with his own hands. And when the Buddha had finished eating and put down his bowl, all the women of the household came before the Buddha and paid homage to him.

But though she sent her maids and serving women to pay homage to the Buddha, Princess Yashodhara remained in her apartments, thinking to herself, "If the Blessed One values me, he will come to see me." So when the meal was finished, the Tathagata gave his bowl to his father to carry, and they went to Yashodhara's apartments. The Buddha entered and sat down on the seat that had been prepared for him. Yashodhara came at once to greet him. Grasping his ankles, she placed his feet on her head. Then King Shuddhodana told the Buddha about Yashodhara's loyalty to him. "When she heard that you wore saffron-colored robes, she too began to wear them. When she heard that you took only one meal a day, this became her custom too. When she heard that you no longer slept on a bed but on the ground, she also slept on a mat on the floor. When she heard that you had given up wearing flowers and perfume, she too gave that up. And when her relatives sent messages for her to return home, since they would gladly care for her, she merely ignored them. This is how loyal and good my daughter was," said the king.

Rahula, the Buddha's son, was now seven years old. One day soon after the Buddha's arrival in Kapilavastu, Rahula went to talk with him and ask him for his inheritance, as his mother had instructed him. The Blessed One did not embrace the boy any more than he had any of his other relatives, yet Rahula told him, "It feels good even to stand in your shadow." And when the Buddha left the palace to return to the Nigrodha Park, the little boy followed just behind him, continuing to ask for his inheritance. Thus the Buddha finally had Shariputra enter Rahula into homelessness, thus making him a novice monk.

By the time the Buddha left the country of the Shakyans to return to Rajagriha, a large number of young Shakyans had entered the order, among them Mahanama, Aniruddha, and Bhadrika. In addition, the Buddha's cousins Ananda and Devadatta decided to join the Sangha, and they brought their friends Brighu and Kimbila. These young nobles brought their barber, Upali, along so he could cut their hair for them when the time came. Later Upali was to become a major disciple of the Buddha, the principal authority on the Sangha's disciplinary rules.

In the course of the rainy season that followed, at Venuvana near Rajagriha, Bhadrika attained arhatship, Aniruddha attained the third level of realization, and Ananda the first. Devadatta acquired supernormal powers arising from powerful concentration, but failed to gain any realization of the truth.

The Buddha spent the next two rainy seasons, the second and third after his enlightenment, at the Venuvana. When that third rainy season was over but the Blessed One had not yet begun his year's wanderings, a wealthy merchant from Rajagriha came to visit the community. The merchant had great respect for the monks and felt bad seeing them living under rough conditions, so he went up to a group of them and asked them if they would live in shelters if he had them built. The monks brought the matter to the Buddha, and he gave his permission for the monks to live in shelters. The merchant immediately had a large number of huts and shelters built. Then he also invited the Buddha and the community to his house for the next day's meal. At the end of the meal, the merchant formally donated the shelters to the Sangha.

The merchant's brother-in-law was also a wealthy merchant. His name was Sudatta, but he was generally called Anathapindada, "Giver to the Defenseless," because of his great charity. With the Buddha's permission, he arranged for a monastery— a *vihara*—to be built for the community in the neighborhood of Shravasti. It was called the Jetavana (Jeta's Grove). Anathapindada had terraces and walkways laid out and leveled, rooms and halls built, storerooms and kitchens and baths fitted out, ponds dug, and outdoor pavilions constructed. All the needs of a large monastic community were provided for, and the Jetavana became the Buddha's favorite sojourning place.

Another great monastery was built for the Buddha's community by King Prasenajit, who reigned over the Koshalans in the capital city of Shravasti. The king was at first skeptical about the Buddha. He especially wondered how the great leader dared to call himself a buddha, when none of the other eminent spiritual teachers of the day thought of doing so. But Prasenajit's wife, Queen Mallika, who was a very able and intelligent woman, often spoke to the king in favor of the Blessed One, and finally convinced Prasenajit to see him in person. After the first time Prasenajit heard the Buddha teach, he asked to be accepted as his follower. As time went on, the king became more and more devoted to the Tathagata. He eventually built a great vihara known as the Rajakarama, in the vicinity of Shravasti. The Buddha pronounced a number of well-known discourses in King Prasenajit's presence.

By this time, the Buddha's community numbered many thousands of bhikshus, and occasionally complaints came to his ears about harm done to vegetation and wildlife as a result of their wandering over the countryside throughout the year. The bhikshus were already held to rules of strict simplicity, making their demand on the world around them as small as possible. Now the Blessed One made it obligatory for bhikshus to remain in a vihara or other retreat place throughout each rainy season.

Thus, for a considerable part of each year, they were able to concentrate on their meditative discipline and remain largely out of the way of the lay population.

The rainy season that the Buddha spent at the Jetavana at Anathapindada's invitation was the fourth after his enlightenment. The fifth rainy season he stayed in the Kutagara Hall in the Mahavana near Vaishali. Not long after this, his father, Shuddhodana, became seriously ill, and the Tathagata went once more to Kapilavastu. When he arrived there, his father was on his deathbed. During his father's last days, the Blessed One was frequently at his bedside. He soothed the king's pain and talked to him a great deal about the Dharma. The understanding between them was so tender and direct that before the king died he was able to gain the realization of an arhat.

Meanwhile, Queen Mahaprajapati Gautami had conceived the desire to devote herself to the spiritual life. Her husband was dead, and both her son Nanda and Rahula, who was like a grandchild to her, had entered homelessness under the Buddha. Now she too wanted to become a member of the Blessed One's Sangha. But there was no such thing as a *bhikshuni*, a nun, of the community of the Buddha. While the Buddha was still at Kapilavastu, she came to him, accompanied by five hundred women, the former wives of men who had entered the Sangha. She prostrated and stood to one side, and said, "Lord, it would be good if women too could enter homelessness under the Tathagata and follow the discipline prescribed for the holy life."

"Enough, Gautami," said the Buddha. "Do not ask this."

The queen repeated her request a second and a third time and received the same answer. There was nothing more she could say, so she prostrated and went away, disappointed and unhappy.

When the Blessed One had stayed in Kapilavastu as long as he chose, he set off for Vaishali. After some days on the way, he arrived and took up residence in the Kutagara Hall.

In the meantime Mahaprajapati, thinking that if the women showed courage and determination, the Buddha would not be able to refuse them, decided to gather them together and follow the Buddha to Vaishali. The women had their hair cut, put on saffron-colored robes, took alms bowls, and set off on foot.

Many of them were pampered noblewomen with soft hands and feet. When they arrived, Mahaprajapati went to the Kutagara Hall and stood waiting outside, hoping for an opportunity to see the Blessed One. Her feet were sore and swollen, she was covered with dust, and she was nearly sobbing with exhaustion.

Ananda found her and asked how she came to be standing there that way. He was filled with pity and sympathy at the sight of her. Ananda told her to wait, and went inside the house where the Buddha was staying to speak to him. He told him of Mahaprajapati standing outside and said, "It would be good if women could leave the householder's life and enter homelessness as part of the order."

The Buddha said, "Enough, Ananda. Do not ask that women be allowed to enter the order."

Twice more Ananda asked and received no better answer. This was equivalent to a refusal, and Ananda should have given up and retired. But instead he thought of asking the Buddha in another way. So he said, "If women did renounce the householder's life and enter homelessness, would they be capable of attaining the four levels of realization?"

"They would," replied the Buddha.

"That being the case," continued Ananda, "since Mahaprajapati nursed and raised the Tathagata like her own son when his own mother died and was benefactor to him in so many ways, and now has come all this way on foot, is standing outside with feet swollen and bleeding, could you not consider allowing women to enter homelessness as members of the Sangha?"

In the face of this plea, the Buddha relented. He said he would accept Mahaprajapati into the Sangha if she would accept eight special conditions having to do with bhikshunis' deferring to and depending upon the authority of bhikshus in a variety of circumstances. When Ananda went outside and told Mahaprajapati the eight conditions, she accepted them with great joy. Thus she became the first bhikshuni.

Mahaprajapati availed herself of every opportunity to receive instruction from the Tathagata. She practiced meditation intensively in seclusion, and after not too long a time was able to attain arhatship. Many of the other women who were ordained at this time soon began to attain the various stages of realization.

The Tathagata's former wife, Yashodhara, also eventually entered the order, and she too was able to attain arhatship. She was particularly gifted in supernormal powers and became foremost among the bhikshunis in that manifestation of awakened mind.

Invited by some wealthy merchants, the Buddha spent the ninth rainy season near Kaushambi on the Yamuna River in the country of the Vatsans. It was after this rainy-season retreat that a petty quarrel arose between two bhikshus in one of the viharas near Kaushambi that grew out of proportion and threatened the unity of the Sangha. One of the bhikshus was a specialist in monastic discipline, which is called vinaya. He was occupied with committing to memory and interpreting the rules made by the Buddha for the behavior of the Sangha in all circumstances of monastic life, and he taught this knowledge to his students. The other bhikshu was a specialist in the Buddha's doctrinal discourses, called sutras. His work was to memorize the sutras and develop an orderly knowledge of their content, and he too passed on his knowledge to his students.

One day the vinaya specialist accused the sutra specialist of a petty infringement of the rules. The sutra specialist denied having committed any wrong. He gathered many supporters, and so did the vinaya specialist. The two parties continued to squabble, and tension and dissension grew. When the matter was brought to the Buddha, he asked the contending parties to put an end to the discord. Their reply was that the Blessed One should stay out of the matter, since all the ugliness of it would never be blamed on him anyhow. The Buddha repeated his request twice more, and twice more got the same answer. Then he got up and went away.

The following morning the Blessed One went into Kaushambi for alms. When he got back, he set his sleeping place in order and picked up his bowl and outer robe. While standing, he began to speak. He spoke about the ludicrous blindness of those embroiled in quarrels, how they always see fault and blame elsewhere. Even thieves and murderers can agree among themselves, he said, but not these warring bhikshus. After speaking thus, he departed.

After some days he came to the Parileyyaka forest. He went

into the thick jungle and stayed for a time in solitary retreat. One day he thought, "Not so long ago I was living in discomfort, tormented by the endless squabbling of those Kaushambi monks who were stirring up strife in the community. Now, alone, I am so very comfortable and at ease without all of them."

At the same time there was in the forest a bull elephant who had been tormented by the carryings-on of all the cow and calf elephants of the herd, having to eat trampled food and drink water dirtied by other elephants, being bumped and shoved by the cow elephants at bathing time. He, too, thought, "Why should I not live alone and get away from all this trouble?" So he too went off to the Parileyyaka forest and into the thick part of the jungle, and found the Blessed One meditating there at the foot of a shala tree. The elephant looked after the Buddda by bringing him food and water and clearing away the thick undergrowth in front of his meditation place so that he could pace back and forth. The elephant thought, "I used to be tormented by the herd, but now, alone, I am so content."

Knowing the elephant's mind, the Blessed One said these words:

> Tusker agrees with tusker here;
> The elephants with tusks as long as [cart] shafts
> delight alone in the woods:
> Their hearts are thus in harmony.

In Kaushambi it was not long before the monks discovered that the Blessed One had put his place in order and disappeared. They became upset and started talking about how terrible it was that the Buddha had gone off by himself without informing anybody. They thought some monks should go after him and find out where he was. But Ananda told them, "When the Blessed One sets his place in order and goes off by himself without telling anyone, it means he wants to live alone. Nobody should follow him."

After some time had passed, a group of monks came to Ananda and said how much they would like to hear a discourse on the Dharma from the Blessed One himself again. So Ananda set off with this party of bhikshus, and they eventually found the Blessed One meditating under the shala tree. They prostrated to him and sat down off to one side. The Blessed One then gave them instruction in the Dharma.

Eventually, after much to-do, the sutra specialist who had been suspended acknowledged having committed an infringement. This made it technically possible for the party of the vinaya specialist to reinstate him as a member of the community, and they did so. Thus the dispute was settled, and the procedural precedent for settling such disputes was noted.

The Buddha passed the thirteenth rainy season at a place called Chalika. In the year following that, Rahula reached the age of twenty and was therefore old enough for full ordination. On the occasion of this ceremony, the Tathagata instructed his son at length and in detail on impermanence, non-ego, and the giving up of attachments. In the course of this talk, through non-clinging, Rahula's mind was entirely liberated from defilements. Thus he reached arhatship and full monkhood on the same day.

In the twentieth year, when the Buddha was fifty-five years old, he decided henceforth to spend all rainy seasons retreats at Shravasti. Most of those retreats were spent at the Jetavana, donated by Anathapindada, but some of them also at the Purvarama (East Park), which was the gift to the Buddha and Sangha of a woman named Vishakha.

It was in this year that the Tathagata decided to appoint Ananda as his permanent personal attendant. Thus Ananda was to be in nearly constant attendance on his lord for twenty-five years, until the Tathagata's death, or *parinirvana*.

It was also in this year that the Blessed One converted Angulimala, a murderous bandit who lived in the neighborhood of Shravasti. He murdered people one after the other and strung a finger of each victim on a cord that he wore around his neck. Hence his name, which means "finger necklace."

One day the Buddha took his bowl and outer robe and went into Shravasti for alms. When he had returned and eaten, he put his sleeping place in order and set off toward Angulimala's territory. As he made his way alone along the road, Angulimala was surveying the scene from a wooded hillside. He saw the Buddha and said to himself, "This is really amazing. Armed men have come along here in large bands, and I've done them all in. Now here comes this monk all by himself. Why shouldn't I kill him too?"

So Angulimala started running after the Buddha. But to his astonishment he found that no matter how fast he ran, he could not catch up with the Blessed One, though the latter was walking at a normal pace. In frustration, Angulimala halted and shouted after the Tathagata, "Stop there, monk! Stop!"

"I have stopped," said the Blessed One. "You should stop too!"

"How can you say you've stopped when you're still walking? And how can you tell me to stop when I already have?" shouted the bandit.

"I have stopped forever doing violence to beings," said the Buddha, "whereas you go on doing violence to nearly every creature you meet. Why don't you stop too?"

When Angulimala heard these words and beheld the Tathagata regarding him serenely from just beyond his grasp, the ferocious bandit suddenly saw the situation just as the Buddha saw it. Then and there he vowed in his heart to renounce evil. He fell down at the Blessed One's feet and asked him to accept him into homelessness. And then and there the Blessed One said, "Come, bhikshu. The Dharma has been properly proclaimed. Live the holy life for the complete ending of suffering."

The time had finally come for the Blessed One to lay down a formal code of behavior for the Sangha. This, he said, would restrain the evil-minded, support the virtuous, curb defilements in this life and prevent them in lives to come, and help greatly to establish the Buddha Dharma firmly in the world.

After proclaiming the pratimoksha, the Buddha gave further shape to the life of his Sangha by having the code periodically recited rule by rule in a full assembly of bhikshus or bhikshunis. Pauses were made during the recitation to permit public acknowledgment of faults. In this connection, the Blessed One remarked that "rain rots what is kept wrapped up, but not what is uncovered."

The Tathagata had long followed a daily routine, which, though not invariable, was fairly constant. The Buddha slept on his right side with his right hand under his head and one foot slightly overlapping the other. This sleeping position of his became known as the lion's posture. It is said that after awakening from sleep before dawn, the Buddha surveyed the panorama of existence with the divine eye and took cognizance of the plight of specific beings. Then he meditated, sitting cross-legged or pacing back and forth in front of his resting place. If he had not been invited for the day's meal by a specific householder, after it was light he would take his bowl and outer robe and walk to the nearest settlement to collect alms. He was usually accompanied by a large following of monks, perhaps several hundred. In collecting alms, he would not go to a specific house where he knew good food might be available, but would start from the end of a given street and proceed house by house. In this way the opportunity for gaining the merit of giving was not reserved for the rich but was spread equally among all. At the door he uttered no request but made his presence known in some inobtrusive way and then stood silently with his bowl in evidence. If alms were given, he accepted in silence anything given in good faith and moved on. If, after a few moments, no alms were given, he passed on in silence. When his bowl was full, he returned to his resting place, washed his feet, and ate his single meal of the day, finishing it before noon.

After finishing the meal, he sat outside near his resting place and gave brief instruction in the Dharma to anyone who was there. When he finished that, he accomplished such work as receiving people into homelessness or granting full ordination. He then retired to an area closed to the public and gave an exposition of the Dharma for the Sangha alone.

If there was an invitation from a householder for the day's meal, there was no alms round. The Buddha and his attendants arrived at the host's house in time to complete the meal before midday. After the meal, the Blessed One gave teaching to the host, his family, and guests. In such cases, he did not teach again in the early part of the day when he returned to the vihara or the monastic camp.

In the heat of the day, he retired to his private place, a simple house if he was in a monastery, and rested. If he wished, he lay down on his right side and slept for a time in a kind of half sleep in which the thread of awareness is not lost. At dusk, large numbers of lay people gathered to hear the Tathagata teach. To

35

them, he delivered a discourse on the Dharma of an hour or more and responded to questions.

After this the Tathagata might bathe and rest for a short time. Then came the conversations with bhikshus or bhikshunis, individually or in groups, that sometimes lasted far into the night.

It is said that the Tathagata slept very little, perhaps only one hour, and then with unbroken mindfulness. In any case, the time between retirement at night and rising at dawn or before was divided between sleeping on his right side, sitting in meditation, and pacing up and down mindfully in front of his sleeping place.

Of course, when the Blessed One was traveling from place to place, after the alms round much of the day was spent walking, except for the rest period in the hot part of the day.

The Sangha followed its master's example, adopting this daily pattern as closely as possible. Those who were not teachers either listened to teaching or meditated at the times of day when the Tathagata taught. Those who were teachers taught the public and their own students at the times of the day when the Tathagata taught the public and his own bhikshus and bhikshunis. Like the Tathagata himself, any member of the Sangha might for a certain time retire to a solitary place to pursue his or her meditation practice intensively.

Year after year the Buddha spent the rainy season at Shravasti and then wandered the central Gangetic plain, for the most part teaching daily, converting lay followers and giving them the triple refuge, and receiving others into the monastic Sangha. Year by year he refined the formulation of various aspects of his doctrine. Case by case, only when occasioned by specific occurrences, he added rules to the pratimoksha until there were two hundred and twenty-seven rules for bhikshus and three hundred and thirty-eight for bhikshunis. The Sangha benefited from the favor of great kings such as King Bimbisara of Magadha and King Prasenajit and countless wealthy householders, so that gradually it came to possess well-appointed viharas throughout the land, and especially many in the neighborhood of Vaishali, Shravasti, and Rajagriha, cities which the Blessed One particularly frequented.

In the thirty-seventh year after the Buddha's enlightenment, when the great sage of the Shakyas was seventy-two years old, there arose a serious menace to his life and the unity of the Sangha: Devadatta, the Blessed One's cousin and his brother-in-law, who had entered homelessness along with the Shakyan princes who came to the Buddha with their barber, Upali. Unlike the others, he had never attained any of the stages of realization. Nevertheless, he was a well-liked person with an extensive following within the Sangha. Moreover, he had become proficient in the exercise of supernormal powers.

Once, when he was meditating alone in retreat, the idea arose in him of gaining fame and power. Instead of letting the idea pass by, Devadatta nurtured it and began to scheme how he might achieve this goal. He hit upon the idea of winning the devotion of Prince Ajatashatru, King Bimbisara's son and heir, through a display of his powers. Having won the discipleship of the prince, Devadatta quickly grew in fame and prestige among the people of Rajagriha. He gloried in this new power, and even greater ambitions came to possess his mind. He thought now of displacing the Buddha and taking over for himself the leadership of the Sangha.

But as these thoughts took shape in Devadatta's mind and firmed into an intention, his supernormal powers vanished as though they had never been.

At this time, pursuing the normal course of his wanderings, the Tathagata arrived in Rajagriha. One day the Buddha was teaching the Dharma to a great gathering of people near the city. Many Rajagrihan notables, including the king, were present, and this was the moment Devadatta chose to approach the Buddha, prostrate himself to him, and in a voice all could hear, address him as follows: "The Blessed One is now old, aged, advanced in years, in the last stage of life, nearing the end. The Blessed One should rest now. The Blessed One should have respite from his work and spend his days in blissful contemplation of the Dharma. For that reason, let the Blessed One hand over leadership of the Sangha to me. I will lead the Sangha well."

"Abandon this idea, Devadatta," said the Buddha. "Do not aspire to lead the Sangha."

Devadatta ignored the Buddha's answer and loudly repeated

his own words. The Buddha met them with the same response. Yet a third time Devadatta uttered his brazen formula. A third time the Buddha replied, "I would not give over the leadership of the Sangha even to the great bhikshus Shariputra and Maudgalyayana. Why then would I give it over to you, who are like something bad-tasting in the mouth that needs to be spit out?"

This was a bitter humiliation for Devadatta. And following this incident, the Blessed One asked Shariputra to make a public denunciation of Devadatta. In response, Devadatta began to plot the murder of the Buddha. He devised several complex plans to have the Buddha assassinated, but all attempts failed. He then decided to kill the Buddha himself.

The vengeance-bent bhikshu went in search of the Tathagata and at last spied him in the distance, pacing back and forth in the shade of the great rock at the top of Vulture Peak Mountain. Devadatta climbed the rock from behind and dislodged a great boulder and sent it tumbling down on the Blessed One. But the boulder caught fast between two rocks just above where the Blessed One was pacing, and the only harm he suffered was from a splinter of the great boulder that deeply penetrated his foot.

This wound caused the Tathagata a great deal of pain, not only in the foot but through his whole body. He bore the pain mindfully and without complaint but had to retire to his house and rest for a few days. This he did lying with unbroken awareness on his right side. As he lay there, Mara came to him and chided him for his indulgence. The Blessed One, however, immediately saw who it was, and as soon as Mara knew he had been caught, he disappeared.

Devadatta then conceived another scheme. In Rajagriha there was a crazed, man-killing elephant named Nalagiri that was kept by the king for purposes of war. To maintain his evil temper, the elephant's daily water supply was laced with large quantities of liquor. On a day, when Devadatta knew that the Buddha would be coming along a certain street for alms, he bribed the great bull elephant's keepers to double its ration of liquor and let it out into the street at the right moment. Nalagiri was released and saw the Blessed One beginning his alms round at the far end of the street. He raised his trunk and trumpeted, then charged, berserk, down the street, bent on the destruction of that tiny robed figure.

Despite the warnings of his companions, the Buddha calmly continued walking. Ananda tried to get in front of the Blessed One so as to take the brunt of the charge. The Buddha took Ananda by the arm and drew him firmly out of the way. Then the Blessed One embraced the charging beast in a great field of lovingkindness. The crazed elephant lowered its trunk and slowed its charge. It came to a confused halt and tossed its huge head from side to side. Then it came on at a slow trot and halted before the Tathagata. The Buddha reached up with his right hand and stroked Nalagiri between the eyes. Then he spoke to him softly in a kind of croon: "O great tusker, do not kill another tusker, a bull elephant, a tathagata. Such an act would bring you an endless destiny of unhappiness. Give up your conceit and madness, great elephant. Tread the path that will bring you future happiness." After the Buddha had spoken to him for a few moments in this way, Nalagiri gathered up dust from about the Tathagata's feet with his trunk and placed it on top of his head. Then he withdrew, walking backward. Only far down the street did he turn and trot back to the stable. There he stood peacefully in his stall.

After this incident there was general condemnation of Devadatta's base attacks on the great monk whose might and wisdom was so clear to see. Most of the discredited schemer's followers in the city fell away. But still Devadatta kept a fair number of adherents within the Sangha itself. He now conspired with his followers to cause a schism in the Sangha.

Knowing that the people idealized self-denial as a high spiritual goal, he went to the Buddha and proposed five points of strict behavior for Sangha members: they must keep to the forests and never live in a settled place; eat only begged alms food and never accept meal invitations; wear only robes pieced together from refuse rags and never accept a gift of cloth; dwell only outdoors and never in shelters; and never eat fish or meat. He proposed that violation of any of these rules be met with expulsion from the Sangha.

The Buddha rejected these rules as too extreme. He ruled that Sangha members were free to dwell in forests or villages, eat alms food or accept invitations, wear refuse-rag robes or accept cloth as they chose. They could dwell either outdoors or in shelters for eight months of the year, but must take shelter during the rainy season. Meat and fish could be eaten if it was not seen, heard, or suspected to have been killed expressly for the eater.

This was the kind of ruling Devadatta had been waiting for. He and his followers at once set talk going in the Sangha that set one faction against another. They depicted their own party under Devadatta's leadership as that of the upholders of the strict and pure Dharma, and implied that those who followed the Buddha were slack, lovers of luxury. "Come to us," they said. "We will follow Devadatta and uphold the five righteous rules." Many followed Devadatta, because they thought greater self-denial was the higher and more noble course.

When the Blessed One heard about this, he spoke with Devadatta personally and tried to bring him to reason. He told Devadatta that he had already laid up horrendous karmic results for himself by shedding the blood of a Tathagata when the rock splinter pierced his foot. "Creating a schism in the Sangha is a very grave thing," he told him, "but reuniting it brings much merit."

This kind of talk had no effect on Devadatta. Shortly after this meeting he let it be known that he intended to lead his own sangha. With his stricter code, Devadatta was able to attract five hundred bhikshus from the region of Vaishali who were new entrants into the Sangha. Thinking, "This is the true teaching," these five hundred decided to follow Devadatta. Thus he succeeded in creating a schism in the Sangha.

The Buddha asked his two leading disciples, Shariputra and Maudgalyayana, to go and save the five hundred bhikshus who had strayed. This they were able to do through their skillful teaching, and the entire assembly was brought back to the Buddha. As a result of this defeat, Devadatta was so stricken that he eventually fell mortally ill. He tried to go to the Buddha to beg his forgiveness, but before he could reach him, he died.

As the Buddha grew older, there was little to differentiate his activities from those of his younger days. Yet in his late seventies, his health began to deteriorate. His back grew bent, his skin grew wrinkled and lost some of its fine radiance, and his senses lost some of their sharpness. He would sit in the late afternoon after rising from the midday retreat, warming his back in the setting sun. Ananda would often massage his limbs to ease the muscles.

In his last year, though flagging physically, the Buddha continued to wander and teach. When the rainy season came, he decided to settle in Venugramaka for his retreat. During the rains, he contracted a serious illness that was accompanied by very severe pain. He bore the pain with equanimity, but still the illness was a dire one that threatened his very life. Thinking that he had not yet taken leave of his close attendants and of the community as a whole, he made a strong effort of will and succeeded in suppressing the illness.

When the illness had passed, Ananda told the Blessed One, "I am so used to seeing you well and at ease that I became very confused and afraid when you were ill. I was only able to console myself because I knew you would not leave us without giving us some instructions for the guidance of the Sangha."

"But Ananda, I have spent forty-five years giving instructions for the guidance of the Sangha. I am not one of those who jealously keep their important teachings in a closed fist. The Dharma has been fully revealed. What more can you expect of me now? Should I declare what direction the Sangha should take? Someone who would do that would be someone who thinks, 'The Sangha is dependent on me.' But a Tathagata does not think that way. How could the Sangha depend on me? I am old and decrepit like a broken-down old cart that has to be held together with thongs. I only experience ease in my body by withdrawing my attention from outward sensations and letting it rest in the heart. So the Sangha cannot depend on me.

"Rather than depending on another, taking refuge in another, each of you should be an island. Let your refuge be the Dharma. And how does one make the Dharma his refuge? By practicing the four foundations of mindfulness, that is the way. Now or after I am gone, whoever makes himself an island or the Dharma his island will be the foremost among the Sangha."

The Blessed One knew that the time was coming soon for him to attain the final nirvana, parinirvana. In the time that remained to him, he traveled northwest by slow stages, stopping sometimes for a period of weeks in one place to rest and give detailed teachings to the large country of bhikshus traveling with him. The way led through Vrijian and then Mallan country along the Hiranyavati River, roughly in the direction of Kapilavastu.

After staying a fairly long time at Bhoganagara, he proceeded to the region of Pava and stopped in the mango grove of a goldsmith named Chunda. When Chunda heard that he was so fortunate as to have the Buddha staying in his mango grove, he hastened to invite the Buddha and the Sangha to his house for the following day's meal.

Chunda had quantities of good food prepared by the next day, including particularly large amounts of a special pork dish. When the Buddha arrived at his house and had taken his seat, he told Chunda, "Serve the pork dish to me alone and serve the other food to the community." Chunda complied.

Within a few hours the Buddha suffered a violent attack of gastric illness with dire pain and severe bleeding of the bowel. He bore the pain with equanimity, mindful and aware. After a time, he said to Ananda, "Come, let us go on to Kushinagara."

When they came to the river, he bathed and drank. Then he crossed the river and lay down on his right side to rest in a mango grove on its far bank. As he was lying there, he said to Ananda, "As for Chunda the goldsmith, it is possible he might be afflicted with remorse when he hears how the Blessed One fared after receiving his last meal from him. You should tell Chunda the smith that the last food given to a tathagata before his enlightenment and the last given before his final nirvana bring particular merit to the giver. He has acquired great merit, and great good fortune will be his in the future. Tell him that I said this; it should counter his remorse."

Realizing that the Blessed One would soon be gone, Ananda began to ask him all manner of questions. "How should we treat the Tathagata's remains?" he asked.

"Do not make a big point of venerating the Tathagata's remains. Strive for your own attainment. Diligent but controlled, devote yourself to your own good. Let the brahmins and householders concern themselves with the Blessed One's remains."

Ananda questioned him further, and the Blessed One spoke about the various circumstances in which it was proper to build stupas, monuments, to house a tathagata's relics and to remind people of the tathagata.

This talk of monuments to commemorate the Tathagata

seemed to be too much for Ananda. He excused himself and went into a nearby shed, where he leaned against the inside of the door and wept. "My teacher who is so compassionate and kind to me is about to attain the ultimate nirvana, and I am still so passion-ridden and have not attained realization!" This is what he thought to himself as the tears poured from his eyes.

The Blessed One was being attended by some other bhikshus. "Where is Ananda?" he asked them.

"He is in that shed, crying," he was told.

"Go to Ananda and tell him, 'Your teacher calls you,' " the Blessed One told one of the bhikshus. The monk brought Ananda this message. Then Ananda returned to the Blessed One and bowed to him with his palms together and stood off to one side. "Ananda," said the Buddha, "have I not often told you we must be separated from what we hold dear? How is it possible that what is born should not die? As for you, you have served me well and with great kindness for many years, served me with your body, with your speech, and with your mind. You have laid up much merit, Ananda. Just be diligent for a little while, and you will attain the goal.

The Buddha then told Ananda to go to Kushinagara and tell the Mallans that the Blessed One's parinirvana would take place that night, in the last watch. Soon those aggrieved and mournful Mallans, children and old people and all, were gathering at the shala grove to bid farewell to the Blessed One. Among the crowds of people was a young wandering ascetic named Subhadra who was permitted to see the Blessed One in his last hour. Subhadra became the last to be received into the order by the Buddha. When he had taken his leave and gone, the Blessed One said to Ananda, "When the Blessed One is gone, you might think that the teacher is gone, that you no longer have a teacher. This is not true. The Dharma, the discipline, and the practice that I taught you will be your teacher after I am gone."

Then he addressed all the bhikshus who were nearby and said, "There might be some among you who have a doubt or a problem concerning the Buddha, the Dharma, or the Sangha. If that is so, ask about it now."

The monks were silent. Finally Ananda spoke up.

"Lord, it is amazing, it is wonderful. I feel confident that there is not one monk here who has any doubts concerning the teacher, the Dharma, the Sangha, the path, or the manner of progressing along the path."

"You speak your words out of confidence, Ananda, but the Tathagata knows with direct knowledge that there is not one bhikshu in all these five hundred who has a doubt concerning the Buddha, the Dharma, the Sangha, the path, or the way of progressing upon it. The least advanced of them has entered the stream, has attained the first stage of realization, is no longer subject to falling away, has achieved certainty, and is destined for enlightenment.

"Truly, monks, I declare this to you. It is in the nature of whatever is formed to dissolve. Attain perfection through diligence."

The Buddha stopped speaking. He entered successively the first, the second, the third, and then the fourth level of meditative absorption. Then he entered the formless realm and progressed through the levels of meditation based on boundless space, boundless consciousness, nothingness, and "neither perception nor nonperception." Then he passed to the cessation of perception and feeling.

Then Ananda said to Aniruddha, who was standing by, "The Blessed One has attained parinirvana."

"No, Ananda," said the other, "not yet. Only the cessation of perception and feeling."

Then the Blessed One passed back down through the levels again until he reached the first level of meditation. Then again he ascended from the first, to the second, to the third, and then to the fourth level. Then he attained the utter extinction of final nirvana, parinirvana.

There was a profound rumbling within the earth and a vast thundering in the heavens.

A Short History of Buddhism   2

SHERAB CHÖDZIN KOHN

THE FOLLOWING ACCOUNT IS MEANT TO GIVE AN overview in short order of the career of the Buddha Dharma in the world following the original impetus given to it by the Buddha. This information will greatly aid the reader in situating the material found in the following chapters, particularly the main section on the development in India. Although many schools and styles of Buddha Dharma developed in response to different cultural and historical situations, the single spirit and essence of the Buddha's message of awakening from confusion by working on one's own mind can be found in all of them.

THE HISTORY OF THE BUDDHA DHARMA BEGINS WITH THE enlightenment of the Buddha, who at the age of thirty-five (probably around 528 BCE) awakened from the sleep of delusion that grips all beings in an endless vicious cycle of ignorance and unnecessary suffering (*samsara*). Having awakened, he decided to "go against the current" and communicate his liberating wakefulness to suffering beings—that is, to teach the Dharma. For forty-five years, he crossed and recrossed India's central Gangetic plain on foot conveying his profound, brilliant wakefulness directly as well as by means of explanations that grew into a great body of spiritual, psychological, and practical doctrine. His enlightenment as well as the doctrine leading to it have been passed down through numerous unbroken lineages of teachers, which have spread to many countries. Many of these lineages still flourish.

At the time of the Buddha's death (ca. 483 BCE), his Dharma was well established in central India. There were many lay followers, but the heart of the Dharma community were the monastics, many of whom were *arhats.* Numerous monasteries had already been built round about such large cities as Rajagriha, Shravasti, and Vaishali.

The first to assume the Buddha's mantle, tradition tells, was his disciple Mahakashyapa, who had the duty of establishing an authoritative version of the Buddha's teachings. Thus, during the first rainy season after the Buddha's *parinirvana,* Mahakashyapa convoked an assembly of five hundred arhats. At this assembly, it is said, Ananda, the Buddha's personal attendant, recited all of the master's discourses (*sutras*), naming the place where each was given and describing the circumstances. A *bhikshu* named Upali recited all the rules and procedures the Buddha has established for the conduct of monastic life. Mahakashyapa himself recited the *matrika,* lists of terms organized to provide analytical synopses of the teachings given in the sutras. These three extensive recitations, reviewed and verified by the assembly, became the basis for the Sutra Pitaka (Discourse Basket), the Vinaya Pitaka (Discipline Basket), and Abhidharma Pitaka (Special Teachings Basket), respectively. The Tripitaka (all three together) is the core of the Buddhist scriptures. This assembly, held at Rajagriha with the patronage of the Magadhan king Ajatashatru, is called the First Council.

In the early centuries after the Buddha's death, the Buddha Dharma spread throughout India and became a main force in the life of its peoples. Its strength lay in its realized (arhat) teachers and large monasteries that sheltered highly developed spiritual and intellectual communities. Monks traveled frequently between the monasteries, binding them into a powerful network.

As the Dharma spread to different parts of India, differences emerged, particularly regarding the Vinaya, or rules of conduct. Roughly a hundred years after the First Council, such discrepancies led to a Second Council in Vaishali, in which seven hun-

dred arhats censured ten points of lax conduct on the part of
the local monks, notably the acceptance of donations of gold
and silver. In spite of this council and other efforts to maintain
unity, gradually, perhaps primarily because of size alone, the
Sangha divided into divergent schools.

Among the principal schools was a conservative faction, the
Sthaviravada (way of the elders), which held firmly to the old
monastic ideal with the arhat at its center and to the original
teaching of the Buddha as expressed in the Tripitaka. Another
school, the Mahasanghikas, asserted the fallibility of arhats. It
sought to weaken the authority of the monastic elite and open
the Dharma gates to the lay community. In this, as well as in
certain metaphysical doctrines, the Mahasanghikas prefigured
the Mahayana. Another important school was that of the Sarvastivadins (from Sanskrit *sarva asti*, "all exists"), who held the
divergent view that past, present, and future realities all exist.
In all, eighteen schools with varying shades of opinion on
points of doctrine or discipline developed by the end of the
third century BCE. However, all considered themselves part of
the spiritual family of the Buddha and in general were accepted
as such by the others. It was not rare for monks of different
schools to live or travel together.

According to the Sthaviravadin tradition (known in Pali as
the Theravada), which continues today in Southeast Asia, a
Third Council took place in the time of King Ashoka (r. 276–
232 BCE) at which the king declared the Sthaviravadin teachings
the standard from which all other schools deviated. Perhaps in
reaction to this, the Sarvastivadins gradually migrated to the
west. They established a bastion in the city of Mathura, from
which their influence continued to spread. Over centuries, they
dominated the northwest, including all of Kashmir and much
of Central Asia. Today a Sarvastivadin Vinaya lineage still sur-
vives in all the schools of Tibetan Buddhism.

King Ashoka was the third emperor of the Mauryan empire,
which covered all of the Indian subcontinent but its southern
tip. His personal espousal of the Dharma and adoption of its
principles for the governance of his immense realm meant a
quantum leap in the spread of the Buddha's teaching. The imperial government promulgated the teachings, supported the
monasteries, and sent proselytizing missions to the Hellenic
states of the northwest and to Southeast Asia. Under King

Ashoka, institutions of compassion and nonviolence were established throughout much of India, such as peaceful relations with all neighboring states, hospitals and animal hospitals, special officials to oversee the welfare of local populations, shady rest stops for travelers, and so on. Thus he remains today the paragon of a Buddhist ruler, and his reign is looked back upon by Buddhists as a golden age.

The Mauryan empire soon fragmented, but the Buddha Dharma continued as a dominant force throughout India in the early centuries of the common era. The kings of the Satavahana dynasty of central India followed Ashoka in adopting the Dharma as a civilizing and unifying force in governing disparate peoples. King Kanishka (r. first–second centuries), whose vast Kushan empire, centered on Gandhara, encompassed northern India and large parts of Central Asia, was a champion of the Dharma, hailed as a second Ashoka. Under his patronage, a Fourth Council was held, at which major new commentaries on the Tripitaka were written, largely under Sarvastivadin influence. Under Kanishka, the Buddha Dharma was firmly planted among the Central Asian peoples whose homelands lay along the Silk Route, whence the way lay open to China. The Kushan Empire also saw the flowering of Gandharan art, which under Hellenistic influences produced Buddha images of extraordinary nobility and beauty.

Traditional accounts of the Fourth Council say that the assembly was composed of arhats under the leadership of the arhat Parshva but also under the accomplished bodhisattva Vasumitra. Indeed it was at this time, about the beginning of the second century, that the way of the bodhisattva, or the Mahayana (Great Vehicle), appeared. It was this form of the Buddha Dharma that was to conquer the north, including China, Japan, Korea, Tibet, and Mongolia.

The most visible manifestation of the Mahayana was a new wave of sutras, scriptures claiming to be the word of the Buddha that had remained hidden until then in other realms of existence. The Mahayana replaced the ideal of the arhat with that of the bodhisattva. Whereas arhats sought to end confusion in themselves in order to escape samsara, bodhisattvas vowed to end confusion in themselves yet remain in samsara to liberate all other sentient beings. The vision of spiritual life broadened beyond the controlled circumstances of cloister and study to include the wide-open situations of the world. Correspondingly, the notion of "buddha" was no longer limited to a series of historical personages, the last of whom was Shakyamuni, but referred also to a fundamental self-existing principle of spiritual wakefulness or enlightenment. While continuing to accept the old Tripitaka, Mahayanists regarded it as a restricted expression of the Buddha's teaching, and they characterized those who held to it exclusively as Hinayanists (adherents of the Hinayana, the Small Vehicle).

Great masters shaped the Mahayana in the early centuries of the common era. Outstanding among them all was Nagarjuna (fl. second or third century), whose name connects him with the *nagas* (serpent deities) from whose hidden realm he is said to have retrieved the *Prajnaparamita* sutras, foundational Mahayana scriptures. Nagarjuna was born in South India and became the head of Nalanda, the great Buddhist university, a few miles north of Rajagriha, which was a major stronghold of the Dharma for a thousand years. Nagarjuna's commentaries and treatises expounded the teachings of the Madhyamaka (Middle Way), one of the two main Mahayana schools. Another great master was Asanga (fl. fourth century), who founded the other main school, the Yogachara, which focused on experience as the ultimate principle.

Through most of the Gupta period (c. 300–c. 600), the Buddha Dharma flourished unhindered in India. In the sixth century, however, hundreds of Buddhist monasteries were destroyed by invading Huns under King Mihirakula. This was a serious blow, but the Dharma revived and flourished once again, mainly in northeastern India under the Pala kings (eight–twelfth centuries). These Buddhist kings patronized the monasteries and built new scholastic centers such as Odantapuri near the Ganges some miles east of Nalanda. Though the Hinayana had largely vanished from India by the seventh century, in this last Indian period the Mahayana continued, and yet another form—known as Mantrayana, Vajrayana, or Tantra—became dominant.

Like the Mahayana, the Vajrayana (Diamond Vehicle) was based on a class of scriptures ultimately attributed to the Buddha, in this case known as Tantras. Vajrayanists regarded the Hinayana and Mahayana as successive stages on the way to the tantric level. The Vajrayana leaped yet further than the Mahayana in acceptance of the world, holding that all experiences, including the sensual, are sacred manifestations of awakened mind, the buddha principle. It emphasized liturgical methods of meditation, or *sadhanas,* in which the practitioner identified with deities symbolizing various aspects of awakened mind. The palace of the deity, identical with the phenomenal world as a whole, was known as a *mandala.* In the place of the arhat and the bodhisattva, the Vajrayana placed the *siddha,* the realized tantric master.

By the thirteenth century, largely as a result of violent suppression by Islamic conquerors, the Buddha Dharma was practically extinct in the land of its birth. However, by this time Hinayana forms were firmly ensconced in Southeast Asia, and varieties of Mahayana and Vajrayana in most of the rest of Asia.

China. The Mahayana entered China through Central Asia at the beginning of the common era. At first it was confused with indigenous Taoism, whose terms it had to borrow. The Kuchean monk Kumarajiva (344–413), brought to China as a prisoner of war, created a new level of precision in Chinese Buddhism. His lucid translation and teaching resulted in the formation of the Chinese Madhyamaka school (San-lun, Three Treatises). Paramartha (499–569) was another great translator and teacher. His work made possible the development of the Fa-hsiang, or Chinese Yogachara, school. Buddha Dharma's golden age in China was the T'ang period (618–907). Monasteries were numerous and powerful and had the support of the emperors. During this time the other main Chinese Dharma schools—Hua-yen, T'ien-t'ai, Ch'an, Pure Land, and the tantric Mi-tsung—made their appearance. In 845, however, came a major persecution of the Dharma community, and the monasteries had to be evacuated. Thereafter the Buddha Dharma in China never recovered its former glory.

The Sung period (960–1279) was a time of blending Taoist, Buddhist, and Confucian ideas and methods. Under the Ming dynasty (1368–1662), a fusion of Ch'an and Pure Land opened the way for a strong lay movement. During the Ch'ing period (1663–1908), the Tibetan Vajrayana made its mark on Chinese Buddhism, mainly through the imperial courts. Communist rule in the twentieth century reduced the Dharma community to a remnant, but in Taiwan the Dharma flourished, predominantly in Pure Land and other popular forms.

Korea. Buddha Dharma came to Korea from China in the fourth century CE. It flourished after the Silla unification in the seventh century. By the tenth century there were Korean versions of most Chinese schools. Paramount were Ch'an, Hua-yen, and a Vajrayana form related to the Chinese Mi-tsung. The heyday of Korean Dharma was the Koryo period (932–1392), during which the comprehensive *Tripitaka Koreana* was published. Under the Yi dynasty (1392–1910), Confucianism became the state religion and the Buddha Dharma was forced into the background. A revival came after the end of Japanese rule in 1945, when the Won movement, a popular Buddhism much influenced by Ch'an, came to the fore. Nowadays, a kind of syncretic Buddhism is widespread in Korea.

Japan. The Buddha Dharma was brought to Japan from Korea in 522. It received its major impetus from the regent prince Shotoku (r. 593–621), a Japanese Ashoka. He established Buddhism as the state religion of Japan, founded monasteries, and himself wrote important commentaries on the sutras. Initially, it was primarily the Sanron (San-lun, Madhyamaka) school that spread. In the ninth century, six Japanese schools, originally brought from China—Kosha, Hosso, Sanron, Jojitsu, Ritsu, and Kegon—were officially recognized, with the imperial house adopting the Kegon Dharma. During the latter part of the Heian period (794–1184), the Tendai and tantric Shingon schools became predominant. From the tenth to fourteenth centuries, various Pure Land sects began to prosper. Zen (Ch'an) came to Japan from China toward the end of the twelfth century, and remained a vital force in Japanese cultural life ever after. Soto and Rinzai are its two main schools. After the appearance of the Nichiren school in the thirteenth century, no further movements developed until modern times. All Japanese schools assimilated aspects of indigenous Shinto *kami* and ancestor worship. Since World War II, various modernizing lay movements such as Soka-gakkai and Rissho Kosei-kai have developed. Japan today boasts an unparalleled variety of Buddhist sects.

Tibet. The Buddha Dharma of Tibet (and Himalayan countries such as Sikkim, Bhutan, and Ladakh) preserved and developed the Vajrayana tradition of late Indian Buddhism and joined it with the Sarvastivadin monastic rule. The first spreading of Buddhism was initiated by King Trisong Detsen (755–797), who invited to Tibet the Indian pandit Shantarakshita, notable for his brilliant synthesis of the Madhayamaka and Yogachara, and the great Indian *siddha* Padmasambhava. The tradition of the Nyingma school stems from this time. After a period of persecution, a second spreading came in the eleventh century, resulting in the foundation of the Kagyu and Shakya schools. A major part of Indian Buddhist writings were translated to form the Tibetan canon, which included tantric scriptures and commentaries, preserving many texts otherwise lost. In the fourteenth century, a reform movement resulted in the formation of the Gelukpa school, the fourth of the principal schools of Tibetan Buddhism. By the late twentieth century, as a result of Chinese repression Buddhism in Tibet was reduced to a vestige, but it remained in Sikkim and Bhutan. Centers of Tibetan Buddhism also developed in northern India and Nepal as well as in Europe, Australia, and North America.

Mongolia. The Mongols were definitively converted to Tibetan Buddhism in the sixteenth century. Scriptures and liturgies were translated into Mongolian, and the four principal Tibetan schools flourished until the Communist takeover of the twentieth century.

Vietnam. Vietnam lay under Chinese influence, and the Chinese Mahayana sects of Ch'an (Thien) and Pure Land (Tindo) were well established in the country by the end of the first millennium. Theravada was introduced by the Khmers but remained largely confined to areas along the Cambodian border. A modern social-action-oriented movement fusing the two Mahayana sects began in Saigon in 1932. In 1963 Theravadans joined this movement, and a United Buddhist Congregation of Vietnam existed fleetingly. Today Buddhists in Vietnam remain intensely involved in politics and social action.

Burma. Emissaries sent by King Ashoka in the third century BCE first brought the Dharma to Burma. By the fifth century, the Theravada was well established, and by the seventh century the Mahayana had appeared in regions near the Chinese border. By the eighth century, the Vajrayana was also present, and all three forms continued to coexist until King Anaratha established the Theravada throughout the land in the eleventh century. Pagan, the royal capital in the north, was adorned with thousands upon thousands of Buddhist stupas and temples, and was the principal bastion of Buddha Dharma on earth until sacked by the Mongols in 1287. In succeeding centuries the Theravada continued strong, interacting closely at times with the Dharma centers of Ceylon. The Burmese form of Theravada acquired a unique flavor through its assimilation of folk beliefs connected with spirits of all kinds known as *nats*. Today 85 percent of Burmese are Buddhist, and Buddhism is the official religion of the country.

Cambodia (Kampuchea). The Buddhism of the Sarvastivadin school spread to Cambodia in the third century BCE and reached a high point in the fifth and sixth centuries. By the end of the eighth century, elements of Mahayana had also appeared. Succeeding centuries brought a fusion of Buddha Dharma with Shaivite Hinduism. In the fourteenth century, however, the Theravada was firmly imposed on the country by the royal house, and it has remained dominant. In 1955 Prince Norodom Sihanouk sought to unite the country under the banner of king, Dharma, and socialism. Buddhism in Burma has remained associated with the political left.

Sri Lanka (Ceylon). In the third century BCE, King Devanampiya Tissa was converted to Theravada Buddhism by King Ashoka's son, Mahinda. The Sinhalese king built the Mahavihara monastery and there enshrined a branch of the Bodhi Tree that had been brought from India. For more than two millennia since that time, the Mahavihara has been a powerful force in the Buddhism of Ceylon and other countries of Southeast Asia, notably Burma and Thailand. The Theravada in Ceylon remains the oldest continuous Dharma tradition anywhere in the world. Nonetheless, factions reflecting the influence of other Indian or Theravada schools played a significant role. These centered around other great Sinhalese monasteries such as the Abhayagirivihara and the Jetavanavihara. Mahayana and tantric influences are also traceable, and Tamil Hinduism had an ongoing influence outside the monasteries. Associated with the Mahavihara was the preeminent teacher and writer Buddhaghosha (fl. fourth–fifth centuries), whose great *Vishuddimagga* (Path of Purity) gives a definitive account of the Theravada. In the twelfth century King Parakkambahu forcibly imposed the Mahaviharan brand of Theravada on the entire country.

The attempted conversion of the country to Christianity by Portuguese and Dutch colonists in the sixteenth and seventeenth centuries greatly weakened the Dharma in Ceylon but made it a rallying point for Sinhalese nationalism. In the following centuries Sinhalese kings turned to Burma and Thailand to refresh Sinhalese monastic lineages. In the nineteenth and twentieth centuries, many Europeans came to the aid of Singhalese Buddhism. By the time of independence in 1948, the Theravada was again thriving in Ceylon and exercising significant influence beyond its borders.

Thailand. Some form of Hinayana Buddhism arrived in Thailand from Burma in about the sixth century; however, the Mahayana seems to have been dominant between the eighth and thirteenth centuries. From the eleventh century, Hinduist Khmers were a major factor in many regions of the country, but in the thirteenth century the Thai royal house established Theravada Buddhism as the national religion. Eventually the Khmers were converted to Theravada and became strong supporters. In the nineteenth century, the reformist Dhammayut school, characterized by strict adherence to Vinaya discipline, arose under royal influence. Today it remains the dominant element in Thai Buddhism and has also influenced other countries of Southeast Asia. Ninety-five percent of the Thai population is Buddhist.

The Western World. Over the last two hundred years many Western intellectuals were drawn to and influenced by Buddhism. Philosophers like Arthur Schopenhauer, Henri Bergson, and others were inspired by the exotic profundity of Buddhist thought. In the twentieth century there has been considerable attention to Buddha Dharma in academic circles, and fairly accurate translations of Buddhist texts have gradually become available since the 1930s. A new level of understanding has come about since the 1950s as authentic Asian meditation masters have established themselves in Western countries and taken on serious Western students. Theravada Buddhism has had a significant impact since the 1930s, Zen since the 1950s, and the tantric Buddhism of Tibet since the 1970s. Recently Westerners have begun assuming leadership in age-old Asian lineages. Of course, significant numbers of Asian Buddhists have reached the West as part of immigrant populations, but thus far there has been little crossover of Buddha Dharma from this source into host cultures.

PART TWO

Basic Teachings

Introduction

THE RANGE AND INTENTION OF THE BUDDHA'S teaching are defined to a great extent by the Four Noble Truths. The Buddha taught these truths to his first disciples at the very beginning in order to give them an overall impression of his message. (One of these disciples got enlightened the first time he heard the Four Noble Truths.) The First Truth is that life is characterized by *duhkha* (Pali, *dukkha*), usually translated as "suffering." This essentially means that all of our experience is pervaded by a kind of frustrating confusion and an irritating sense of inadequacy. We often feel that the way things are going is "a pain." A lot of situations seem to be "a drag." A general murmur of complaint and worry resonates throughout the human world, punctuated by cries of indignation, resentment, and grief. Serious troubles easily breed in a medium such as this. The newscast is usually bad news tinctured with worrisome implications that has to be relieved with a lovable human-interest story. Moments of happiness and satisfaction derive their poignancy, their preciousness, from the general background of duhkha. This condition of duhkha is what makes the spiritual path worthwhile and interesting—for getting out of it, that is.

The Second Truth declares that the cause of duhkha is *trishna* (Pali, *tanha*), "craving" or "desire" or "attachment." The problem seems to be that we are always wanting something, feeling we are lacking something, or wanting an existing something to go away (aversion is also a form of attachment). We could say that the cause of suffering is a generalized mentality of poverty.

The Third Truth is that of Cessation. Duhkha can cease, because its cause can cease. There is a way out—which is the Fourth Truth, the truth of the path that leads to the cessation of suffering by extirpating its cause. This is described as an Eightfold Path. A key element of this path is meditation. Through the eightfold path we can entirely awaken from the poverty mentality of trishna and stop generating duhkha.

Other important basic teachings described in the chapters that follow are the three marks of existence (impermanence, suffering, and egolessness), a description of the nature of things, which explains why the process of craving and possessing can't function successfully in bringing happiness; and the *pratitya-samutpada,* often translated as "conditioned origination," which gives a very complete and subtle picture of how of all of experience that is characterized by duhkha (samsara) fits together inseparably and so can all come apart at once (nirvana); and of course, there is karma.

These and a few other basic teachings make the Buddha Dharma the Buddha Dharma. From a historical point of view, these might be looked on as the old teachings. All the schools of Buddha Dharma that appeared later in time—the various forms of the Mahayana and the Vajrayana—assimilated and made use of these teachings, though these later forms sometimes reshaped the original teachings.

By the time the Mahayana ("great vehicle") appeared, five or six hundred years after the death (*parinirvana*) of the Buddha, the eighteen schools that rejected the new Mahayana teachings and stuck to the old were classed together derogatorily by the Mahayanists as the Hinayana ("small vehicle"). Only one of the eighteen old schools remain today, appropriately called the Theravada ("way of the elders"). It flourishes in Sri Lanka and much of Southeast Asia. Though Theravadans still reject the term *Hinayana*, the majority of writers on Buddha Dharma—with no derogatory intent whatsoever—have adopted the term to distinguish the eighteen original schools and their teachings from the Mahayana and Vajrayana.

The Theravadans preserve the oldest and most complete version of the Hinayana sutras, written in Pali, a language related to Sanskrit. They consider them to preserve the actual words of the Buddha and to represent his complete, pure, and unadulterated teaching. As in the time of the Buddha himself, great emphasis is placed by the Theravada on monasticism, the way of the arhat, and on sudden enlightenment. In this last point, the Theravada has common ground with Zen, a prominent Mahayana school.

The Buddha's Teaching   3

BHIKKU BODHI

 THE THERAVADA MONK Bhikku Bodhi presents here an astonishingly concise and precise summary of the essential Theravada teachings we discussed in the introduction to Part Two. Note that he has divided the eightfold path into *shila, samadhi,* and *prajna,* which he translates as "morality," "concentration," and "wisdom" (and which can also be translated as divergently as "discipline," "meditation," and "knowledge"). In the last months of the Buddha's life, when the time came to fix the essentials of his teaching in his followers' minds, he repeated again and again—sometimes more than once a day—a short talk explaining how these three elements of training on the spiritual path support each other and should be inseparable. If the three elements are applied in concert, he repeatedly assured his hearers, enlightenment will speedily follow.

THE BUDDHA'S TEACHING, CALLED THE DHARMA, IS THE DOC-trine of deliverance which he himself discovered through the Enlightenment and proclaimed on the basis of his own clear comprehension of reality. The most concise expression of the Dharma, its unifying framework, is the teaching of the Four Noble Truths: suffering, its origin, its cessation, and the way leading to its cessation. This was the great realization that broke upon the Buddha's mind as he sat in meditation under the Bodhi Tree after six hard years of striving. It is not only the formulated content of his Enlightenment, but the ongoing significance of his message to the world, setting forth the crucial undeceptive truths upon which the whole prospect of deliverance depends.

The four truths all revolve around the recognition of suffering (duhkha) as the central problem of human existence, and in the first truth the Buddha enumerates its diverse forms:

> What now is the noble truth of suffering? Birth is suffering; decay is suffering; death is suffering; sorrow, lamentation, pain, grief, and despair are suffering; not to get what one wants is suffering; in short, the five aggregates of clinging are suffering.

This last clause—referring to a fivefold grouping of all the factors of existence—implies a deeper dimension to suffering than is covered by our ordinary ideas of pain, sorrow, and despondency. What it points to, as the fundamental meaning of the first noble truth, is the unsatisfactoriness and radical inadequacy of everything conditioned, owing to the fact that whatever is conditioned is impermanent and ultimately bound to perish. This aspect of suffering comes to light most clearly in the most comprehensive manifestation of impermanence and peril: the beginningless round of rebirths in which all living beings revolve, samsara. Thus, to appreciate the first noble truth in its full depth and range, it is not enough to consider merely the sufferings of a single lifetime. One must take into account the entire round of becoming with its ever-repeated phases of birth, aging, sickness and death.

In the second noble truth the Buddha traces suffering to its origin or cause, which he identifies as craving:

> What now is the noble truth of the origin of suffering? It is craving, which gives rise to repeated existence, is bound up with pleasure and lust, and always seeks fresh enjoyment here and

there; that is, sensual craving, craving for existence and craving for nonexistence.

Itself the product of ignorance, an unawareness of the true nature of things, craving springs up wherever there is the prospect of pleasure and enjoyment, bringing along with it the multitude of mental defilements responsible for so much human misery: greed and ambition, hatred and anger, selfishness and envy, conceit, vanity, and pride.

Craving gives rise to suffering, not only by engendering the immediate pain of want, the sense of lack, but more specifically in the context of the four truths by generating rebirth and thus maintainng bondage to samsara. But the process of rebirth, in the Buddhist view, does not involve the transmigration of a self or soul, for the thesis that everything is in flux precludes a durable entity passing from life to life. Continuity through the sequence of rebirths is maintained, not by a self-identical ego subsisting through the change, but by the transmission of impressions and tendencies along the individual "mental continuum" or stream of consciousness in which they arise. The direction the continuum takes from life to life is governed by a force called *karma*, a word meaning "volitional action." According to the teaching on karma, it is our own willed actions, bodily, verbal, and mental, that determine the forms of existence we assume in each of our successive sojourns through samsara. The law connecting the two is essentially moral in its mode of operation: good actions lead to happiness and higher forms of rebirth, bad actions to misery and lower forms of rebirth. But whether one's destiny moves upwards or downwards, as long as craving and ignorance persist in the deep recesses of the mind, the cycle of birth and death, the great round of suffering, will continue to turn.

This cycle, however, does not have to go on forever, and in the third noble truth the Buddha announces the key to stopping it:

What now is the noble truth of the cessation of suffering? It is the complete fading away and cessation of craving, its forsaking and abandonment, liberation and detachment from it.

Since suffering arises through craving, with the destruction of craving, suffering too must cease: a relationship as tight and inevitable as logical law. The state that then supervenes, the goal of all striving for Theravada Buddhism, is *nirvana*, the unconditioned, the deathless, the imperishable peace beyond the round of birth and death. The attainment of nirvana takes place in two stages. The first is the "nirvana element with a residue remaining," the liberation of mind achieved when all defilements have been extinguished but the mind-body combination brought into being at birth continues to live on until the end of the lifespan. The second is the "nirvana element with no residue remaining," the liberation from existence itself, the cessation of becoming attained with the liberated one's final passing away.

In the fourth noble truth, the Buddha teaches the way to nirvana, "the way leading to the cessation of suffering." This is the Noble Eightfold Path with its eight factors arranged into three groups thus:

1. Right understanding 2. Right thought	III. Wisdom (*prajna*)
3. Right speech 4. Right action 5. Right livelihood	I. Morality (*shila*)
6. Right effort 7. Right mindfulness 8. Right concentration	II. Concentration (*samadhi*)

The path begins with the minimal degree of right understanding and right thought needed to take up the training, and then unfolds through its three groups as a systematic strategy designed to uproot the defilements that generate suffering. Morality restrains the defilements in their coarsest form, their outflow in unwholesome actions; concentration removes their more refined manifestations as distractive and restless thoughts; and wisdom eradicates their subtle latent tendencies by penetrating with direct insight the three basic facts of existence, summed up by the Buddha in the three characteristics of impermanence, suffering, and egolessness.

To each of the four truths the Buddha assigns a specific function, a task to be mastered by the disciple in training. The truth of suffering is to be fully understood, the craving and defilements which originate it are to be abandoned, nirvana as deliverance from suffering is to be realized, and the Noble Eightfold Path that leads to deliverance is to be developed. The individual who has completed these four functions is the ideal figure of Theravada Buddhism. This is the *arhat*, the liberated one, who has broken all bonds binding to the round of becoming and lives in the experienced freedom of nirvana.

4   *Words of the Buddha*

TRANSLATED BY THE VENERABLE
BALANGODA ANANDA MAITREYA

THE FOLLOWING SELECTIONS ARE THREE LITTLE chapters from the *Dhammapada,* a collection of 426 verses of simple moral advice preserved in the Theravada (Pali) canon, which are attributed to the Buddha himself. The essence of the message seems to be: keep always mindful and aware, so that your heart will not slip into sidetracks that will lead to unhappiness.

The first selection, "Twins," refers in verse 15 to "here" and "hereafter." The use of "hereafter" should not be understood as a realm "beyond" in which sinners are punished and the good rewarded. The phrase really means "this birth and the next." As we go along from moment to moment, day to day, life to life, awareness and our thoughts keep shaping the life we lead. Cumulatively the effect is tremendous. We can create for ourselves a tunnel lined with rags and deprivation or an open world of wealth and genuine communication—dark worlds, bright worlds, moderate worlds—so many different worlds can be created based on the karma we keep creating through our thoughts and projections.

The translation is by Ven. Ananda Maitreya, a Sri Lankan monk esteemed as a scholar and master in both the Theravada and Mahayana schools of Buddhism.

Twins

1 MIND IS THE FORERUNNER OF ALL ACTIONS.
All deeds are led by mind, created by mind.
If one speaks or acts with a corrupt mind, suffering
    follows,
As a wheel follows the hoof of an ox pulling a cart.

2 Mind is the forerunner of all actions.
All deeds are led by mind, created by mind.
If one speaks or acts with a serene mind, happiness
    follows,
As surely as one's shadow.

3 "He abused me, mistreated me, defeated me, robbed
    me."
Harboring such thoughts keeps hatred alive.

4 "He abused me, mistreated me, defeated me, robbed
    me."
Releasing such thoughts banishes hatred for all time.

5 Animosity does not eradicate animosity.
Only by loving kindness is animosity dissolved.
This law is ancient and eternal.

6 There are those who are aware
That we are always facing death.
Knowing this, they put aside all contentiousness.

7 The one who lives for sensation,
Unrestrained, indulgent in eating, irreverent, lazy,
The tempter Mara* breaks,
Just as the wind breaks a frail tree.

8 The one who lives mindfully, senses under control,
Moderate in eating, devout, energetic,
Cannot be overthrown by Mara,
Just as the wind cannot shake a rocky mountain.

---

* In Buddhist scriptures Mara is a metaphor for temptations or passions
personified, being neither male nor female; hence, the use of "tempter."

9 The monk's robe does not in itself
Render one free from stain.
If the one who wears that robe
Is lacking in self-control and honesty,
He is unworthy of such a robe.

10 Only one who is free from stain,
Well-disciplined, honest,
And endowed with self-control,
Is worthy of the monk's robe.

11 Those who fail to distinguish
The nonessential from the essential
And the essential from the nonessential,
Will, in feeding on wrong thoughts,
Fail to attain the essential.

12 On the other hand, those who correctly perceive
The essential as essential
And the nonessential as nonessential
Will, in feeding on right thoughts,
Attain the essential.

13 As rain pours through badly thatched houses,
So does desire penetrate the undeveloped mind.

14 As rain fails to pour through a well-thatched house,
So does desire fail to penetrate the well-developed
mind.

15 For the doer of evil there is only grief,
Here as well as hereafter.
In both states he experiences grief,
Seeing his own unwholesome acts.

16 For the doer of good deeds there is rejoicing,
Here as well as hereafter.
Joy and more joy are his,
As he sees his own right action.

17 The doer of evil reaps suffering,
Here and hereafter,
In both states remembering, "I have committed
evil."

Not only here, but hereafter, he experiences more
	suffering,
Because he has gone to a state of suffering.

18   The doer of good deeds reaps happiness,
Here and hereafter,
In both states remembering, "I have done good
	deeds."
And there is more joy,
Because he has gone to a blissful state.

19   A careless person,
Quoting much of the scriptural text but not living it,
Cannot share the abundance of the holy life,
Just as the cowherd, counting other people's cattle,
Cannot taste the milk or ghee.

20   Reciting a small portion of the scriptures,
But putting it diligently into practice;
Letting go of passion, aggression, and confusion;
Revering the truth with a clear mind;
And not clinging to anything, here or hereafter;
Brings the harvest of the holy life.

Mindfulness

1   Mindfulness is the path to immortality.
Negligence is the path to death.
The vigilant never die,
Whereas the negligent are the living dead.

2   With this understanding,
The wise, having developed a high degree of
	mindfulness,
Rejoice in mindfulness,
Paying heed to each step on the path.

3   These awakened ones,
Dedicated to meditation,
Striving actively and vigorously,
Attain nirvana, the ultimate security.

4   The radiance of the man who is committed,
Aware, unsullied,

Acting with consideration and restraint,
Becomes more luminous.

5   The wise man,
By vigor, mindfulness, restraint, and self-control,
Creates for himself an island
Which no flood can submerge.

6   The foolish, the unwise,
Surrender themselves to negligence,
Whereas the wise man protects mindfulness
As his most valuable possession.

7   "Don't lose yourself in negligence,
Don't lose yourself in sensuality."
These admonitions lead to joy and fulfillment
In the mindful and meditative man.

8   When the enlightened man frees himself
From careless behavior through mindfulness,
Free of sorrow, he gazes on the sorrowing masses,
As one on the mountaintop gazes on the plain
below.

9   The mindful person among the mindless,
The aware person among the unaware,
Surpasses the rest with his wisdom,
Like a superb racehorse outstripping an old worn-
out horse.

10 By mindfulness did the Maghavat,* Lord of Two
Realms,
Reach a position of authority among the gods.
So does mindfulness ever surpass carelessness.

11 A seeker,† concentrating on mindfulness,
Advances like a fire,

---

* According to the belief of ancient Indians, Maghavat was the king of a
certain heavenly realm. He was born into that realm and became its over-
lord as a result of good deeds he had performed in his immediate previous
life as a man on earth. During that time he fulfilled all his duties toward
others mindfully.
† Originally the term here was *bhikku*, or monk. When the Buddha was
speaking to his hearers the bhikkus were always sitting near him. That is
why in his general talks he addressed monks. One meaning of *bhikku* is
"one who discerns the fears of the round of rebirths."

Consuming the chains of bondage
Both great and small.

12   A monk, or lay person, rejoicing in mindfulness,
Seeing the danger of negligence,
Is protected on the way to his perfect state
And is close to nirvana.

The Pleasant

1   When anyone mistakenly pursues only what is
          pleasant,
Avoiding the true path,
Forgetting their true purpose, attached to the senses,
When anyone sees another on the true path,
They will experience their loss and be full of
          reproach.

2   Avoid attachment to both what is pleasant
And what is unpleasant.
Losing the pleasant causes grief.
Dwelling on the unpleasant also causes grief.

3   Do not cling to the pleasant.
Let it pass,
So that the separation will not diminish you.

4   Clinging to what is dear brings sorrow.
Clinging to what is dear brings fear.
To one who is entirely free from endearment
There is no sorrow or fear.

5   Sorrow springs from affection.
Fear springs from affection.
To loosen those bonds
Is to be free from sorrow and fear.

6   Sorrow springs from indulgence in sensual pleasures.
Fear springs from indulgence in sensual pleasures.
Whoever is free from such indulgence
Knows neither sorrow nor fear.

7   Sorrow springs from preoccupation with lustful
          pleasures.

Fear springs from preoccupation with lustful
    pleasures.
Whoever is free from such preoccupation
Knows neither sorrow nor fear.

8 Sorrow springs from craving.
Fear springs from craving.
Whoever is free from craving
Knows neither sorrow nor fear.

9 People cherish the person committed to right action
And rich in understanding.
That person, knowing the truth,
Walks steadfastly on the path.

10 The person who reaches the sacred, the inexpressible,
Who has permeated his mind with it,
Who is in control of his senses,
Is one bound upstream.

11 Friends and relatives welcome with joy a loved one,
Returning from abroad after a long absence.
In exactly the same way will the fruits of right action
Welcome the doer as he travels from one life to the
    next.

The Development of Ego 5

CHÖGYAM TRUNGPA

THE TIBETAN MASTER CHÖGYAM Trungpa (1940–1987) was one of the first from his tradition to assimilate the Western mentality fully. Thus he was able to formulate the traditional Buddhist teachings in a new way, speaking directly to the Westerner. Here we have a complete lesson in basic Buddhist psychology. One of the most central of Buddhist ideas is that there is no self. The sense of self that we naively cling to is seen by the naked eye of meditation to be only a tenuous, ever-shifting amalgam of psychological elements, known traditionally as the five *skandhas*, or "heaps." Here Trungpa gives these as form, feeling, perception, concept, and consciousness and provides an intimate inner account of their development.

A key point is duality, which arises at the level of the first skandha, form. Duality is a description for the most basic characteristic of the confused world of ego, the rudimentary building block of the suffering world of samsara. It is the fundamental sense that there is "something else." The sense of something else draws awareness out of the primordial directness of the here and now. It perceives the "other" and in a panic perceives itself as another something else across from that other. At that point we have the situation of duality, of self and other, and the struggle of relating to an alien world that must be grasped, warded off, or ignored has begun. Here Trungpa connects this with the moment of the birth of time.

I THINK IT WOULD BE BEST TO START WITH SOMETHING VERY concrete and realistic, the field we are going to cultivate. It would be foolish to study more advanced subjects before we are familiar with the starting point, the nature of ego. We have a saying in Tibet that, before the head has been cooked properly, grabbing the tongue is of no use. Any spiritual practice needs this basic understanding of the starting point, the material with which we are working.

If we do not know the material with which we are working, then our study is useless; speculations about the goal become mere fantasy. Speculations may take the form of advanced ideas and descriptions of spiritual experiences, but they only exploit the weaker aspects of human nature, our expectations and desires to see and hear something colorful, something extraordinary. If we begin our study with these dreams of extraordinary, "enlightening" and dramatic experiences, then we will build up our expectations and preconceptions so that later, when we are actually working on the path, our minds will be occupied largely with what *will be* rather than with what *is*. It is destructive and not fair to people to play on their weaknesses, their expectations and dreams, rather than to present the realistic starting point of what they are. . . .

Fundamentally there is just open space, the *basic ground*, what we really are. Our most fundamental state of mind, before the creation of ego, is such that there is basic openness, basic freedom, a spacious quality; and we have now and have always had this openness. Take, for example, our everyday lives and thought patterns. When we see an object, in the first instant there is a sudden perception which has no logic or conceptualization to it at all; we just perceive the thing in the open ground. Then immediately we panic and begin to rush about trying to add something to it, either trying to find a name for it or trying to find pigeon-holes in which we could locate and categorize it. Gradually things develop from there.

This development does not take the shape of a solid entity. Rather, this development is illusory, the mistaken belief in a "self" or "ego." Confused mind is inclined to view itself as a solid, on-going thing, but it is only a collection of tendencies, events. In Buddhist terminology this collection is referred to as the five skandhas, or five heaps. So perhaps we could go through the whole development of the five skandhas.

The beginning point is that there is open space, belonging to no one. There is always primordial intelligence connected with the space and openness, *vidya*—which means "intelligence" in Sanskrit—precision, sharpness, sharpness with space, sharpness with room in which to put things, exchange things. It is like a spacious hall where there is room to dance about, where there is no danger of knocking things over or tripping over things, for there is completely open space. We *are* this space, we are *one* with it, with vidya, intelligence, and openness.

But if we are this all the time, where did the confusion come from, where has the space gone, what has happened? Nothing has happened, as a matter of fact. We just became too active in that space. Because it is spacious, it brings inspiration to dance about; but our dance became a bit too active, we began to spin more than was necessary to express the space. At this point we became *self*-conscious, conscious that "I" am dancing in the space.

At such a point, space is no longer space as such. It becomes solid. Instead of being one with the space, we feel solid space as a separate entity, as tangible. This is the first experience of duality—space and I, I am dancing in this space, and this spaciousness is a solid, separate thing. Duality means "space and I," rather than being completely one with the space. This is the birth of "form," of "other."

Then a kind of blackout occurs, in the sense that we forget what we were doing. There is a sudden halt, a pause; and we turn around and "discover" solid space, as though we had never before done anything at all, as though we were not the creators of all that solidity. There is a gap. Having already created solidified space, then we are overwhelmed by it and begin to become lost in it. There is a blackout and then, suddenly, an awakening.

When we awaken, we refuse to see the space as openness, refuse to see its smooth and ventilating quality. We completely ignore it, which is called *avidya. A* means "negation," *vidya* means "intelligence," so it is "unintelligence." Because this extreme intelligence has been transformed into the perception of solid space, because this intelligence with a sharp and precise and flowing luminous quality has become static, therefore it is called avidya, "ignorance." We deliberately ignore. We are not satisfied just to dance in the space but we want to have a partner, and so we choose the space as our partner. If you choose space as your partner in the dance, then of course you want it to dance with you. In order to possess it as a partner, you have to solidify it and ignore its flowing, open quality. This is avidya, ignorance, ignoring the intelligence. It is the culmination of the first skandha, the creation of ignorance-form.

In fact, this skandha, the skandha of ignorance-form, has three different aspects or stages which we could examine through the use of another metaphor. Suppose in the beginning there is an open plain without any mountains or trees, completely open land, a simple desert without any particular characteristics. That is how we are, what we are. We are very simple and basic. And yet there is a sun shining, a moon shining, and there will be lights and colors, the texture of the desert. There will be some feeling of the energy which plays between heaven and earth. This goes on and on.

Then, strangely, there is suddenly someone to notice all this. It is as if one of the grains of sand had stuck its neck out and begun to look around. We are that grain of sand, coming to the conclusion of our separateness. This is the "birth of ignorance" in its first stage, a kind of chemical reaction. Duality has begun.

The second stage of ignorance-form is called "the ignorance born within." Having noticed that one is separate, then there is the feeling that one has always been so. It is an awkwardness, the instinct toward self-consciousness. It is also one's excuse for remaining separate, an individual grain of sand. It is an aggressive type of ignorance, though not exactly aggressive in the sense of anger; it has not developed as far as that. Rather it is aggression in the sense that one feels awkward, unbalanced, and so one tries to secure one's ground, create a shelter for oneself. It is the attitude that one is a confused and separate individual, and that is all there is to it. One has identified oneself as separate from the basic landscape of space and openness.

The third type of ignorance is "self-observing ignorance,"

watching oneself. There is a sense of seeing oneself as an external object, which leads to the first notion of "other." One is beginning to have a relationship with a so-called "external" world. This is why these three stages of ignorance constitute the skandha of form-ignorance; one is beginning to create the world of forms.

When we speak of "ignorance" we do not mean stupidity at all. In a sense, ignorance is very intelligent, but it is a completely two-way intelligence. That is to say, one purely reacts to one's projections rather than just seeing what is. There is no situation of "letting be" at all, because one is ignoring what one is all the time. That is the basic definition of ignorance.

The next development is the setting up of a defense mechanism to protect our ignorance. This defense mechanism is feeling, the second skandha. Since we have already ignored open space, we would like next to feel the qualities of solid space in order to bring complete fulfillment to the grasping quality we are developing. Of course space does not mean just bare space, for it contains color and energy. There are tremendous, magnificent displays of color and energy, beautiful and picturesque. But we have ignored them altogether. Instead there is just a solidified version of that color; and the color becomes captured color, and the energy becomes captured energy, because we have solidified the whole space and turned it into "other." So we begin to reach out and feel the qualities of "other." By doing this we reassure ourselves that we exist. "If I can feel that out there, then I must be here."

Whenever anything happens, one reaches out to feel whether the situation is seductive or threatening or neutral. Whenever there is a sudden separation, a feeling of not knowing the relationship of "that" to "this," we tend to feel for our ground. This is the extremely efficient feeling mechanism that we begin to set up, the second skandha.

The next mechanism to further establish ego is the third skandha, perception-impulse. We begin to be fascinated by our own creation, the static colors and the static energies. We want to relate to them, and so we begin gradually to explore our creation.

In order to explore efficiently there must be a kind of switchboard system, a controller of the feeling mechanism. Feeling transmits its information to the central switchboard, which is the act of perception. According to that information, we make judgments, we react. Whether we should react for or against or indifferently is automatically determined by this bureaucracy of feeling and perception. If we feel the situation and find it threatening, then we will push it away from us. If we find it seductive, then we will draw it to us. If we find it neutral, we will be indifferent. These are the three types of impulse: hatred, desire, and stupidity. Thus perception refers to receiving information from the outside world and impulse refers to our response to that information.

The next development is the fourth skandha, concept. Perception-impulse is an automatic reaction to intuitive feeling. However, this kind of automatic reaction is not really enough of a defense to protect one's ignorance and guarantee one's security. In order to really protect and deceive oneself completely, properly, one needs intellect, the ability to name and categorize things. Thus we label things and events as being "good," "bad," "beautiful," "ugly," and so on, according to which impulse we find appropriate to them.

So the structure of ego is gradually becoming heavier and heavier, stronger and stronger. Up to this point ego's development has been purely an action and reaction process; but from now on ego gradually develops beyond the ape instinct and becomes more sophisticated. We begin to experience intellectual speculation, confirming or interpreting ourselves, putting ourselves into certain logical, interpretive situations. The basic nature of intellect is quite logical. Obviously there will be the tendency to work for a positive condition: to confirm our experience, to interpret weakness into strength, to fabricate a logic of security, to confirm our ignorance.

In a sense, it might be said that the primordial intelligence is operating all the time, but it is being employed by the dualistic fixation, ignorance. In the beginning stages of the development of ego this intelligence operates as the intuitive sharpness of feeling. Later it operates in the form of intellect. Actually it seems that there is no such thing as the ego at all; there is no such thing as "I am." It is an accumulation of a lot of stuff. It is a "brilliant work of art," a product of the intellect which says, "Let's give it a name, let's call it something, let's call it 'I am'," which is very clever. "I" is the product of intellect, the label

7.   Ambulatory of the Great Stupa at Sanchi. India, first century CE, stone. Photo by John C. Huntington.

The relics from the Buddha's cremation were enshrined in memorial monuments called stupas. In its oldest form, the stupa is a solid hemispherical mound. One pays respect at a stupa by performing the rite of circumambulation, walking around it in a clockwise direction. In the third century BCE, Emperor Ashoka supported Buddhism by commissioning the building of many stupas. The Great Stupa at Sanchi is believed to contain an Ashoka-ordered core monument, around which the present casing and ambulatory were later added.

8.   Phra Pathom Chedi at Nakhon Pathom. Thailand, restored nineteenth century. Photo by John C. Huntington.

The stupa became the unique and fundamental monument of Buddhism. As the practice of building stupas spread across Asia, many local variations in form evolved. The golden dome of Phra Pathom Chedi, the largest *chedi* (or stupa) in Thailand, displays the bell-shaped outline often favored in Southeast Asia. Roofed niches containing images of the Buddha mark the four directions. The huge dome and mighty spire of Phra Pathom Chedi express powerfully the ancient symbolism of the stupa as the world mountain whose vertical axis exemplifies cosmic order.

9. Wat Phumin, Nan. Thailand, nineteenth century. Photo by John Ringis.

Buddhist temples contain at least one hall that enshrines images and provides shelter for teaching, practice, and ritual. Wat Phumin is an example of a hall built in the distinctive local architectural style of northern Thailand. The roof consists of overlapping sections topped with soaring finials. An undulating balustrade represents the bodies of *naga*s, mythical serpents whose tails "emerge" from the building to form the balustrade of the rear entrance.

10. WALKING BUDDHA. Thailand, 1426 CE, bronze. Wat Praya Pu, Nan. Photo courtesy of Stratton/Scott Archives.

In Theravada Buddhism, the principal subject of sculpture is the historic Buddha Shakyamuni. The Thais introduced a significant variant on this theme. Abandoning the still symmetry of the usual way of representing the Buddha, they showed him walking forward with fluid grace.

11. BODHISATTVA ON CLOUDS. Japan, 1053 CE, wood. Byodoin, Kyoto.

Mahayana art admits a wealth of iconographic variety. One of its hallmarks is the image of the bodhisattva, the embodiment of great compassion. Bodhisattvas wear a crown, scarves, and jewelry to signify bringing worldly experience onto the path. This small sculpture belongs to an ensemble of fifty-two bodhisattvas who form the entourage of Amitabha Buddha, one of the many Buddhas acknowledged in the Mahayana tradition. The bodhisattvas descend on clouds to welcome those who are born into Sukhavati, Amitabha's Pure Land in the West.

12. LOHAN. China, tenth–twelfth century, glazed pottery. The Nelson-Atkins Museum of Art,
Kansas City, Missouri (Purchase: Nelson Trust), 34–6.

Lohan (Skt. *arhat*) is the Chinese term for a personal disciple of Shakyamuni Buddha. The
Chinese revered the *lohan*s and visualized them as elders dwelling in remote mountain fastnesses. In many Chinese temples, a hall enshrining a Buddha image displays a set of sixteen,
eighteen, or even five hundred *lohan* statues along its side walls. This life-sized *lohan* is from
such a set. It conveys almost uncannily the immediate presence of a person engaged in meditation. The openwork base suggests the rocks of the *lohan*s' mountain home.

which unifies into one whole the disorganized and scattered development of ego.

The last stage of the development of ego is the fifth skandha, consciousness. At this level an amalgamation takes place: the intuitive intelligence of the second skandha, the energy of the third, and the intellectualization of the fourth combine to produce thoughts and emotions. Thus at the level of the fifth skandha we find the six realms as well as the uncontrollable and illogical patterns of discursive thought.

This is the complete picture of ego. It is in this state that all of us have arrived at our study of Buddhist psychology and meditation.

In Buddhist literature there is a metaphor commonly used to describe this whole process, the creation and development of ego. It speaks of a monkey locked in an empty house, a house with five windows representing the five senses. This monkey is inquisitive, poking its head out of each window and jumping up and down, up and down, restlessly. He is a captive monkey in an empty house. It is a solid house, rather than the jungle in which the monkey leapt and swung, rather than the trees in which he could hear the wind moving and the rustling of the leaves and branches. All these things have become completely solidified. In fact, the jungle itself has become his solid house, his prison. Instead of perching in a tree, this inquisitive monkey has been walled in by a solid world, as if a flowing thing, a dramatic and beautiful waterfall, had suddenly been frozen. This frozen house, made of frozen colors and energies, is completely still. This seems to be the point where time begins as past, future and present. The flux of things becomes solid tangible time, a solid idea of time.

The inquisitive monkey awakens from his blackout, but he does not awaken completely. He awakens to find himself trapped inside of a solid, claustrophobic house with just five windows. He becomes bored, as though captured in a zoo behind iron bars, and he tries to explore the bars by climbing up and down. That he has been captured is not particularly important; but the idea of capture is magnified a thousand times because of his fascination with it. If one is fascinated, the sense of claustrophobia becomes more and more vivid, more and more acute, because one begins to explore one's imprisonment. In fact fascination is part of the reason he remains imprisoned. He is captured by his fascination. Of course at the beginning there was the sudden blackout which confirmed his belief in a solid world. But now having taken solidity for granted, he is trapped by his involvement with it.

Of course this inquisitive monkey does not explore all the time. He begins to become agitated, begins to feel that something is very repetitive and uninteresting, and he begins to become neurotic. Hungry for entertainment, he tries to feel and appreciate the texture of the wall, attempting to make sure that this seeming solidity is really solid. Then, assured that the space is solid, the monkey begins to relate to it by grasping it, repelling it or ignoring it. If he attempts to grasp the space in order to possess it as his own experience, his own discovery, his own understanding, this is desire. Or, if the space seems a prison to him so that he tries to kick and batter his way out, fighting harder and harder, then this is hatred. Hatred is not just the mentality of destruction alone; but it is even more a feeling of defensiveness, defending oneself against claustrophobia. The monkey does not necessarily feel that there is an opponent or enemy approaching; he simply wants to escape his prison.

Finally the monkey might try to ignore that he is imprisoned or that there is something seductive in his environment. He plays deaf and dumb and so is indifferent and slothful in relation to what is happening around him. This is stupidity.

To go back a bit, you might say that the monkey is born into his house as he awakens from the blackout. He does not know how he arrived in this prison, so he assumes he has always been there, forgetting that he himself solidified the space into walls. Then he feels the texture of the walls, which is the second skandha, feeling. After that, he relates to the house in terms of desire, hatred, and stupidity, the third skandha, perception-impulse. Then, having developed these three ways of relating to his house, the monkey begins to label and categorize it: "This is a window. This corner is pleasant. That wall frightens me and is bad." He develops a conceptual framework with which to label and categorize and evaluate his house, his world, according to whether he desires, hates, or feels indifferent to it. This is the fourth skandha, concept.

The monkey's development through the fourth skandha has been fairly logical and predictable. But the pattern of development begins to break down as he enters the fifth skandha, consciousness. The thought pattern becomes irregular and unpredictable and the monkey begins to hallucinate, to dream.

When we speak of "hallucination" or "dream," it means that we attach values to things and events which they do not necessarily have. We have definite opinions about the way things are and should be. This is projection: we project our version of things onto what is there. Thus we become completely immersed in a world of our own creation, a world of conflicting values and opinions. Hallucination, in this sense, is a misinterpretation of things and events, reading into the phenomenal world meanings which it does not have.

This is what the monkey begins to experience at the level of the fifth skandha. Having tried to get out and having failed, he feels dejected, helpless, and so he begins to go completely insane. Because he is so tired of struggling, it is very tempting for him to relax and let his mind wander and hallucinate. This is the creation of the six *lokas,* or realms. There is a great deal of discussion in the Buddhist tradition about hell beings, people in heaven, the human world, the animal realm, and other psychological states of being. These are the different kinds of projections, the dream worlds we create for ourselves.

Having struggled and failed to escape, having experienced claustrophobia and pain, this monkey begins to wish for something good, something beautiful and seductive. So the first realm he begins to hallucinate is the *deva* loka, the god realm, "heaven," a place filled with beautiful, splendid things. The monkey dreams of strolling out of his house, walking in luxuriant fields, eating ripe fruit, sitting and swinging in the trees, living a life of freedom and ease.

Then he also begins to hallucinate the *asura* realm, or the realm of the jealous gods. Having experienced the dream of heaven, the monkey wants to defend and maintain his great bliss and happiness. He suffers from paranoia, worrying that others may try to take his treasures from him, and so he begins to feel jealousy. He is proud of himself, has enjoyed his creation of the god realm, and this has led him into jealousy of the asura realm.

Then he also perceives the earth-bound quality of these experiences. Instead of simply alternating between jealousy and pride, he begins to feel comfortable, at home in the "human world," the "earthy world." It is the world of just leading a regular life, doing things ordinarily, in a mundane fashion. This is the human realm.

But then the monkey also senses that something is a bit dull, something is not quite flowing. This is because, as he progresses from the realm of the gods to the realm of the jealous gods to the realm of human beings and his hallucinations become more and more solid, then this whole development begins to feel rather heavy and stupid. At this point he is born into the animal realm. He would rather crawl or moo or bark than enjoy the pleasure of pride or envy. This is the simplicity of the animals.

Then the process is intensified, and the monkey starts to experience a desperate feeling of starvation, because he really does not want to descend to any lower realms. He would like to return to the pleasure realms of the gods; so he begins to feel hunger and thirst, a tremendous feeling of nostalgia for what he remembers once having had. This is the realm of the hungry ghosts, or *preta* realm.

Then there is a sudden losing of faith and the monkey begins to doubt himself and his world, begins to react violently. All this is a terrible nightmare. He realizes that such a nightmare could not be true and he begins to hate himself for creating all this horror. This is the dream of the hell realm, the last of the six realms.

Throughout the entire development of the six realms the monkey has experienced discursive thoughts, ideas, fantasies, and whole thought patterns. Up to the level of the fifth skandha his process of psychological evolution has been very regular and predictable. From the first skandha each successive development arose in a systematic pattern, like an overlay of tiles on a roof. But now the monkey's state of mind becomes very distorted and disturbed, as suddenly this mental jigsaw puzzle erupts and his thought patterns become irregular and unpredictable. This seems to be our state of mind as we come to the teachings and the practice of meditation. This is the place from which we must start our practice.

Seeing Things as They Are   6

NYANAPONIKA THERA

NYANAPONIKA THERA (*THERA* means "elder") was born in 1901 in Germany of Jewish parents. He became a Buddhist at the age of twenty and in 1936 moved to Ceylon, where he became a monk. He remained mainly in Ceylon from then on and founded the Buddhist Publication Society in Kandy, which played a key role in the twentieth-century revival of the Theravada.

In this selection, Nyanaponika Thera helps us to grasp the significance of the Buddha's teaching of the three marks of existence: impermanence, suffering, and not-self, or egolessness. Particularly he makes clear how, from the point of view of experience, suffering can be a general characteristic of existence even though it seems to be only a subjective psychological quality. Egolessness, too, as the absence of personal essence, can be applied to phenomena as well as to people, for the things of the world are also devoid of an essence. Thus the world built up by the dualistic outlook that separates self and other turns out to be a shifting phantasm. Those who relate to it as solid and real are doomed to the frustration described in the First Noble Truth.

IF WE CONTEMPLATE EVEN A MINUTE SECTOR OF LIFE'S VAST range, we are faced with a variety of living forms so tremendous that it defies all description. Yet three basic features can be discerned as common to everything that has animate existence, from the microbe to man, from the simplest sensations to the thoughts of a creative genius:

impermanence or change (*anitya*)

suffering or unsatisfactoriness (*duhkha*)

not-self or insubstantiality (*anatman*)

These three basic facts were first found and formulated over 2,500 years ago by the Buddha, who was rightly called "the Knower of the World." They are designated, in Buddhist terminology, the three characteristics—the invariable marks or signs of everything that springs into being, the "signata" stamped upon the very face of life itself.

Of the three, the first and third apply directly to inanimate existence as well as to the animate, for every concrete entity by its very nature undergoes change and is devoid of substance. The second feature, suffering, is of course only an experience of the animate. But the Buddha applies the characteristic of suffering to all conditioned things, in the sense that, for living beings, everything conditioned is a potential cause of experienced suffering and is at any rate incapable of giving lasting satisfaction. Thus the three are truly universal marks pertaining even to what is below or beyond our normal range of perception.

The Buddha teaches that life can be correctly understood only if these three basic facts are understood. And this understanding must take place, not only logically, but in confrontation with one's own experience. Insight-wisdom, which is the ultimate liberating factor in Buddhism, consists in just this experiential understanding of the three characteristics as applied to one's own bodily and mental processes, and deepened and matured in meditation.

To see things as they really are means to see them consistently in the light of the three characteristics. Not to see them in this way, or to deceive oneself about their reality and range of application, is the defining mark of ignorance, and ignorance is by itself a potent cause of suffering, knitting the net in which man is caught—the net of false hopes, of unrealistic and harmful desires, of delusive ideologies and of perverted values and aims.

Ignoring or distorting the three basic facts ultimately leads only to frustration, disappointment and despair. But if we learn to see through deceptive appearances, and discern the three characteristics, this will yield immense benefits, both in our daily life and in our spiritual striving. On the mundane level, the clear comprehension of impermanence, suffering and not-self will bring us a saner outlook on life. It will free us from unrealistic expectations, bestow a courageous acceptance of suffering and failure and protect us against the lure of deluded assumptions and beliefs. In our quest for the supramundane, comprehension of the three characteristics will be indispensable. The meditative experience of all phenomena as inseparable from the three marks will loosen, and finally cut, the bonds binding us to an existence falsely imagined to be lasting, pleasurable and sustantive. With growing clarity, all things internal and external will be seen in their true nature: as constantly changing, as bound up with suffering and as unsubstantial, without an eternal soul or abiding essence. By seeing thus, detachment will grow, bringing greater freedom from egoistic clinging and culminating in *nirvana*, mind's final liberation from suffering.

Our Real Home

AJAHN CHAH

IN THIS SELECTION THE Venerable Ajahn Chah—a Thai monk whose simple, direct style of teaching attracted many Western students to his monastery—addresses an aging disciple approaching her death. In tones bespeaking profound composure, the master reminds the dying woman of the facts of impermanence. He goes on to provide her with concrete means for dealing with her suffering—first mantra, then mindfulness of the breath. The use of mantra here has nothing in common with magical incantation of any kind. It merely protects the mind by providing a word with wholesome connotations as an alternative to the painful associations that beset a person agonizing in bed. As attention is gradually drawn away from the mechanical flow of associations and relates to this thread of wholesomeness, anxiety falls away and enough composure develops to make it possible to attend to the rising and falling of the breath.

Mindfulness of the breath is the most basic of all Buddhist meditation techniques, practiced in all traditions. The unmanipulated movement of the breath comes by itself, a continual and natural expression of the simplicity of here and now. Two

Sanskrit terms are used, *dharmas*, and *samskaras*. The most familiar use of the term *dharma* is as part of *Buddha Dharma*. There it means something like "way" or "norm." But in Buddhist writings it is frequently employed, as it is here, to mean a phenomenon or fact. Anything that becomes the object of attention is a dharma. A *samskara* in the narrow sense is a mental impulse; in the broad sense it is any formation that has come about in dependence on conditions. This includes just about everything that arises. And the Buddha was continually reminding his disciples, "Whatever is subject to arising is subject to cessation."

NOW DETERMINE IN YOUR MIND TO LISTEN WITH RESPECT TO the dharma. During the time that I am speaking, be as attentive to my words as if it was the Lord Buddha himself sitting in front of you. Close your eyes and make yourself comfortable, compose your mind and make it one-pointed. Humbly allow the Triple Gem of wisdom, truth and purity to abide in your heart as a way of showing respect to the Fully Enlightened One.

Today I have brought nothing material of any substance to offer you, only Dharma, the teachings of the Lord Buddha. Listen well. You should understand that even the Buddha himself, with his great store of accumulated virtue, could not avoid physical death. When he reached old age he relinquished his body and let go of its heavy burden. Now you too must learn to be satisfied with the many years you've already depended on your body. You should feel that it's enough.

You can compare it to household utensils that you've had for a long time—your cups, saucers, plates, and so on. When you first had them, they were clean and shining, but now, after using them for so long, they're starting to wear out. Some are already broken, some have disappeared, and those that are left are deteriorating, they have no stable form, and it's their nature to be like that. Your body is the same way—it's been continually changing right from the day you were born, through childhood and youth, until now it's reached old age. You must accept that. The Buddha said that conditions (*samskaras*), whether they are internal conditions, bodily conditions or external conditions are not-self, their nature is to change. Contemplate this truth until you see it clearly.

This very lump of flesh that lies here in decline is *satyadharma*, the truth. The truth of this body is *satyadharma*, and it is the unchanging teaching of the Buddha. The Buddha taught us to look at the body, to contemplate it and to come to terms with its nature. We must be able to be at peace with the body, whatever state it is in. The Buddha taught that we should ensure that it's only the body that is locked up in jail and not let the mind be imprisoned along with it. Now as your body begins to run down and deteriorate with age don't resist that, but don't let your mind deteriorate with it, keep the mind separate. Give energy to the mind by realizing the truth of the way things are. The Lord Buddha taught that this is the nature of the body, it can't be any other way, having been born it gets old and sick and then it dies. This is a great truth that you are presently encountering. Look at the body with wisdom and realize it.

Even if your house is flooded or burnt to the ground, whatever the danger that threatens it, let it concern only the house. If there's a flood, don't let it flood your mind. If there's a fire, don't let it burn your heart, let it be merely the house, that which is external to you, that is flooded and burned. Allow the mind to let go of its attachments. The time is ripe.

You've been alive a long time. Your eyes have seen any number of forms and colours, your ears have heard so many sounds, you've had any number of experiences. And that's all they were—just experiences. You've eaten delicious foods and all the good tastes were just good tastes, nothing more. The unpleasant tastes were just unpleasant tastes, that's all. If the eye sees a beautiful form that's all it is, just a beautiful form. An ugly form is just an ugly form. The ear hears an entrancing, melodious sound and it's nothing more than that. A grating, disharmonious sound is simply so.

The Buddha said that rich or poor, young or old, human or animal, no being in this world can maintain itself in any one state for long, everything experiences change and estrangement. This is a fact of life that we can do nothing to remedy. But the Buddha said that what we can do is to contemplate the body and mind so as to see their impersonality, see that neither of them is "me" or "mine." They have a merely provisional reality. It's like this house, it's only nominally yours, you couldn't take it with you anywhere. It's the same with your wealth, your possessions and your family—they're all yours only in name, they don't really belong to you, they belong to nature. Now this truth doesn't apply to you alone, everyone is in the same position, even the Lord Buddha and his enlightened disciples. They differed from us in only one respect and that was in their acceptance of the way things are, they saw that it could be no other way.

So the Buddha taught us to scan and examine this body, from the soles of the feet up to the crown of the head and then back down to the feet again. Just take a look at the body. What sort of things do you see? Is there anything intrinsically clean there? Can you find any abiding essence? This whole body is steadily degenerating and the Buddha taught to see that it doesn't belong to us. It's natural for the body to be this way, because all conditioned phenomena are subject to change. How else would you have it be? Actually there's nothing wrong with the way the body is. It's not the body that causes you suffering, it's your wrong thinking. When you see the right wrongly, there's bound to be confusion.

It's like the water of a river. It naturally flows down the gradient, it never flows against it, that's its nature. If a person was to go and stand on a river bank and seeing the water flowing swiftly down its course, foolishly want it to flow back up the gradient, he would suffer. Whatever he was doing his wrong thinking would allow him no peace of mind. He would be unhappy because of his wrong view, thinking against the stream. If he had right view he would see that the water must inevitably flow down the gradient and until he realized and accepted that fact the man would be agitated and upset.

The river that must flow down the gradient is like your body. Having been young your body's become old and now it's meandering towards its death. Don't go wishing it was otherwise, it's not something you have the power to remedy. The Buddha told us to see the way things are and then let go of our clinging to them. Take this feeling of letting go as your refuge. Keep meditating even if you feel tired and exhausted. Let your mind dwell with the breath. Take a few deep breaths and then establish the mind on the breath using the mantra BUDDHO. Make this practice habitual. The more exhausted you feel the more subtle and focused your concentration must be, so that you can cope with the painful sensations that arise. When you start to feel fatigued then bring all your thinking to a halt, let the mind gather itself together and then turn to knowing the breath. Just keep up the inner recitation BUD-DHO, BUD-DHO. Let go of all externals. Don't go grasping at thoughts of your children and relatives, don't grasp at anything whatsoever. Let go. Let the mind unite in a single point and let that composed mind dwell with the breath. Let the mind unite in a single point and let that composed mind dwell with the breath. Let the breath be its sole object of knowledge. Concentrate until the mind becomes increasingly subtle, until feelings are insignificant and there is great inner clarity and wakefulness. Then when painful sensations arise they will gradually cease of their own accord. Finally you'll look on the breath as if it was a relative come to visit you. When a relative leaves, we follow him out and see him off. We watch until he's walked or driven out of sight, and then we go back indoors. We watch the breath in the same way. If the breath is coarse, we know that it's coarse; if it's subtle, we know that it's subtle. As it becomes increasingly fine, we keep following it, while simultaneously awakening the mind. Eventually the breath disappears altogether and all that remains is the feeling of wakefulness. This is called meeting the Buddha. We have that clear wakeful awareness that is called "Buddho," the one who knows, the one who is awake, the radiant one. It is meeting and dwelling with the Buddha, with knowledge and clarity. For it was only the historical flesh-and-blood Buddha that entered Parinirvana, the true Buddha, the Buddha that is clear radiant knowing, we can still experience and attain today, and when we do, the heart is one.

So let go, put everything down, everything except the knowing. Don't be fooled if visions or sounds arise in your mind during meditation. Put them all down. Don't take hold of anything at all. Just stay with this nondual awareness. Don't worry about the past or the future, just be still and you will reach the place where there's no advancing, no retreating and no stopping, where there's nothing to grasp at or cling to. Why? Because there's no self, no "me" or "mine." It's all gone.

The Buddha taught us to be emptied of everything in this way, not to carry anything with us. To know, and having known, let go.

Realizing the Dharma, the path to freedom from the round

of birth and death, is a task that we all have to do alone. So keep trying to let go and to understand the teachings. Really put effort into your contemplation. Don't worry about your family. At the moment they are as they are, in the future they will be like you. There's no one in the world who can escape this fate. The Buddha told us to put down everything that lacks a real abiding substance. If you put everything down you will see the truth, if you don't you won't. That's the way it is and it's the same for everyone in the world. So don't worry and don't grasp at anything.

Even if you find yourself thinking, well that's all right too, as long as you think wisely. Don't think foolishly. If you think of your children think of them with wisdom, not with foolishness. Whatever the mind turns to, then think and know that thing with wisdom, aware of its nature. If you know something with wisdom then you let it go and there's no suffering. The mind is bright, joyful and at peace, and turning away from distractions it is undivided. Right now what you can look to for help and support is your breath.

This is your own work, nobody else's. Leave others to do their own work. You have your own duty and responsibility and you don't have to take on those of your family. Don't take anything else on, let it all go. That letting go will make your mind calm. Your sole responsibility right now is to focus your mind and bring it to peace. Leave everything else to others. Forms, sounds, odours, tastes—leave them to others to attend to. Put everything behind you and do your own work, fulfill your own responsibility. Whatever arises in your mind, be it fear of pain, fear of death, anxiety about others or whatever, say to it, "Don't disturb me. You're not my business anymore." Just keep saying this to yourself when you see those dharmas arise.

What does the word *dharma* refer to? Everything is a dharma. There is nothing that is not a dharma. And what about "world"? The world is the very mental state that is agitating you at this moment. "What will this person do? What will that person do? When I'm dead who will look after them? How will they manage?" This is all just "the world." Even the mere arising of a thought fearing death or pain is the world. Throw the world away! The world is the way it is. If you allow it to arise in the mind and dominate consciousness then the mind becomes obscured and can't see itself. So whatever appears in the mind just say, "This isn't my business. It's impermanent, unsatisfactory and not-self."

Thinking you'd like to go on living for a long time will make you suffer. But thinking you'd like to die right away or die very quickly isn't right either, it's suffering, isn't it? Conditions don't belong to us; they follow their own natural laws. You can't do anything about the way the body is. You can prettify it a little, make it look attractive and clean for a while, like the young girls who paint their lips and let their nails grow long, but when old age arrives, everyone's in the same boat. That's the way the body is, you can't make it any other way. But what you can improve and beautify is the mind.

Anyone can build a house of wood and bricks, but the Buddha taught that that sort of home is not our real home, it's only nominally ours. It's a home in the world and it follows the ways of the world. Our real home is inner peace. An external material home may well be pretty but it is not very peaceful. There's this worry and then that, this anxiety and then that. So we say it's not our real home, it's external to us, sooner or later we'll have to give it up. It's not a place we can live in permanently because it doesn't truly belong to us, it's part of the world. Our body is the same, we take it to be self, to be "me" and "mine," but in fact it's not really so at all, it's another worldly home. Your body has followed its natural course from birth until now, it's old and sick and you can't forbid it from doing that, that's the way it is. Wanting to be different would be as foolish as wanting a duck to be like a chicken. When you see that that's impossible; that a duck has to be a duck, that a chicken has to be a chicken and that bodies have to get old and die, you will find strength and energy. However much you want the body to go on and last for a long time, it won't do that.

The Buddha said,

> *Anicca vata sankhara*
> *Uppadavayadhammino*
> *Upajjhitva nirujjhanti*
> *Tesam vupasamo sukho.*

The Pali word *sankhara* (*samskara*) refers to this body and mind. Sankharas are impermanent and unstable, having come into being they disappear, having arisen they pass away and yet everyone wants them to be permanent. This is foolishness. Look at the breath.

Having come in, it goes out, that's its nature, that's how it has to be. The inhalation and exhalation have to alternate, there must be change. Sankharas exist through change, you can't prevent it. Just think: could you exhale without inhaling? Would it feel good? Or could you just inhale? We want things to be permanent but they can't be, it's impossible. Once the breath has come in, it must go out, when it's gone out it comes in again and that's natural, isn't it? Having been born we get old and sick and then we die, and that's totally natural and normal. It's because sankharas have done their job, because the in-breaths and out-breaths have alternated in this way, that the human race is still here today.

As soon as we're born, we're dead. Our birth and our death are just one thing. It's like a tree: when there's a root, there must be twigs. When there are twigs, there must be a root. You can't have one without the other. It's a little funny to see how at a death people are so grief-stricken and distracted, fearful and sad, and at a birth how happy and delighted. It's delusion; nobody has ever looked at this clearly. I think if you really want to cry, then it would be better to do so when someone's born. For actually birth is death, death is birth, the root is the twig, the twig is the root. If you've got to cry, cry at the root, cry at the birth. Look closely: if there was no birth, there would be no death. Can you understand this?

Don't think a lot. Just think, "This is the way things are." It's your work, your duty. Right now nobody can help you, there is nothing that your family and your possessions can do for you. All that can help you now is the correct awareness.

So don't waver. Let go. Throw it all away.

Even if you don't let go, everything is starting to leave anyway. Can you see that, how all the different parts of your body are trying to slip away? Take your hair: when you were young, it was thick and black; now it's falling out. It's leaving. Your eyes used to be good and strong and now they're weak and your sight is unclear. When the organs have had enough, they leave; this isn't their home. When you were a child, your teeth were healthy and firm; now they're wobbly; perhaps you've got false ones. Your eyes, ears, nose, tongue—everything is trying to leave because this isn't their home. You can't make a permanent home in a samskara, you can stay for a short while and then you have to go. It's like a tenant watching over his tiny little house with failing eyes. His teeth aren't so good, his ears aren't so good, his body's not so healthy, everything is leaving.

So you needn't worry about anything because this isn't your real home, it's just a temporary shelter. Having come into this world you should contemplate its nature. Everything there is, is preparing to disappear. Look at your body. Is there anything there that's still in its original form? Is your skin as it used to be? Is your hair? It's not the same is it? Where has everything gone? This is nature, the way things are. When their time is up, conditions go their way. This world is nothing to rely on—it's an endless round of disturbance and trouble, pleasures and pain. There's no peace.

When we have no real home, we're like an aimless traveler out on the road, going this way for a while and then that way, stopping for a while and then setting off again. Until we return to our real home, we feel ill-at-ease whatever we're doing, just like one who's left his village to go on a journey. Only when he gets home again can he really relax and be at ease.

Nowhere in the world is any real peace to be found. The poor have no peace and neither do the rich. Adults have no peace, children have no peace, the poorly educated have no piece, and neither do the highly educated. There's no peace anywhere. That's the nature of the world.

Those who have few possessions suffer and so do those who have many. Children, adults, the aged, everyone suffers. The suffering of being old, the suffering of being young, the suffering of being wealthy, and the suffering of being poor—it's all nothing but suffering.

When you've contemplated things in this way, you'll see *anitya,* impermanence, and *duhkha,* unsatisfactoriness. Why are things impermanent and unsatisfactory? It's because they're *an-atman,* not-self.

Both your body that is lying here sick and painful and the mind that is aware of its sickness and pain, are called dharmas. That which is formless, the thoughts, feelings and perceptions, is called namadharma. That which is racked with aches and pains is called rupadharma. The material is dharma and the im-material is dharma. So we live with dharmas, in dharmas, and we are dharma. In truth there's no self anywhere to be found, there are only dharmas continually arising and passing away, as is their nature. Every single moment we're undergoing birth and death. This is the way things are.

8 Moral Conduct, Concentration, and Wisdom

S. N. GOENKA

S. N. GOENKA IS AN INDIAN LAY-man, born in Burma, who was authorized as a teacher of *Vipassana* (Skt. *vipashyana*), or insight, meditation by U Ba Khin in 1969. He now lives near Bombay, India, and teaches in the West as well. In this selection, as in chapter 3, we again find the Eightfold Path divided into *shila, samadhi,* and *prajna,* the three inseparable elements of a practitioner's training insisted upon by the Buddha, which Mr. Goenka translates as moral conduct (*shila*), concentration (*samadhi*), and wisdom (*prajna*). His description of the Eightfold Path is explicit and detailed, and leads into a thorough examination of the two basic forms of Buddhist meditation, *shamatha-bhavana* and *vipashyana-bhavana,* the development of tranquillity and the development of insight. The first is based on the mindfulness of breathing we encountered earlier, in chapter 7. The second begins with attention to bodily sensation, which naturally leads to direct and concrete understanding of the three marks of existence—impermanence, suffering, and egolessness, which we have studied in more conceptual terms in previous chapters. Mr. Goenka's writing, with its firm moral quality, brings us unerringly to a clear and genuine understanding of the Eightfold Path.

The Training of Moral Conduct

Our task is to eradicate suffering by eradicating its causes: ignorance, craving, and aversion. To achieve this goal the Buddha discovered, followed, and taught a practical way to this attainable end. He called this way the Noble Eightfold Path.

Once, when asked to explain the path in simple words, the Buddha said,

> "Abstain from all unwholesome deeds,
> perform wholesome ones,
> purify your mind"—
> this is the teaching of enlightened persons.

This is a very clear exposition which appears acceptable to all. Everyone agrees that we should avoid actions that are harmful and perform those that are beneficial. But how does one define what is beneficial or harmful, what is wholesome or unwholesome? When we try to do this we rely on our views, our traditional beliefs, our preferences and prejudices, and consequently we produce narrow, sectarian definitions that are acceptable to some but unacceptable to others. Instead of such narrow interpretations the Buddha offered a universal definition of wholesome and unwholesome, of piety and sin. Any action that harms others, that disturbs their peace and harmony, is a sinful action, an unwholesome action. Any action that helps others, that contributes to their peace and harmony, is a pious action, a wholesome action. Further, the mind is truly purified not by performing religious ceremonies or intellectual exercises, but by experiencing directly the reality of oneself and working systematically to remove the conditioning that gives rise to suffering.

The Noble Eightfold Path can be divided into three stages of training: *shila, samadhi,* and *prajna. Shila* is moral practice, abstention from all unwholesome actions of body and speech. *Samadhi* is the practice of concentration, developing the ability to consciously direct and control one's own mental processes.

Prajna is wisdom, the development of purifying insight into one's own nature.

THE VALUE OF MORAL PRACTICE

Anyone who wishes to practice Dharma must begin by practicing *shila*. This is the first step without which one cannot advance. We must abstain from all actions, all words and deeds, that harm other people. This is easily understood; society requires such behavior in order to avoid disruption. But in fact we abstain from such actions not only because they harm others but also because they harm ourselves. It is impossible to commit an unwholesome action—to insult, kill, steal, or rape—without generating great agitation in the mind, great craving and aversion. This moment of craving or aversion brings unhappiness now, and more in the future.

There is another reason for undertaking the practice of *shila*. We wish to examine ourselves, to gain insight into the depths of our reality. To do this requires a very calm and quiet mind. It is impossible to see into the depths of a pool of water when it is turbulent. Introspection requires a calm mind, free from agitation. Whenever one commits unwholesome action, the mind is inundated with agitation. When one abstains from all unwholesome actions of body or speech, only then does the mind have the opportunity to become peaceful enough so introspection may proceed.

There is still another reason why *shila* is essential: One who practices Dharma is working toward the ultimate goal of liberation from all suffering. While performing this task he cannot be involved in actions that will reinforce the very mental habits he seeks to eradicate. Any action that harms others is necessarily caused and accompanied by craving, aversion, and ignorance. Committing such actions is taking two steps back for every step forward on the path, thwarting any progress toward the goal.

Shila, then, is necessary not only for the good of society but for the good of each of its members, and not only for the worldly good of a person but also for his progress on the path of Dharma.

Three parts of the Noble Eightfold Path fall within the training of *shila:* right speech, right action, and right livelihood.

Speech must be pure and wholesome. Purity is achieved by removing impurity, and so we must understand what constitutes impure speech. Such acts include telling lies, that is, speaking either more or less than the truth; carrying tales that set friends at odds; backbiting and slander; speaking harsh words that disturb others and have no beneficial effect; and idle gossip, meaningless chatter that wastes one's own time and the time of others. Abstaining from all such impure speech leaves nothing but right speech.

Nor is this only a negative concept. One who practices right speech, the Buddha explained,

> speaks the truth and is steadfast in truthfulness, trustworthy, dependable, straightforward with others. He reconciles the quarreling and encourages the united. He delights in harmony, seeks after harmony, rejoices in harmony, and creates harmony by his words. His speech is gentle, pleasing to the ear, kindly, heartwarming, courteous, agreeable, and enjoyable to many. He speaks at the proper time, according to the facts, according to what is helpful, according to Dharma and the Code of Conduct. His words are worth remembering, timely, well-reasoned, well-chosen, and constructive.

RIGHT ACTION

Action must also be pure. As with speech, we must understand what constitutes impure action so that we may abstain from it. Such acts include killing a living creature; stealing; sexual misconduct, for example, rape or adultery; and intoxication, losing one's senses so that one does not know what one says or does. Avoiding these four impure actions leaves nothing but right action, wholesome action.

Again this is not only a negative concept. Describing one who practices right physical action, the Buddha said, "Laying aside the rod and sword, he is careful to harm none, full of kindness, seeking the good of all living creatures. Free of stealth, he himself lives like a pure being."

THE PRECEPTS

For ordinary people involved in worldly life, the way to implement right speech and right action is to practice the five precepts, which are

1. to abstain from killing any living creature;
2. to abstain from stealing;
3. to abstain from sexual misconduct;
4. to abstain from false speech;
5. to abstain from intoxicants.

These five precepts are the essential minimum needed for moral conduct. They must be followed by anyone who wishes to practice Dharma.

RIGHT LIVELIHOOD

Each person must have a proper way of supporting himself or herself. There are two criteria for right livelihood. First, it should not be necessary to break the five precepts in one's work, since doing so obviously causes harm to others. But further, one should not do anything that encourages other people to break the precepts, since this will also cause harm. Neither directly nor indirectly should our means of livelihood involve injury to other beings. Thus any livelihood that requires killing, whether of human beings or of animals, is clearly not right livelihood. But even if the killing is done by others and one simply deals in the parts of slaughtered animals, their skins, flesh, bones, and so on, still this is not right livelihood, because one is depending on the wrong actions of others. Selling liquor or other drugs may be very profitable, but even if one abstains from them oneself, the act of selling encourages others to use intoxicants and thereby to harm themselves. Operating a gambling casino may be very lucrative, but all who come there to gamble cause themselves harm. Selling poisons or weapons— arms, ammunition, bombs, missiles—is good business, but it injures the peace and harmony of multitudes. None of these is right livelihood.

Even though a type of work may not actually harm others, if it is performed with the intention that others should be harmed, it is not right livelihood. The doctor who hopes for an epidemic and the trader who hopes for a famine are not practicing right livelihood.

Each human being is a member of society. We meet our obligations to society by the work we do, serving our fellows in different ways. In return for this we receive our livelihood. Even a monk, a recluse, has his proper work by which he earns the alms he receives: the work of purifying his mind for his good and the benefit of all. If he starts exploiting others by deceiving people, performing feats of magic or falsely claiming spiritual attainments, then he is not practicing right livelihood.

Whatever remuneration we are given in return for our work is to be used for the support of ourselves and our dependents. If there is any excess, at least a portion of it should be returned to society, given to be used for the good of others. If the intention is to play a useful role in society in order to support oneself and to help others, then the work one does is right livelihood.

The Training of Concentration

By practicing *shila* we attempt to control our speech and physical actions. However, the cause of suffering lies in our mental actions. Merely restraining our words and deeds is useless if the mind continues to boil in craving and aversion, in unwholesome mental actions. Divided against ourselves in this way, we can never be happy. Sooner or later the craving and aversion will erupt and we shall break *shila,* harming others and ourselves.

Intellectually one may understand that it is wrong to commit unwholesome actions. After all, for thousands of years every religion has preached the importance of morality. But when the temptation comes, it overpowers the mind and one breaks *shila.* An alcoholic may know perfectly well that he should not drink because alcohol is harmful to him, and yet when the craving arises he reaches for the alcohol and becomes intoxicated. He cannot stop himself, because he has no control over his mind. But when one learns to cease committing unwholesome *mental* actions, it becomes easy to refrain from unwholesome words and deeds.

Because the problem originates in the mind, we must confront it at the mental level. In order to do so, we must undertake the practice of *bhavana*—literally, "mental development," or, in common language, meditation. . . . *Bhavana* includes the two trainings of concentration (*samadhi*) and wisdom (*prajna*). The practice of concentration is also called "the development of tranquility" (*samatha-bhavana*), and that of wisdom is called "the development of insight" (*vipashyana-bhavana*). The practice of *bhavana* begins with concentration, which is the second division of the Noble Eightfold Path. This is the wholesome action of learning to take control of the mental processes, to become master of one's own mind. Three parts of the path fall within this training: right effort, right awareness, and right concentration.

RIGHT EFFORT

Right effort is the first step in the practice of *bhavana*. The mind is easily overcome by ignorance, easily swayed by craving or aversion. Somehow we must strengthen it so that it becomes firm and stable, a useful tool for examining our nature at the subtlest level in order to reveal and then remove our conditioning.

A doctor, wishing to diagnose the disease of a patient, will take a blood sample and place it under a microscope. Before examining the sample, the doctor must first focus the microscope properly and fix it in focus. Only then is it possible to inspect the sample, discover the cause of the disease, and determine the proper treatment to cure the disease. Similarly, we must learn to focus the mind, to fix and maintain it on a single object of attention. In this way we make it an instrument for examining the subtlest reality of ourselves.

The Buddha prescribed various techniques for concentrating the mind, each suited to the particular person who came to him for training. The most suitable technique for exploring inner reality, the technique the Buddha himself practiced, is that of *anapanasati*, "awareness of respiration."

Respiration is an object of attention that is readily available to everyone, because we all breathe from the time of birth until the time of death. It is a universally accessible, universally acceptable object of meditation. To begin the practice of *bhavana*, meditators sit down, assume a comfortable, upright posture, and close their eyes. They should be in a quiet room with little to distract the attention. Turning from the outer world to the world within, they find that the most prominent activity is their own breathing; so they give attention to this object: the breath entering and leaving the nostrils.

This is not a breathing exercise; it is an exercise in awareness. The effort is not to control the breath but instead to remain conscious of it as it naturally is: long or short, heavy or light, rough or subtle. For as long as possible one fixes the attention on the breath, without allowing any distractions to break the chain of awareness.

As meditators we find out at once how difficult this is. As soon as we try to keep the mind fixed on respiration, we begin to worry about a pain in the legs. As soon as we try to suppress all distracting thoughts, a thousand things jump into the mind: memories, plans, hopes, fears. One of these catches our attention, and after some time we realize that we have forgotten completely about breathing. We begin again with renewed determination, and again after a short time we realize that the mind has slipped away without our noticing.

Who is in control here? As soon as one begins this exercise, it becomes very clear very quickly that in fact the mind is out of control. Like a spoiled child who reaches for one toy, becomes bored, and reaches for another, and then another, the mind keeps jumping from one thought, one object of attention to another, running away from reality.

This is the ingrained habit of the mind; this is what it has been doing all our lives. But once we start to investigate our true nature, the running away must stop. We must change the mental habit pattern and learn to remain with reality. We begin by trying to fix the attention on the breath. When we notice that it has wandered away, patiently and calmly we bring it back again. We fail and try again, and again. Smilingly, without tension, without discouragement, we keep repeating the exercise. After all, the habit of a lifetime is not changed in a few minutes. The task requires repeated, continuous practice as well as patience and calmness. This is how we develop awareness of reality. This is right effort.

The Buddha described four types of right effort:

to prevent evil, unwholesome states from arising;

to abandon them if they should arise;

to generate wholesome states not yet existing;

to maintain them without lapse, causing them to develop and to reach full growth and perfection.

By practicing awareness of respiration, we practice all four right efforts. We sit down and fix attention on the breath without any intervening thought. By doing so, we initiate and maintain the wholesome state of self-awareness. We prevent ourselves from falling into distraction, or absent-mindedness, from losing sight of reality. If a thought arises, we do not pursue it, but return our attention once again to the breath. In this way, we develop the ability of the mind to remain focused on a single object and to resist distractions—two essential qualities of concentration.

RIGHT AWARENESS

Observing respiration is also the means for practicing right awareness. Our suffering stems from ignorance. We react because we do not know what we are doing, because we do not know the reality of ourselves. The mind spends most of the time lost in fantasies and illusions, reliving pleasant or unpleasant experiences and anticipating the future with eagerness or fear. While lost in such cravings or aversions, we are unaware of what is happening now, what we are doing now. Yet surely this moment, now, is the most important for us. We cannot live in the past; it is gone. Nor can we live in the future; it is forever beyond our grasp. We can live only in the present.

If we are unaware of our present actions, we are condemned to repeating the mistakes of the past and can never succeed in attaining our dreams for the future. But if we can develop the ability to be aware of the present moment, we can use the past as a guide for ordering our actions in the future, so that we may attain our goal.

Dharma is the path of here-and-now. Therefore we must develop our ability to be aware of the present moment. We require a method to focus our attention on our own reality in this moment. The technique of *anapanasati* is such a method. Practicing it develops awareness of oneself in the here-and-now: at this moment breathing in, at this moment breathing out. By practicing awareness of respiration, we become aware of the present moment.

Another reason for developing awareness of respiration is that we wish to experience ultimate reality. Focusing on breathing can help us explore whatever is unknown about ourselves, to bring into consciousness whatever has been unconscious. It acts as a bridge between the conscious and unconscious mind, because the breath functions both consciously and unconsciously. We can decide to breathe in a particular way, to control the respiration. We can even stop breathing for a time. And yet when we cease trying to control respiration, it continues without any prompting.

For example, we may begin by breathing intentionally, slightly hard, in order to fix the attention more easily. As soon as the awareness of respiration becomes clear and steady, we allow the breath to proceed naturally, either hard or soft, deep or shallow, long or short, fast or slow. We make no effort to regulate the breath; the effort is only to be aware of it. By maintaining awareness of natural breath we have started observing the autonomic functioning of the body, an activity which is usually unconscious. From observing the gross reality of intentional breathing, we have progressed to observing the subtler reality of natural breathing. We have begun to move beyond superficial reality toward awareness of a subtler reality.

Yet another reason for developing awareness of respiration is in order to become free of craving, aversion, and ignorance, by first becoming aware of them. In this task the breath can help, because respiration acts as a reflection of one's mental state. When the mind is peaceful and calm, the breath is regular and gentle. But whenever negativity arises in the mind, whether anger, hatred, fear, or passion, then respiration becomes more rough, heavy, and rapid. In this way, our respiration alerts us to our mental state and enables us to start to deal with it.

There is yet another reason for practicing awareness of breathing. Since our goal is a mind free of negativity, we must be careful that every step we take toward that goal is pure and wholesome. Even in the initial stage of developing *samadhi* we must use an object of attention which is wholesome. Breath is such an object. We cannot have craving or aversion toward the breath, and it is a reality, totally divorced from illusion or delusion. Therefore it is an appropriate object of attention.

In the moment when the mind is fully focused on respiration, it is free from craving, free of aversion, and free of ignorance. However brief that moment of purity may be, it is very powerful, for it challenges all one's past conditioning. All the accumulated reactions are stirred up and begin to appear as various difficulties, physical as well as mental, which hinder one's efforts to develop awareness. We may experience impatience for progress, which is a form of craving; or else aversion may arise in the form of anger and depression because progress seems slow. Sometimes lethargy overwhelms us and we doze off as soon as we sit to meditate. Sometimes we may be so agitated that we fidget or find excuses to avoid meditating. Sometimes skepticism undermines the will to work—obsessive, unreasoning doubts about the teacher, or the teaching, or our own ability to meditate. When suddenly faced with these difficulties, we may think of giving up the practice altogether.

At such a moment we must understand that these hindrances have arisen only in reaction to our success in practicing awareness of respiration. If we persevere they will gradually disappear. When they do, the work becomes easier, because even at this early stage of practice, some layers of conditioning have been eradicated from the surface of the mind. In this way, even as we practice awareness of breathing, we begin to cleanse the mind and advance toward liberation.

RIGHT CONCENTRATION

Fixing the attention on respiration develops awareness of the present moment. Maintaining this awareness from moment to moment, for as long as possible, is right concentration.

In the daily actions of ordinary life, concentration is also required, but it is not necessarily the same as right concentration. A person may be concentrating on satisfying a sensual desire or forestalling a fear. A cat waits with all its attention focused on a mousehole, ready to pounce as soon as a mouse appears. A pickpocket is intent on the victim's wallet, waiting for the moment to remove it. A child in bed at night stares fearfully at the darkest corner of the room, imagining monsters hidden in the shadows. None of these is right concentration, concentration that can be used for liberation. *Samadhi* must have as its focus an object that is free from all craving, all aversion, all illusion.

In practicing awareness of breathing one finds how difficult it is to maintain unbroken awareness. Despite a firm determination to keep the attention fixed on the object of the breath, somehow it slips away unnoticed. We find we are like a drunken man trying to walk a straight line, who keeps straying to one side or the other. In fact we *are* drunk with our own ignorance and illusions, and so we keep straying into past or future, craving or aversion. We cannot remain on the straight path of sustained awareness.

As meditators, we would be wise not to become depressed or discouraged when faced with these difficulties, but instead to understand that it takes time to change the ingrained mental habits of years. It can be done only by working repeatedly, continuously, patiently, and persistently. Our job is simply to return attention to our breathing as soon as we notice that it has strayed. If we can do that, we have taken an important step toward changing the wandering ways of the mind. And by repeated practice, it becomes possible to bring the attention back more and more quickly. Gradually, the periods of forgetfulness becomes shorter and the periods of sustained awareness—*samadhi*—becomes longer.

As concentration strengthens, we begin to feel relaxed, happy, full of energy. Little by little the breath changes, becoming soft, regular, light, shallow. At times it may seem that respiration has stopped altogether. Actually, as the mind becomes tranquil, the body also becomes calm and the metabolism slows down, so that less oxygen is required.

At this stage some of those who practice awareness of respiration may have various unusual experiences: seeing lights or visions while sitting with eyes closed or hearing extraordinary sounds, for example. All these so-called extrasensory experiences are merely indications that the mind has attained a heightened level of concentration. In themselves these phenomena have no importance and should be given no attention. The object of awareness remains respiration; anything else is a distraction. Nor should one expect such experiences; they occur in some cases and not in others. All these extraordinary experiences are simply milestones that mark progress on the path. Sometimes the milestone may be hidden from view, or we may be so intent on the path that we stride ahead without noticing it. But if we take such a milestone as the final goal and cling to it, we cease making progress altogether. After all, there are countless extraordinary sensory experiences to be had. Those practicing dharma are not seeking such experiences but rather insight into their own nature, so as to attain freedom from suffering.

Therefore we continue to give attention only to respiration.

As the mind becomes more concentrated, the breath becomes finer and more difficult to follow, thereby requiring still greater efforts to remain attentive. In this way we continue to hone the mind, to sharpen the concentration, to make of it a tool with which to penetrate beyond apparent reality in order to observe the subtlest reality within.

There are many other techniques to develop concentration. One may be taught to concentrate on a word by repeating it, or on a visual image, or even to perform over and over again a certain physical aciton. In doing so one become absorbed in the object of attention, and attains a blissful state of trance. Although such a state is no doubt very pleasant so long as it lasts, when it ends one finds oneself back in ordinary life with the same problems as before. These techniques work by developing a layer of peace and joy at the surface of the mind, but in the depths the conditioning remains untouched. The objects used to attain concentration in such techniques have no connection with the moment-to-moment reality of oneself. The bliss that one attains is superimposed, intentionally created, rather than arising spontaneously from the depths of a purified mind. Right *samadhi* cannot be spiritual intoxication. It must be free from all artificiality, all illusions.

Even within the teaching of the Buddha, there are various states of trance—*dhyana*—that can be attained. The Buddha himself was taught eight states of mental absorption before he became enlightened, and he continued to practice them throughout his life. However, states of trance alone could not liberate him. When he taught the states of absorption, therefore, he emphasized their function only as stepping-stones to the development of insight. Meditators develop the faculty of concentration not in order to experience bliss or ecstasy, but rather to forge the mind into an instrument with which to examine their own reality and to remove the conditioning that causes their suffering. This is right concentration.

The Training of Wisdom

Neither *shila* nor *samadhi* is unique to the teaching of the Buddha. Both were well known and practiced before his enlightenment; in fact, while searching for the way to liberation, the future Buddha was trained in *samadhi* by two teachers with whom he studied. In prescribing these trainings the Buddha did not differ from the teachers of conventional religion. All religions insist on the necessity of moral behavior, and they also offer the possibility of attaining states of bliss, whether by prayer, by rituals, by fasting and other austerities, or by various forms of meditation. The goal of such practices is simply a state of deep mental absorption. This is the "ecstasy" experienced by religious mystics.

Such concentration, even if not developed to the level of the trance states, is very helpful. It calms the mind by diverting attention from the situations in which one would otherwise react with craving and aversion. Counting slowly to ten to prevent an outburst of anger is a rudimentary form of *samadhi*. Other, perhaps more obvious forms are repetition of a word or mantra, or concentration on a visual object. They all work: When the attention is diverted to a different object, the mind appears to become calm and peaceful.

The calm achieved in this way, however, is not real liberation. Certainly the practice of concentration confers great benefits, but it works only at the conscious level of the mind. Nearly twenty-five centuries before the invention of modern psychology, the Buddha realized the existence of the unconscious mind, which he called the *anushaya*. Diverting the attention, he found, is a way to deal effectively with craving and aversion at the conscious level, but it does not actually eliminate them. Instead it pushes them deep into the unconscious, where they remain as dangerous as ever even though dormant. At the surface level of the mind there may be a layer of peace and harmony, but in the depths is a sleeping volcano of suppressed negativity which sooner or later will erupt violently. The Buddha said,

> If the roots remain untouched and firm in the ground,
> a felled tree still puts forth new shoots.
> If the underlying habit of craving and aversion is not
>   uprooted,
> suffering arises anew over and over again.

So long as conditioning remains in the unconscious mind, it will put forth fresh shoots at the first opportunity, causing suffering. For this reason, even after reaching the highest states attainable by the practice of concentration, the future Buddha was not satisfied that he had achieved liberation. He decided that he must continue his search for the way out of suffering and the path to happiness.

He saw two choices. The first is the path of self-indulgence, of giving oneself free license to seek the satisfaction of all one's desires. This is the worldly path which most people follow, whether they realize it or not. But he saw clearly that it cannot lead to happiness. There is no one in the universe whose desires are always fulfilled, in whose life everything that is wished for happens and nothing happens that is not wished. People who follow this path inevitably suffer when they fail to achieve their desires; that is, they suffer disappointment and dissatisfaction. But they suffer equally when they attain their desires: they suffer from the fear that the desired object will vanish, that the moment of gratification will prove transitory, as in fact it must. In seeking, in attaining, and in missing their desires, such people always remain agitated. The future Buddha had experienced this path himself before leaving worldly life to become a recluse, and therefore he knew that it cannot be the way to peace.

The alternative is the path of self-restraint, of deliberately refraining from satisfying one's desires. In India 2,500 years ago, this path of self-denial was taken to the extreme of avoiding all pleasurable experiences and inflicting on oneself unpleasurable ones.

The rationale for this self-punishment was that it would cure the habit of craving and aversion and thereby purify the mind. The practice of such austerities is a phenomenon of religious life throughout the world. The future Buddha had experienced this path as well in the years following his adoption of the homeless life. He had tried different ascetic practices to the point that his body was reduced to skin and bones, but still he found that he was not liberated. Punishing the body does not purify the mind.

Self-restraint need not be carried to such an extreme, however. One may practice it in more moderate form by abstaining from gratifying those desires that would involve unwholesome actions. This kind of self-control seems far preferable to self-indulgence since in practicing it, one would at least avoid immoral actions. But if self-restraint is achieved only by self-repression, it will increase the mental tensions to a dangerous degree. All the suppressed desires will accumulate like floodwater behind the dam of self-denial. One day the dam is bound to break and release a destructive flood.

So long as conditioning remains in the mind, we cannot be secure or at peace. *Shila,* beneficial though it is, cannot be maintained by sheer force of will. Developing *samadhi* will help, but this is only a partial solution that will not work at the depths of the mind where the roots of the problem lie, the roots of the impurities. So long as these roots remain buried in the unconscious, there can be no real, lasting happiness, no liberation.

But if the roots of conditioning themselves can be removed from the mind, then there will be no danger of indulgence in unwholesome actions, no necessity for self-repression, because the very impulse for performing unwholesome action will be gone. Freed of the tensions either of seeking or denying, one can live at peace.

To remove the roots a method is required with which we can penetrate to the depths of the mind in order to deal with the impurities where they begin. This method is what the Buddha found: the training of wisdom, or *prajna,* which led him to enlightenment. It is also called *vipashyana-bhavana,* the development of insight into one's own nature, insight by means of which one may recognize and eliminate the cause of suffering. This was the discovery of the Buddha—what he practiced for his own liberation, and what he taught others throughout his life. This is the unique element in his teachings, to which he gave the highest importance. He repeatedly said, "If it is supported by morality, concentration is very fruitful, very beneficial. If it is supported by concentration, wisdom is very fruitful, very beneficial. If it is supported by wisdom, the mind becomes freed of all defilements."

In themselves, morality and concentration, *shila* and *samadhi,* are valuable, but their real purpose is to lead to wisdom. It is only in developing *prajna* that we find a true middle path between the extremes of self-indulgence and self-repression. By practicing morality, we avoid actions that cause the grossest forms of mental agitation. By concentrating the mind, we further calm it and at the same time shape it into an effective tool with which to undertake the work of self-examination. But it is only by developing wisdom that we can penetrate into the reality within and free ourselves of all ignorance and attachments.

Two parts of the Noble Eightfold Path are included within the training of wisdom: right thought and right understanding.

RIGHT THOUGHT

It is not necessary for all thoughts to cease in meditation before one begins *vipashyana-bhavana*. Thoughts may still persist, but if awareness is sustained from moment to moment, that is sufficient to start the work.

Thoughts may remain, but the nature of the thought pattern changes. Aversion and craving have been calmed down by awareness of breathing. The mind has become tranquil at least at the conscious level, and has begun to think about Dharma, about the way to emerge from suffering. The difficulties that arose on initiating awareness of respiration have now passed or at least have been overcome to some extent. One is prepared for the next step, right understanding.

RIGHT UNDERSTANDING

It is right understanding that is real wisdom. Thinking about truth is not enough. We must realize truth ourselves, we must see things as they really are, not just as they appear to be. Apparent truth is a reality, but one that we must penetrate in order to experience the ultimate reality of ourselves and eliminate suffering.

There are three kinds of wisdom (*prajna*): received wisdom, intellectual wisdom, and experiential wisdom. The literal meaning of the phrase for "received wisdom" is "heard wisdom"— wisdom learned from others, by reading books or listening to sermons or lectures, for example. This is another person's wisdom which one decides to adopt as one's own. The acceptance may be out of ignorance. For example, people who have grown up in a community with a certain ideology, a system of beliefs, religious or otherwise, may accept without questioning the ideology of the community. Or the acceptance may be out of craving. Leaders of the community may declare that accepting the established ideology, the traditional beliefs, will guarantee a wonderful future; perhaps they claim that all believers will attain heaven after death. Naturally the bliss of heaven is very attractive, and so willingly one accepts. Or the acceptance may be out of fear. Leaders may see that people have doubts and questions about the ideology of the community, so they warn them to conform to the commonly held beliefs, threatening them with terrible punishment in the future if they do not conform, perhaps claiming that all unbelievers will go to hell after death. Naturally, people do not want to go to hell, so they swallow their doubts and adopt the beliefs of the community.

Whether it is accepted out of blind faith, out of craving, or out of fear, received wisdom is not one's own wisdom, not something experienced for oneself. It is borrowed wisdom.

The second type of wisdom is intellectual understanding. After reading or hearing a certain teaching, one considers it and examines whether it is really rational, beneficial, and practical. And if it is satisfying at the intellectual level, one accepts it as true. Still this is not one's own insight, but only an intellectualization of the wisdom one has heard.

The third type of wisdom is that which arises out of one's own experience, out of personal realization of truth. This is the wisdom that one lives, real wisdom that will bring about a change in one's life by changing the very nature of the mind.

In worldly matters, experiential wisdom may not always be necessary or advisable. It is sufficient to accept the warnings of others that fire is dangerous, or to confirm the fact by deductive reasoning. It is foolhardy to insist on plunging oneself into fire before accepting that it burns. In Dharma, however, the wisdom that comes of experience is essential, since only this enables us to become free from conditioning.

Wisdom acquired through listening to others and wisdom acquired through intellectual investigation are helpful if they inspire and guide us to advance to the third type of *prajna*, experiential wisdom. But if we remain satisfied simply to accept received wisdom without questioning, it becomes a form of bondage, a barrier to the attainment of experiential understanding. By the same token, if we remain content merely to contemplate truth, to investigate and understand it intellectually, but make no effort to experience it directly, then all our intellectual understanding becomes a bondage instead of an aid to liberation.

Each one of us must live truth by direct experience, by the

practice of *bhavana;* only this living experience will liberate the mind. No one else's realization of truth will liberate us. Even the enlightenment of the Buddha could liberate only one person, Siddhartha Gautama. At most, someone else's realization can act as an inspiration for others, offering guidelines for them to follow, but ultimately we each must do the work ourselves. As the Buddha said,

> You have to do your own work;
> those who have reached the goal will only show the way.

Truth can be lived, can be experienced directly, only within oneself. Whatever is outside is always at a distance from us. Only within can we have actual, direct, living experience of reality.

Of the three types of wisdom, the first two are not peculiar to the teaching of the Buddha. Both existed in India before him, and even in his own time there were those who claimed to teach whatever he taught. The unique contribution of the Buddha to the world was a way to realize truth personally and thus to develop experiential wisdom, *bhavana-maya prajna.* This way to achieve direct realization of truth is the technique of *vipashyana-bhavana.*

VIPASHYANA-BHAVANA

Vipashyana is often described as being a flash of insight, a sudden intuition of truth. The description is correct, but in fact there is a step-by-step method which meditators can use to advance to the point that they are capable of such intuition. This method is *vipashyana-bhavana,* the development of insight, commonly called vipashyana meditation.

The word *pashyana* means "seeing," the ordinary sort of vision that we have with open eyes. *Vipashyana* means a special kind of vision: observation of the reality within oneself. This is achieved by taking as the object of attention one's own physical sensations. The technique is the systematic and dispassionate observation of sensations within oneself. This observation unfolds the entire reality of mind and body.

Why sensation? First because it is by sensations that we experience reality directly. Unless something comes into contact with the five physical senses or the mind, it does not exist for us. These are the gates through which we encounter the world, the bases for all experience. And whenever anything comes into contact with the six sensory bases, a sensation occurs. The Buddha described the process as follows: "If someone takes two sticks and rubs one against the other, then from the friction heat is generated, a spark is produced. In the same way, as the result of a contact to be experienced as pleasant, a pleasant sensation arises. As the result of a contact to be experienced as unpleasant, an unpleasant sensation arises. As the result of a contact to be experienced as neutral, a neutral sensation arises."

The contact of an object with mind or body produces a spark of sensation. Thus sensation is the link through which we experience the world with all its phenomena, physical and mental. In order to develop experiential wisdom, we must become aware of what we actually experience; that is, we must develop awareness of sensations.

Further, physical sensations are closely related to the mind, and like the breath they offer a reflection of the present mental state. When mental objects—thoughts, ideas, imaginations, emotions, memories, hopes, fears—come into contact with the mind, sensations arise. Every thought, every emotion, every mental action is accompanied by a corresponding sensation within the body. Therefore by observing the physical sensations, we also observe the mind.

Sensation is indispensable in order to explore truth to the depths. Whatever we encounter in the world will evoke a sensation within the body. Sensation is the crossroads where mind and body meet. Although physical in nature, it is also one of the four mental processes. It arises within the body and is felt by the mind. In a dead body or inanimate matter, there can be no sensation, because mind is not present. If we are unaware of this experience, our investigation of reality remains incomplete and superficial. Just as to rid a garden of weeds one must be aware of the hidden roots and their vital function, similarly we must be aware of sensations, most of which usually remain hidden to us, if we are to understand our nature and deal with it properly.

Sensations occur at all times throughout the body. Every contact, mental or physical, produces a sensation. Every biochemical reaction gives rise to sensation. In ordinary life, the conscious mind lacks the focus necessary to be aware of all but the most intense of them, but once we have sharpened the mind by the practice of *anapanasati* and thus developed the faculty of awareness, we become capable of experiencing consciously the reality of every sensation within.

In the practice of awareness of respiration the effort is to observe natural breathing, without controlling or regulating it. Similarly, in the practice of *vipashyana-bhavana,* we simply observe bodily sensations. We move attention systematically throughout the physical structure from head to feet and feet to head, from one extremity to the other, but while doing so we do not search for a particular type of sensation, nor try to avoid sensations of another type. The effort is only to observe objectively, to be aware of whatever sensations manifest themselves throughout the body. They may be of any type: heat, cold, heaviness, lightness, itching, throbbing, contraction, expansion, pressure, pain, tingling, pulsation, vibration, or anything else. The meditator does not search for anything extraordinary but tries merely to observe ordinary physical sensations as they naturally occur.

Nor is any effort made to discover the cause of a sensation. It may arise from atmospheric conditions, because of the posture in which one sits, because of the effects of the food one has eaten. The reason is unimportant and beyond one's concern. The important thing is to be aware of the sensation that occurs at this moment in the part of the body where the attention is focused.

When we first begin this practice, we may be able to perceive sensations in some parts of the body and not in others. The faculty of awareness is not yet fully developed, so we only experience the intense sensations and not the finer, subtler ones. However, we continue giving attention to every part of the body in turn, moving the focus of awareness in systematic order, without allowing the attention to be drawn unduly by the more prominent sensations. Having practiced the training of concentration, we have developed the ability to fix the attention on an object of conscious choosing. Now we use this ability to move awareness to every part of the body in an orderly progression, neither jumping past a part where sensation is unclear to another part where it is prominent, nor lingering over some sensations, nor trying to avoid others. In this way, we gradually reach the point where we can experience sensations in every part of the body.

When one begins the practice of awareness of respiration, the breathing often will be rather heavy and irregular. Then it gradually calms and becomes progressively lighter, fine, subtler. Similarly, when beginning the practice of *vipashyana-bhavana*, one often experiences gross, intense, unpleasant sensations that seem to last for a long time. At the same time, strong emotions or long-forgotten thoughts and memories may arise, bringing with them mental or physical discomfort, even pain. The hindrances of craving, aversion, sluggishness, agitation, and doubt which impeded one's progress during the practice of awareness of breathing may now reappear and gain such strength that it is altogether impossible to maintain the awareness of sensation. Faced with this situation one has no alternative but to revert to the practice of awareness of respiration in order once again to calm and sharpen the mind.

Patiently, without any feeling of defeat, as meditators we work to reestablish concentration, understanding that all these difficulties are actually the results of our initial success. Some deeply buried conditioning has been stirred up and has started to appear at the conscious level. Gradually, with sustained effort but without any tension, the mind regains tranquility and one-pointedness. The strong thoughts or emotions pass away, and one can return to the awareness of sensations. And with repeated, continuous practice, the intense sensations tend to dissolve into more uniform, subtler ones and finally into mere vibrations, arising and falling with great rapidity.

But whether the sensations are pleasant or unpleasant, intense or subtle, uniform or varied is irrelevant in meditation. The task is simply to observe objectively. Whatever the discomforts of the unpleasant sensations, whatever the attractions of the pleasant ones, we do not stop our work, do not allow ourselves to become distracted or caught up in any sensation; our job is merely to observe ourselves with the same detachment as a scientist observing in a laboratory.

IMPERMANENCE, EGOLESSNESS, AND SUFFERING

As we persevere in meditation, we soon realize one basic fact: our sensations are constantly changing. Every moment, in every part of the body, a sensation arises, and every sensation is an indication of a change. Every moment changes occur in every part of the body, electromagnetic and biochemical reactions. Every moment, even more rapidly, the mental processes change and are manifested in physical changes.

This is the reality of mind and matter: It is changing and impermanent—*anitya*. Every moment the subatomic particles of which the body is composed arise and pass away. Every moment the mental functions appear and disappear, one after another. Everything inside oneself, physical and mental, just as the world outside, is changing every moment. Previously, we may have known that this was true; we may have understood it intellectually. Now, however, by the practice of *vipashyana-bhavana*, we experience the reality of impermanence directly within the framework of the body. The direct experience of the transitory sensations proves to us our ephemeral nature.

Every particle of the body, every process of the mind is in a state of constant flux. There is nothing that remains beyond a single moment, no hard core to which one can cling, nothing that one can call "I" or "mine." This "I" is really just a combination of processes that are always changing.

Thus the meditator comes to understand another basic reality: *anatman*—there is no real "I," no permanent self or ego. The ego to which one is so devoted is an illusion created by the combination of mental and physical processes, processes in constant flux. Having explored body and mind to the deepest level, one sees that there is no immutable core, no essence that remains independent of the processes, nothing that is exempt from the law of impermanence. There is only an impersonal phenomenon, changing beyond one's control.

Then another reality becomes clear. Any effort to hold on to something, saying "This is I, this is me, this is mine" is bound to make one unhappy, because sooner or later this something to which one clings passes away, or else this "I" passes away. Attachment to what is impermanent, transitory, illusory, and beyond one's control is suffering, *duhkha*. We understand all this not because someone tells us it is so, but because we experience it within, by observing sensations within the body.

EQUANIMITY

Then how is one not to make oneself unhappy? How is one to live without suffering? By simply observing without reacting:

Instead of trying to keep one experience and to avoid another, to pull this close, to push that away, one simply examines every phenomenon objectively, with equanimity, with a balanced mind.

This sounds simple enough, but what are we to do when we sit to meditate for an hour, and after ten minutes feel a pain in the knee? At once we start hating the pain, wanting the pain to go away. But it does not go away; instead, the more we hate it, the stronger it becomes. The physical pain becomes a mental pain, causing great anguish.

If we can learn for one moment just to observe the physical pain; if even temporarily we can emerge from the illusion that it is *our* pain, that *we* feel pain; if we can examine the sensation objectively like a doctor examining someone else's pain, then we see that the pain itself is changing. It does not remain forever; every moment it changes, passes away, starts again, changes again.

When we understand this by personal experience, we find that the pain can no longer overwhelm and control us. Perhaps it goes away quickly, perhaps not, but it does not matter. We do not suffer from the pain any more because we can observe it with detachment.

THE WAY TO LIBERATION

By developing awareness and equanimity, one can liberate oneself from suffering. Suffering begins because of ignorance of one's own reality. In the darkness of this ignorance, the mind reacts to every sensation with liking and disliking, craving and aversion. Every such reaction creates suffering now and sets in motion a chain of events that will bring nothing but suffering in the future.

How can this chain of cause and effect be broken? Somehow, because of past actions taken in ignorance, life has begun, the flow of mind and matter has started. Should one then commit suicide? No, that will not solve the problem. At the moment of killing oneself the mind is full of misery, full of aversion. Whatever comes next will also be full of misery. Such an action cannot lead to happiness.

Life has started, and one cannot escape from it. Then should one destroy the six bases of sensory experience? One could pluck out the eyes, cut out the tongue, destroy the nose and ears. But how could one destroy the body? How could one destroy the mind? Again it would be suicide, which is useless.

Should one destroy the objects of each of the six bases, all the sights and sounds, and so on? This is not possible. The universe is full of countless objects; one could never destroy them all. Once the six sensory bases exist, it is impossible to prevent their contact with their respective objects. And as soon as contact occurs, there is bound to be a sensation.

But this is the point at which the chain can be broken. The crucial link occurs at the point of sensation. Every sensation gives rise to liking or disliking. These momentary, unconscious reactions of liking and disliking are immediately multiplied and intensified into great craving and aversion, into attachment, producing misery now and in the future. This becomes a blind habit which one repeats mechanically.

By the practice of *vipashyana-bhavana*, however, we develop awareness of every sensation. And we develop equanimity: We do not react. We examine the sensation dispassionately, without liking or disliking it, without craving, aversion, or attachment. Instead of giving rise to fresh reactions, every sensation now gives rise to nothing but wisdom, *prajna*, insight: "This is impermanent, bound to change, arising to pass away."

The chain has been broken, suffering has been stopped. There is no fresh reaction of craving or aversion, and therefore no cause from which sufferings can arise. The cause of suffering is the *karma*, the mental deed, that is, the blind reaction of craving and aversion, the *samskara*. When the mind is aware of sensation but maintains equanimity, there is no such reaction, no cause that will produced suffering. We have stopped making suffering for ourselves.

The Buddha said,

> All *samskaras* are impermanent.
> When you perceive this with true insight,
> then you become detached from suffering;
> this is the path of purification.

Here the word *samskara* has a very wide meaning. A blind reaction of the mind is called *samskara*, but the result of that action, its fruit, is also known as *samskara*; like seed, like fruit.

Everything that we encounter in life is ultimately the result of our own mental actions. Therefore in the widest sense, *samskara* means anything in this conditioned world, whatever has been created, formed, composed. Hence, "All created things are impermanent," whether mental or physical, everything in the universe. When one observes this truth with experiential wisdom through the practice of *vipashyana-bhavana*, then suffering disappears, because one turns away from the causes of suffering; that is, one gives up the habit of craving and aversion. This is the path of liberation.

The entire effort is to learn how not to react, how not to produce a new *samskara*. A sensation appears, and liking or disliking begins. This fleeting moment, if we are unaware of it, is repeated and intensified into craving and aversion, becoming a strong emotion that eventually overpowers the conscious mind. We become caught up in the emotion, and all our better judgment is swept aside. The result is that we find ourselves engaged in unwholesome speech and action, harming ourselves and others. We create misery for ourselves, suffering now and in the future, because of one moment of blind reaction.

But if we are aware at the point where the process of reaction begins—that is, if we are aware of the sensation—we can choose not to allow any reaction to occur or to intensify. We observe the sensation without reacting, neither liking nor disliking it. It has no chance to develop into craving or aversion, into powerful emotion that can overwhelm us; it simply arises and passes away. The mind remains balanced, peaceful. We are happy now, and we can anticipate happiness in the future, because we have not reacted.

This ability not to react is very valuable. When we are aware of the sensations within the body, and at the same time maintain equanimity, in those moments the mind is free. Perhaps at first these may be only a few moments in a meditation period, and the rest of the time the mind remains submerged in the old habit of reaction to sensations, the old round of craving, aversion, and misery. But with repeated practice those few brief moments will become seconds, will become minutes, until finally the old habit of reaction is broken, and the mind remains continuously at peace. This is how suffering can be stopped. This is how we can cease producing misery for ourselves.

9   *Karma and Its Fruit*

NYANAPONIKA THERA

NYANAPONIKA THERA, WHO WAS ALREADY AN accomplished scholar and meditator, experienced a significant deepening in his understanding after spending a considerable time in Burma in the 1950s training in insight meditation (vipashyana-bhavana) under the Venerable Mahasi Sayadaw, the famous Burmese meditation master. Here the Theravada elder gives us first of all a wonderfully lucid description of the complexity of karma's workings, emphasizing the freedom inherent in the karmic situation. Then, against the background of the potential for liberation, he depicts the double-edged quality of karmic action, affecting the doer and object of the deed at the same time. At last he makes us understand how "karma is the womb from which we spring, the true creator of the world and of ourselves as the experiencers of the world."

MOST WRITINGS ON THE DOCTRINE OF KARMA EMPHASIZE THE strict lawfulness governing karmic actions, ensuring a close correspondence between our deeds and their fruits. While this emphasis is perfectly in place, there is another side to the working of karma—a side rarely noted, but so important that it deserves to be stressed and discussed as an explicit theme in itself. This is the modifiability of karma, the fact that the lawfulness which governs karma does not operate with mechanical rigidity but allows for a considerably wide range of modifications in the ripening of the fruit.

If karmic action were always to bear fruits of invariably the same magnitude, and if modification or annulment of karma-result were excluded, liberation from the samsaric cycle of suffering would be impossible; for an inexhaustable past would ever throw up new obstructive results of unwholesome karma. Hence the Buddha said:

> If one says that 'in whatever way a person performs a karmic action, in that very same way he will experience the result'—in that case there will be no (possibility of a) religious life and no opportunity would appear for the complete ending of suffering.
>
> But if one says that 'a person who performs a karmic action (with a result) that is variably experienceable, will reap its results accordingly'—in that case there will be (a possibility of) a religious life and an opportunity for making a complete end of suffering. [*Anguttara Nikaya*, 3: 110]

Like any physical event, the mental process constituting a karmic action never exists in isolation but in a field, and thus its efficacy in producing a result depends not only on its own potential, but also upon the variable factors of its field, which can modify it in numerous ways. We see, for example, that a particular karma, either good or bad, may sometimes have its result strengthened by supportive karma, weakened by counter-active karma, or even annulled by destructive karma. The occurrence of the result can also be delayed if the conjunction of outer circumstances required for its ripening is not complete; and that delay may again give a chance for counteractive or destructive karma to operate.

It is, however, not only these extraneous conditions which can cause modification. The ripening also reflects the karma's "internal field" or internal conditions—that is, the total qualitytive structure of the mind from which the action issues. To one rich in moral or spiritual qualities, a single offense may not entail the weighty results the same offense will have for one who is poor in such protective virtues. Also, analogously to human law, a first-offender's punishment will be milder than that of a reconvicted criminal.

Of this type of modified reaction the Buddha speaks in the continuation of the discourse quoted above:

"Now take the case when a minor evil deed has been committed by a certain person and it takes him to hell. But if the same minor offense is committed by another person, its results might be experienced during his lifetime and not even the least (residue of a reaction) will appear (in the future), not to speak about a major (reaction).

"Now what is the kind of person whom a minor offense takes to hell: It is one who has not cultivated (restraint of) the body, not cultivated virtue and thought, nor has he developed any wisdom; he is narrow-minded, of low character and even for trifling things he suffers. It is such a person whom even a minor offense may take to hell.

"And what is the person by whom the result of the same small offense will be experienced in his lifetime, without the least (future residue)? He is one who has cultivated (restraint of) the body, who has cultivated virtue and thought and who has developed wisdom; he is not limited (by vices), is a great character and he lives unbounded (by evil). It is such a person who experiences the result of the same small offense during this lifetime, without the least future residue.

"Now suppose a man throws a lump of salt into a small cup of water. What do you think, monks: would that small quantity of water in the cup become salty and undrinkable through that lump of salt?"

"It would, lord."

"And why so?"

"The water in the cup is so little that a lump of salt can make it salty and undrinkable."

"But suppose, monks, that lump of salt is thrown into the river Ganges. Would it make the river Ganges salty and undrinkable?"

"Certainly not, lord."

"And why not?"

"Great, lord, is the mass of water in the Ganges. It will not become salty and undrinkable by a lump of salt."

"Further, O monks, suppose a person has to go to jail for a matter of a halfpenny or a penny or a hundred pence. And another man does not have to go to jail on that account.

"Now, what is the kind of person that has to go to jail for a matter of a halfpenny, a penny or a hundred pence? It is one who is poor, without means or property. But he who is rich, a man of means and property, does not have to go to jail for such a matter." [*Anguttara Nikaya*, 3: 110]

Hence we may say that it is an individual's accumulation of good or evil karma and also his dominating character traits, good or evil, which affect the karmic result. They determine the greater or lesser weight of the result and may even spell the difference between whether or not it occurs at all.

But even this does not exhaust the existing possibilities of modifications in the weight of karmic reaction. A glance into the life histories of people we know may well show us a person of good and blameless character, living in secure circumstances; yet a single mistake, perhaps even a minor one, suffices to ruin his entire life—his reputation, his career, and his happiness— and it may also lead to a serious deterioration of his character. This seemingly disproportionate crisis might have been due to a chain reaction of aggravating circumstances beyond his control, to be ascribed to a powerful counteractive karma of his past. But the chain of bad results may have been precipitated by the person's own action—decisively triggered by his initial mistake and reinforced by subsequent carelessness, indecision or wrong decisions, which, of course, are unskilled karma in themselves. This is a case when even a predominately good character cannot prevent the ripening of bad karma or soften the full force of the results. The good qualities and deeds of that person will certainly not remain ineffective; but their future outcome might well be weakened by any presently arisen negative character changes or actions, which might form a bad counteractive karma.

Consider too the converse situation: A person deserving to be called a thoroughly bad character may, on a rare occasion, act on an impulse of generosity and kindness. This action may turn out to have unexpectedly wide and favourable repercussions on his life. It might bring about a decisive improvement in his external circumstances, soften his character, and even initiate a thorough "change of heart."

How complex, indeed, are situations in human life, even when they appear deceptively simple! This is so because the situations and their outcome mirror the still greater complexity of the mind, their inexhaustible source. The Buddha himself has said: "The mind's complexity surpasses even the countless varieties of the animal kingdom" (*Samyutta Nikaya*, 12: 100). For any single individual, the mind is a stream of ever-changing mental processes driven by the currents and cross-currents of karma accumulated in countless past existences. But this complexity, already great, is increased still very much more by the fact that each individual life-stream is interwoven with many other individual life-streams through the interaction of their respective karmas. So intricate is the net of karmic conditioning that the Buddha declared karma-result to be one of four "unthinkables" and warned against treating it as a subject of speculation. But though the detailed workings of karma escape our intellection, the practically important message is clear: the fact that karmic results are modifiable frees us from the bane of determinism and its ethical corollary, fatalism, and keeps the road to liberation constantly open before us.

The potential "openness" of a given situation, however, also has a negative side, the element of risk and danger: a wrong response to the situation might open a downward path. It is our own response which removes the ambiguity of the situation, for better or worse. This reveals the karma doctrine of the Buddha as a teaching of moral and spiritual responsibility for oneself and others. It is truly a "human teaching" because it corresponds to and reflects man's wide range of choices, a range much wider than that of an animal. Any individual's moral choice may be severely limited by the varying load of greed, hatred and delusion and their results which he carries around; yet every time he stops to make a decision or a choice, he is potentially free to throw off that load, at least temporarily. At this precarious and precious moment of choice he has the opportunity to rise above all the menacing complexities and pressures of his unfathomable karmic past. Indeed, in one short moment he can transcend aeons of karmic bondage. It is through right mindfulness that man can firmly grasp that fleeting moment, and it is mindfulness again that enables him to use it for making wise choices.

Every karmic action, as soon as it is performed, first of all affects the doer of the deed himself. This holds with as much truth for bodily and verbal deeds directed towards others as it does for volitional thoughts that do not find outward expres-

sion. To some extent we can control our own response to our
actions, but we cannot control the way others respond to them.
Their response may turn out to be quite different from what we
expect or desire. A good deed of ours might be met with in-
gratitude, a kind word may find a cold or even hostile reception. But though these good deeds and kind words will then be
lost to the recipient, to his own disadvantage, they will not be
lost to the doer. The good thoughts that inspired them will en-
noble his mind, even more so if he responds to the negative
reception with forgiveness and forbearance rather than anger
and resentment.

Again, an act or word meant to harm or hurt another, may
not provoke him to a hostile reaction but only meet with self-
possessed calmness. Then this "unaccepted present will fall
back to the giver," as the Buddha once told a brahmin who had
abused him. The bad deeds and words, and the thoughts mo-
tivating them, may fail to harm the other, but they will not fail
to have a damaging effect on the character of the doer; and it
will affect him even worse if he reacts to the unexpected response by rage or a feeling of resentful frustration. Hence the
Buddha says that beings are the responsible owners of their
karma, which is their inalienable property. They are the only
legitimate heirs of their actions, inheriting their legacy of good
or bad fruits.

It will be a wholesome practice to remind oneself often of the
fact that one's deeds, words, and thoughts first of all act upon
and alter one's own mind. Reflecting thus will give a strong
impetus to true self-respect which is preserved by protecting
oneself against everything mean and evil. To do so will also
open a new, practical understanding of a profound saying of
the Buddha:

In this fathom-long body with its perceptions and thoughts
there is the world, the origin of the world, the ending of the
world and the path to the ending of the world. [*Anguttara Nikaya*, 4: 45]

The "world" of which the Buddha speaks is comprised in this
aggregate of body-and-mind. For it is only by the activity of our
physical and mental sense faculties that a world can be experienced and known at all. The sights, sounds, smells, tastes, and

bodily impressions which we perceive, and our various mental functions, conscious and unconscious—this is the world in which we live. And this world of ours has its origin in that very aggregate of physical and mental processes that produces the karmic act of craving for the six physical and mental sense objects.

> "If, Ananda, there were no karmic ripening in the sphere of the senses, would there appear any sense sphere existence?"
> "Surely not, O lord." [*Anguttara Nikaya*, 3: 76]

Thus karma is the womb from which we spring, the true creator of the world and of ourselves as the experiencers of the world. And through our karmic actions in deed, word and thought, we unceasingly engage in building and rebuilding *this* world and worlds beyond. Even our good actions, as long as they are still under the influence of craving, conceit, and ignorance, contribute to the creation and preservation of this world of suffering. The Wheel of Life is like a treadmill set in perpetual motion by karma, chiefly by its three unwholesome roots—greed, hatred, and delusion. The "end of the world" cannot be reached by walking on a treadmill; this only creates the illusion of progress. It is only by stopping that vain effort that the end can be reached.

It is "through the elimination of greed, hatred and delusion that the concatenation of karma comes to an end" (*Anguttara Nikaya*, 10: 174). And this again can happen nowhere else than in the same aggregate of body-and-mind where suffering and its causes originate. It is the hopeful message of the third noble truth that we *can* step out of the weary round of vain effort and misery. If, despite our knowledge of the possibility of release, we keep walking on the treadmill of life, that is because of an age-old addiction hard to break, the deeply rooted habit of clinging to the notions of "I," "mine," and "self." But here again there is the hopeful message in the fourth noble truth with its eightfold path, the therapy that can cure the addiction and gradually lead us to the final cessation of suffering. And all that is required for the therapy is again found in our own body and mind.

The treatment proper starts with correctly understanding the true nature of karma and thereby our situation in the world.

This understanding will provide a strong motivation for ensuring a prevalence of good karma in one's life. And as it deepens by seeing the human condition still more clearly, this same understanding will become the spur for breaking the chains of karmic bondage. It will impel one to strive diligently along the path, and to dedicate all one's actions and their fruits to the greatest end of action—the final liberation of oneself and all sentient beings.

The Practice of Recollection

BHIKKHU MANGALO

HERE BHIKKU MANGALO, A British monk, gives us a remarkable meditator's-eye view of the untamed mind's inner theater, then proceeds to explain how to work with it through the practice of recollection. Recollection is another name for mindfulness (*smriti*), and the practice described here is closely connected with the mindfulness-of-breathing exercises we have encountered in previous chapters. Here, however, we are given much more practical detail in the technique of practice along with a number of wise tips about sidetracks Westerners might be drawn into. Doubtless it would be interesting—and quite harmless—for the reader to experiment with the technique described here. But if one becomes earnestly interested and wishes to continue, it is best to seek the advice of an experienced meditator or teacher.

The Mad Monkey

The best way to start is to see where one starts from.

Let us take a look at the mind of an ordinary worldly person.

What we find is a grasshopper mind, a butterfly mind, chasing its fancies and impulses of the moment, the prey of stimuli and its own emotional reaction to them—a reaction that is largely a purely conditioned and blind one. A chain of linked associations, hopes, fears, memories, fantasies, regrets, stream constantly through the mind, triggered off by momentary contact with the outside world through the senses. It is a blind, neverceasing, never-satisfied search for satisfaction, bewildered, aimless, suffering. This is not reality, but a waking dream, a sequence of concepts and fantasies. The world is split up into recognizable identified forms, each of which has its name, and on the basis of these names—conceptual images of the reality around—the mind spins its web of thought in which it entangles itself. Objects change, but their "name" remains the same, and the mind, left clinging to empty names and images, loses touch with reality, trying to find in the products of its own imagination the satisfaction and security for which it thirsts. No wonder the mind has been called an "idol-factory," and no wonder that the Buddha described such a mind as a restless monkey swinging from branch to branch in the quest for satisfying fruit through the endless jungle of conditioned events. The futility, unreality, and frustration inherent in such a mode of existence is startlingly self-apparent once one begins to see it clearly.

It is the purpose of Buddhism, and of religion in general, to reunite one with the Reality one has thus lost sight of due to one's ignorance in seeking the happiness for which one thirsts where it is not to be found—in the shadows and illusions of one's own mind. That modern man allows his mind to continue this blind, tormented rat-race in undisciplined confusion is perhaps the wonder of wonders in an age that likes to consider itself "scientific." Man has amassed a phenomenal amount of information—concepts all of it—about the forms and names that inhabit the universe, and he has harnessed and disciplined forces of nature in a way that would have staggered his forefathers. To gain electrical power he will build structures of enormous size and cost in both money and labor, damming back great rivers in midstream, yet still his knowledge of reality fails him, and his own nature escapes him, while he, almost unbelievably, omits to expend the slightest labor to stem and discipline his own thoughts, even when he half perceives they delude and torment him.

Down through countless generations a few, going against the stream of human patterns, have undertaken this task, often in the face of almost incredible privations and discouragement, at first blind, and often teacherless. Some broke through triumphantly, some stumbled through after great sufferings, yet all in their different languages declare a unanimous find—there is a "something," by knowing which one knows all. It is the Uncreated, the only lasting Reality; it is our own true Being, and its "discovery" is, all are agreed, the supreme happiness, beside which all the suffering of ages is suddenly quite insignificant. And in some strange yet certain way, those who find It find the Deathless, they step outside of both birth and death. This is beyond the senses, though in it resides the power by and in which we see and hear and think. It is veiled by the flow of ignorant thoughts, by which we see not what is, but what we think about it. It is the old story of the man who seeing a piece of rope hanging from a tree in the twilight, mistakes it for a snake and is panicked.

So it goes on. Taking our own thoughts, mere images of reality, for reality, we allow the emotions to be aroused by them. These emotions produce more thoughts in the desire to satisfy this disturbance, and the vicious circle is complete. Without ignorance of reality one would not think about it, without the stream of thoughts there would be no distressing emotions, the mind would be at peace, and then there would be no *need* to think.

The Stopping of Conceptual Thought

The first step, therefore, is to cut off the chain of associated concepts and words that flood the mind, holding it with recollection on the present, on what *is*. Thus in a famous verse, the Buddha used to say,

> Don't chase after the past,
> Don't seek the future;
> The past is gone

The future hasn't come
But see clearly on the spot
That object which *is now*,
While finding and living in
A still, unmoving state of mind.

This is the beginning of mental discipline, and the *remembering* to do so is recollection. Without this recollection the stream of thoughts takes over again, agitating, distressing and befouling the mind like muddy water in a lake on which the wind is blowing up waves. Clarity of vision, peace of mind and self-recollection are lost in a single instant. It is for this reason that the Buddha recalled recollection "the only way." Or as he vividly described it by a metaphor,

Whatever streams flow in the world,
Recollection is their damming-back.

As it is said in Zen, "The mad mind does not halt; if it halts it is Enlightenment."

The practice of recollection is a gradual training. Perfection of self-recollection is the "art of arts and the science of sciences," to which a due apprenticeship is necessary. To train one's own mind, "ours" as it is, is even harder than training a dog or horse, for the mind is no less headstrong, and has all the ingenuity and trickery of man to help it find ways to break loose. Yet this is a far more worthwhile training, bringing already in early stages great peace and joy, and in its train innumerable riches. With an unrecollected, self-willed mind there is little hope of happiness—even the simple happiness of a peaceful, purposeful and balanced life, how much less the supreme goal of life.

What Is Recollection?

What then is the "practice" of recollection? How does one go about it?

Recollection is, quite simply, remembering to establish the attention with full awareness on the present, on the here and now. It is the "unsupported thought," the "fast of the mind," the true "noble silence." As each object arises into consciousness, through whichever of the six entrances (the five senses and the imagination), it must be seen *as it is,* without welcoming it or rejecting it, without clinging to it or trying to push it aside—just "letting it go as though it were a piece of rotten wood," as the great Huang Po puts it. This is the real meaning of the "Middle Way" of Buddhism, to see each (and every) object as it arises, with a mind that is "alert, fully-conscious and self-recollected, avoiding either attachment or aversion to anything." "Do not like, do not dislike, all will then be clear." The Buddha used to define recollection and full consciousness as "seeing the arising, presence and passing of all perceptions, feelings and thoughts." He often used to say that his teaching "in brief" was "To see only the seen in what is seen; and in the heard to hear only what is heard." It is all the same.

But when we try to *do* this, what do we find? We find that, at first, to do so for even a few minutes is quite impossible; the mind is swept away by a stream of erupting thoughts and a restlessness that makes it quite impossible to be clear and detailed enough to avoid reacting to the thoughts and objects that arise. One just cannot begin. It is for this reason that the Buddha, in his wisdom, compassion and "skill in means," taught the practice of recollection as a gradual method of training, whereby, from the initial chaos and confusion of an undisciplined, wild-dull mind, the mind can be weaned from "whoring after strange gods," to be still and know THAT WHICH IS.

The Foundations of Recollection

First, though, a word of warning. Proper *samadhi,* or stillness of mind, the last step on the Buddha's Noble Eightfold Path leading to Realization, is only possible with proper recollection, the step before it. Similarly, this recollection is dependent on the steps preceding it, which comprise, in brief, right understanding, morality, and determination. There must be at least a good foundation of understanding to realize the futility of the transient and conditioned in the light of the Unconditioned— and of all objects—when one is looking for "*me,*" the subject.

Else the mind will not be able to detach itself enough from thinking about the ever-changing objects, so as to practice poised self-recollection in the here and now. It will want to be off thinking of its "idols," for where one's treasure is, there will one's heart be also. Similarly, without at least a good foundation on a moral attitude to life, recollection is being built on sand. An evil conscience is indeed like muddied water in which nothing can be seen clearly "as it is." Without peace of mind there is little hope of stemming the flow of thoughts, not with all the determination in the world—even so it is hard enough. Of course none of us is perfect—far from it—and we all fail to live up to what we know we should be, but without at least a sincere and manful effort to put the basic Buddhist precepts into practice, one is just accelerating and braking at the same time. Later, increased self-awareness and peace will bring greater self-control, but at lest the sincere *will* and effort to goodness must be there, and a sincere regret (and if possible restitution) for any evil done.

Above all the mind must be starting to turn away from the old patterns, which is the true meaning of "repentance"— metanoia. . . .

Related to this question is the Westerner's preoccupation with the concepts of psychology—"making the unconscious conscious" and the like, so that he even starts to *look* for "upsurges from the unconscious," "problems presenting themselves for solution" and so forth. It should be impressed most firmly that psychological analysis is not a part of the practice of recollection, the sole purpose of which is to see more clearly, *without thinking discursively about it*, what *is*, at each moment, *now* in the present. Analysis deals with concepts. Meditation aims at stilling the mind and watching what *is*, dispassionately. No thoughts—no "me," no "me"—no neurosis. Just, moreover, as the mind refreshes itself in sleep, or when by occupational therapy it is kept off its preoccupations, and just as a cut in one's finger if cleaned and left to rest is cured by "nature," so the mind will best cure itself by rest, and by being kept clean, clean of emotional stimulants and harassing preoccupations. Nothing effects this so well as the practice of recollection. If one perseveres in the practice, moreover, one comes more and more to see the unreality of the "me" concept, which cuts the foundation away from all mental illness and distress. No device or way of looking at things, and no amount of "making the un-conscious conscious" will deliver one from (for example) "in-security," so long as it is for "me," this body and mind, that one is seeking security. They *are* impermanent, and no juggling will alter that fact or lend them a false security. Once the idea of "me" in the body drops out, the whole problem drops out with it. For this reason, during the practice of recollection at least, psychological analysis is best put aside. The "me" thought itself is the problem—not its preoccupations, nor the forms it takes.

The Western need to intellectualize over one's own medita-tional practice is one of the main reasons why Westerners usu-ally find it much harder, and take much longer, to complete a course of meditation than do their Eastern equivalents. Many Easterners, by simply and conscientiously getting down to it in accordance with their instructor's guidance, will complete a course inside a few weeks. Most Westerners tend to take at least double the time. . . .

Basic Breathing Exercise

The best way to start the practice of recollection is, as the Bud-dha clearly describes in the "Discourse on the Practice of Rec-ollection" (*Satipatthana-sutta*), to sit down and establish the at-tention on the one most visible constant function of the body—the breathing. This is a semi-automatic function (*samskara*) that is always present with us in normal life, and which is emo-tionally quite neutral. For these reasons it is the ideal object of use for learning to become recollected, and to hold one's atten-tion on what is going on *now*, in the present, and *here, in* us. Most people agree that in practice (theoretical considerations quite apart) the most conducive position to sit in, if one can manage it, is cross-legged. This need not be in the famous "full-lotus" position, with the feet lifted back up on to the opposite thigh, nor even in the "half-lotus" position—which can cause many people almost as much pain as a "half-nelson." The sim-ple "easy" posture, with the legs just placed crosswise on the floor is quite sufficient, and if necessary a strategic cushion can be placed under a troublesome knee. If sitting cross-legged is not convenient, however, it is of no great importance. Nowadays even many meditation instructors in the East do their meditation sitting in a chair. The only important considerations are that one should have an alert, upright, perfectly straightbacked posture which can be held without indescribable agony for a minimum of one hour or so. While doing the practice one should be sitting still (without fidgeting) and relaxed but alert, with the hands either in the usual position to be seen in statuettes of the Buddha in meditation, or simply lying lightly cupped one inside the other. The head should be held upright, the eyes closed, and all muscles, in so far as is possible, relaxed and easy. Once taken up, one should try to avoid unnecessary readjusting of the posture for the given period.

The proper place to concentrate the attention on the breathing is at the face wherever it is most prominent. This varies slightly from person to person. Some find the best spot is just above the upper lip, others just at the tip of the nose, others again on the inside of the nostrils. It is immaterial. What is important is that it should be wherever one, oneself, finds it most clear. A few experimental breaths should soon establish that. The attention should be on the *physical sensation* of the touch of the air, not the *concept* of breathing. Nor should the breathing be interfered with or deliberately regulated. At first, this may be a little difficult, and in the preliminary states it is not easy to dissociate *pure attention* from *control.* However, in that case one should just try to avoid unnecessary and unnatural control of the breath in any way, and just breathe easily, naturally and at a normal rhythm, but with the mind held on the sensation of the touch of the air. At first, too, it may well be found difficult to catch this touch of air clearly. Press on regardless. Practice and persistence will greatly improve this. One should try, moreover, to be aware of the sensation of the breath from the time it starts the inbreath until it stops, and then, again, from the start of the outbreath to its end. As one breathes in one should repeat, "In," and as one breathes out one should repeat, "Out." This is a check to see that the mind is really doing the practice and not wandering.

DISTRACTIONS

Before he has been going on with the practice for very long, the beginner will find a constant tendency for the mind to be torn away from the observation of the breathing. Thoughts and memories of the past, hopes and fears for the future, imaginations, fantasies, intelletualizations on theory, doubts and worries about one's meditation, pictures and shapes in front of the mind's eye, and distracting external stimuli such as noises, pains, itches, impulses to move, etc., all tend perpetually to beckon the mind aside into "interesting sidelines." There is no need to be unduly upset or discouraged by this. After all, it is the state of mind to which one has been long accustomed. Discipline has only just begun. Rome was not built in a day. Indeed, if it were so easy as all that to govern the mind, enlightened men would be a penny-a-dozen. The Buddha has pointed out that the mind, when one starts to try to withdraw it from its evil resorts, is like a fish taken from its native water and lying thrashing on the bank. Here we have it in practice—but everyone finds, or has found, the same problem. Enlightened men are made from those who do not despair, but persevere in keeping bringing the mind back to heel, just as one does with an overexuberant puppy one is patiently but firmly training to obedience. Here, as everywhere, one should try to take the razor's edge of the Middle Way. There should be the determination to press on—but a *calm* determination—not the sort that moves in fits and starts between the poles of despair and fanaticism. This merely shows an overstrong ego involved in the question ("*I* want to be a good meditator"). A relaxed determination is what is needed—or as the classic Buddhist commentators describe it, the perfect balance between peace (*samadhi*) and energy (*virya*). These two, like discrimination (*prajna*) and faith (*shraddha*), should be perfectly in balance.

The way to deal with these distractions is to notice immediately, or at least as soon as possible, the fact of distraction, identifying it with an appropriate word, such as "Thinking." Then the mind should revert to its proper activity—noting the sensation of the breath. . . . All tendencies to wander should be noted as soon as possible after they have arisen—when one is more practiced one can even catch them *before* they arise, by the feel of the mind starting to turn—but one should not *jump* at them, or jerk the mind in so doing. The noting should be done neither too fast nor too slowly—the middle way, that is— immediately, firmly and clearly, but not overhurriedly. This only further agitates and distracts the mind.

It has been well said, "There is no need to be afraid of rising thoughts, but only of the delay in becoming aware of them."

If one patiently perseveres in catching the thoughts—like bringing the puppy back to heel each time he wanders—this *is* meditation, and things are going very well. What is *not* meditation is, on the one hand, to be lazy about it and sit daydreaming and, on the other, to get upset and full of despair over the feeling that the mind will just not stay put.

Another sort of thought that can be a great distraction at times are so-called "running commentary" thoughts such as, "Now I am not thinking of anything," "Things are going very well now," "This is dreadful; my mind just won't stay still"—and the like. Often these take the form of wondering what one is going to say in one's report to one's instructor, and virtually imagining the whole conversation. All such thoughts should simply be noted as "Thinking," and, as Huang Po says, just "dropped like a piece of rotten wood." "Dropped," notice, not *thrown* down. A piece of rotten wood is not doing anything to irritate you, but is just of no use, so there is no point in hanging on to it. . . . Nor is there any need to try to retrace the links in a chain of associated thoughts, nor to try to ascertain what it was that first started the chain. Any such impulse should itself be noted simply as "Thinking," and the mind should revert to the breathing. However badly things have just been going, one should take up again at the only place one can—where one is—and go on from there. Psychological analyses are also "Thinking." . . .

This practice of the Basic Breathing Exercise should be continued for one-hourly stretches (or for whatever period the instructor may recommend).

In between sessions the following basic walking exercise should be practised—also for hourly stretches—alternately with the breathing exercise, turn and turn about.

Basic Walking Exercise

Between sessions of the sitting practice the meditator should find a quiet stretch of ground where he can walk up and down relatively undisturbed. It need not be long. If one's room is not too small, it can easily be done there, or along a corridor, garden path, or hall. It is best, for this exercise, if one walks deliberately much more slowly than one usually does. Something about the speed of a good slow march is ideal, but of course one should walk nonetheless in as simple and natural a manner as the speed allows. . . . During this period of walking up and down, the attention should be on the movement of the feet and legs. One should note, as the right foot begins to rise from the ground, "Lifting"; as it moves forward, "Moving"; and as it places again on the ground, "Placing." Similarly for the left foot, and so on.

In exactly the same manner as during the sitting, breathing practice, all distracting thoughts or sensations should be noted in the apposite manner. If one happens to look up at something while walking, one should immediately register "Looking," and revert to the movement of the feet. Looking about one and noticing the details of objects, even those on one's path, is "lust of the eyes" and is *not* part of the practice.

Unlimited Friendliness   11

THE METTA SUTTA

LIKE ALL SUTRAS, *METTA SUTTA* (PALI, ''KIND-ness Sutra'') is attributed to the Buddha himself. It is a teaching about loving-kindness (Pali, *Metta*; Skt., *Maitri*). We all have latent within us a wish for the welfare of all beings. That is why we all find ourselves from time to time spontaneously helping others—whether by coming to the aid of an old person struggling with his grocery bags or by supplying a friend with the words she needs to complete the expression of her thought. The idea expressed in this sutra with great dignity, simplicity, and beauty is that if we are humble and relinquish our own attachments, our natural kindness can flow out to all beings without limitation. The sutra points to the model of fathomless kindness that nature itself has provided in suggesting that we could relate to all beings as a mother relates to her only child.

This sutra is recited daily by Buddhists throughout the Theravadin countries of Southeast Asia. It provides the root vision for the Theravada practice of *maitri-bhavana,* the development of kindness. Yet its message of unreserved kindness to all makes it the perfect link between the Hinayana and the Mahayana. (As we shall see in chapter 15, the Mahayana has also developed a special meditative practice that opens the gates of kindness by helping us let go of our attachment to our own point of view.)

THIS IS THE WORK OF THOSE WHO ARE SKILLED AND PEACEFUL, who seek the good:

> May they be able and upright, straightforward, of gentle speech and not proud.
> May they be content and easily supported, unburdened with their senses calmed.
> May they be wise, not arrogant and without desire for the possessions of others.
> May they do nothing mean or that the wise would reprove.
>
> May all beings be happy.
> May they live in safety and joy.
> All living beings, whether weak or strong, tall, stout, medium or short, seen or unseen, near or distant, born or to be born, may they all be happy.
>
> Let no one deceive another or despise any being in any state, let none by anger or hatred wish harm to another.
>
> As a mother watches over her child, willing to risk her own life to protect her only child, so with a boundless heart should one cherish all living beings, suffusing the whole world with unobstructed loving-kindness.
>
> Standing or walking, sitting or lying down, during all one's waking hours, may one remain mindful of this heart and this way of living that is the best in the world.
>
> Unattached to speculations, views and sense desires, with clear vision, such a person will never be reborn in the cycles of suffering.

PART THREE

The Teachings
of the
Great Vehicle

Introduction

THE MAHAYANA (''GREAT VEHICLE'') AP-
peared in the first and second centuries of the common era
in a burst of creativity that produced a new wave of sutras
greatly differing in flavor and content from the sutras that
had existed until then. These new sutras, which also claimed
to record the words of the Buddha, were said to have been
hidden away in other realms of existence until the right time
for their emergence should come. They emphasized a principle that was inherent in the Hinayana teachings but had
remained undeveloped—the notion of emptiness (*shunyata*).
According to the Buddha's teaching of conditional arising
(*pratitya-samutpada*), which he had enunciated from the beginning as an integral part of his enlightenment, everything
that arises—all phenomena physical and psychological, all
dharmas—are interdependent and mutually condition each
other. Since they are essentially interdependent, they have no

individual essences of their own. They appear to be independent entities, but as such, they are empty.

The Hinayana had mainly applied the notion of emptiness to the ego, the self. Now the Mahayana went further and applied it to all things. A flower, your friend's happiness, your friend, a dog, your nose, a hellish case of resentment, a postage stamp, your "I," a love affair, an automobile—all are essentially a changing nexus of causes and conditions. Naked, direct experience, which sees through concepts, reveals this. The world as something that could be grasped by dualistic mind is empty. Our experience is a dance of appearances without an essential root.

But this doesn't mean that the world we experience doesn't count, or that we don't have to care about it. As appearances it does exist and must be dealt with properly. It cannot be said to be real or unreal. It is as it is, because it isn't.

The tendency to regard the phenomenal world as something unreal that doesn't really matter is rejected by Buddhists as nihilism. The tendency to regard it as something permanent, real in itself, that matters utterly and everlastingly is rejected as eternalism. Nihilism and eternalism are known in the Buddha Dharma as the two extremes.

The Mahayana emphasis on emptiness had the effect of causing a vast new vision to burst forth, a vision of countless worlds inhabited by countless beings and countless buddhas. Within the immensity of this universal vision, individual liberation, which had hitherto been the object of spiritual practice, became too narrow a goal. Turning from this inward focus, practice was now directed outward to encompass everything. The figure of the arhat seeking the extinction of his or her own suffering was replaced as a spiritual model by that of the bodhisattva willing to delay entering into nirvana in order to engage the whole universe and save all its beings from delusion. With this new outlook came an emphasis on the notion of buddha-nature—that the inherent basic nature of all beings is enlightenment itself with all its brilliant qualities. With countless buddhas in countless worlds and buddha-nature present in every being, existence/nonexistence was thronged with buddhahood, and there came to be far less emphasis on the figure of Shakyamuni, the "historical Buddha."

The Mahayana teachings spread and became prevalent throughout northern Asia—in Central Asia, China, Tibet, Mongolia, Korea, Japan, and also in Vietnam. One of the most influential of Mahayana schools over the centuries has been and remains the school first developed in China as Ch'an (from the Sanskrit *dhyana*, "meditation") and now best known in its Japanese form, Zen. The Ch'an/Zen schools focus on sitting meditation as an act of "buddhahood on the spot," and its masters cultivate the art of bringing about "sudden enlightenment." Ch'an/Zen is also a prime example of the Mahayana's extraordinary fertility as a medium for the development of many art forms.

On Trust in the Mind

SENG-TS'AN

TRANSLATED BY BURTON WATSON

THE *HSIN-HSIN-MING,* OR "INSCRIPTION ON TRUST in the Mind," is a Chinese poem in 146 rhymed four-character lines attributed to Seng-ts'an (c. 600), the third Chinese patriarch of Ch'an and the thirtieth in line from Shakyamuni Buddha. *Hsin,* translated here as "mind," is also often translated as "heart" or "heart-mind" and corresponds to the Japanese *kokoro.*

Almost nothing is known about Seng-ts'an apart from legends describing the transmission of enlightenment "from heart-mind to heart-mind," so characteristic of Cha'n/Zen, which occurred between him and the second patriarch, Hui-k'o. This transmission is said not only to have brought Seng-ts'an enlightenment but to have cured him of leprosy as well.

In this poem, which is one of the earliest of Cha'n writings and much influenced in its terminology by Taoism, nonduality appears as a positive theme. If the heart-mind abides in nonduality, without being drawn into the distinction between subject and object, genuine self-existing trust arises, natural confidence that needs no external confirmation. Experience arises accurately as suchness, the nature of things as they are. Suchness, like rubble or debris, does not need to be maintained. It just rests as it is, the indestructible expression of things as they are.

The term "ten thousand phenomena" used in the poem is a conventional Chinese Taoist designation for all phenomena.

THE HIGHEST WAY ASKS NOTHING HARD,
but detests any picking or choosing.
Only do without love and hatred
and all will come clear and open.

With the smallest degree of differentiation, though,
things grow farther apart than heaven and earth!
If you want the Way right here before you,
have nothing to do with assent or dissent.

Where acceptance and rejection vie for mastery,
this is sickness to the mind.
Without comprehending the Dark Meaning[1]
you strive in vain to still your thoughts.

The Way is round, a vast emptiness,
nothing lacking, nothing left over.
Only because you choose and reject
does it cease to be so.

Never tag after the realm of entanglements;
do not dwell in Emptiness either.
When mind achieves unity in repose,
all else will vanish of itself.

Mind moves, you return it to stillness,
but thus stilled, it moves all the more.
While you persist in two extremes,
how can you understand unity?

And where unity no longer reigns,
both extremes forfeit their merit.
Cast aside being and you find it swamping you;
pursue Emptiness and you stray farther from it still.

[1] "The Dark Meaning" stands for the ultimate truth of Buddhism.

Much talk, much worry,
and you're less than ever able to face things.
Be done with talk, be done with worry,
and there's no place you cannot pass through.

Return to the root and you'll grasp the meaning,
but trail after lights and you lose their source.
For a moment shine your own light—
then you can master the Emptiness before you.

The shifts and turns of this Emptiness
all spring from deluded views.
No need to go seeking truth—
simply put an end to such views!

Dualism is no place to dwell;
take care, never go that way!
No sooner do we have "right" and "wrong"
than the mind is lost in confusion.

Two come about because of One,
but don't cling to the One either!
So long as the mind does not stir,
the ten thousand things stay blameless;
no blame, no phenomena,
no stirring, no mind.

The viewer disappears along with the scene,
the scene follows the viewer into oblivion,
for scene becomes scene only through the viewer,
viewer becomes viewer because of the scene.

If you wish to understand both,
see them as from the first a single Emptiness,
a single Emptiness in which both are identical,
embracing all the ten thousand forms alike.

When you perceive things as neither coarse nor fine,
how could you favor one above another?
The Great Way is the soul of latitude,
nothing about it easy, nothing about it hard.

People of petty outlook are fretful, doubting;
the more they hurry, the more they fall behind.

Sticklers always miss the proper measure,
certain to set off on wrong roads.

Leave it! Let things take their course!
In the end there's neither going nor staying.
Follow your nature, blend with the Way,
be free and easy, a stranger to all care.

Fetter your thoughts and you turn aside from truth,
sinking in darkness, no longer well.
No longer well, you wear out your spirit—
what use to covet one thing, shun another?

If you want to grasp the One Vehicle,[2]
never despise the six senses.
So long as the six senses are not despised,
you're at one with correct perception.

Wise men take no special action;
fools fashion their own shackles.
The Law knows no "this" Law or "that,"
yet you persist in your witless attachments.

Using mind to stir up more mind—
what grosser error than this?
Delusion breeds concepts such as "tranquil" or
    "disordered";
enlightenment tells you there's no good or bad.

All these pairs of opposites
spring from faulty reckoning.
Dreams, phantoms, empty flowers—
why trouble trying to grasp them?

Gain, loss, right, wrong—
throw them away at once!
When eyes do not close in sleep,
dreams vanish of themselves.

When the mind refrains from differentiation,
the ten thousand phenomena are a single Suchness,
a single Suchness dark in entity,
lumpish, forgetful of entanglements.

[2] "One Vehicle" here stands for the principle of nondualism.

View the ten thousand phenomena as equal
and all will revert to naturalness.
The very basis of their being wiped out,
impossible to rate one above another!

Arrest motion, and motion ceases to exist;
move stillness and stillness is gone.
But when neither comes into being,
how can even a single thing exist?

In the ultimate realm, the farthest extreme,
norms and standards no longer hold.
Once achieve true impartiality of mind
and purposive actions will cease completely.

All fret, all doubt cleansed
in the harmony and directness of true faith.
Nothing whatsoever remains,
nothing to be thought of, to recall.

In empty brightness your light shines of itself,
without labor to mind or sinew,
there in the place past reckoning,
beyond the ken of cognition or feeling.

The Dharma-realm of Suchness
knows no "other," no "self."
If you desire to approach and enter it,
only say to yourself "not two."

Where there are "not two," all is uniform,
nothing not enfolded there.
Wise ones of the ten directions
all make their way to this Source.

In this Source, no long or short time spans:
one moment is ten thousand years;
no "here" or "not here,"
all ten directions right before your eyes.

The tiniest is one with the huge,
all boundaries and realms wiped out.
The largest is one with the tiny,
extremes no longer to be seen.

Being—this is nonbeing,
nonbeing—this is being.
Any view at variance with this
must not be held!

One—this is all,
all—this is one.
When you can see in this manner,
what worries will not fade?

When trust and mind are not two,
not two, trust and mind,
there all words break off,
no past, no future, no now.

The Heart Sutra 13

TRANSLATED BY
THE NĀLANDĀ TRANSLATION COMMITTEE

THIS IS A TRANSLATION OF ONE OF THE MOST important of all the Mahayana sutras, treating as it does the central theme of emptiness *(shunyata),* which it presents in an extraordinarily concise and penetrating way. It is the shortest of the forty sutras comprising the *Prajnaparamita* ("Transcendental Knowledge") *Sutra.* Its full name is "Heart of the Great Transcendental Knowledge Sutra" *(Mahaprajnaparamita-hridaya Sutra).*

In the scene depicted here, though it is the Buddha who enters a profound meditative state, it is his disciple, the bodhisattva Avalokiteshvara, who has the vision of emptiness and who proceeds to utter the sutra in response to the questioning of another leading disciple, the bodhisattva Shariputra. At the end of this utterance, the Buddha merely approves. Then all praise the words of the Blessed One, the Buddha. The implication is that the whole event arises out of the power of the Buddha's meditation.

The heart of the *Heart Sutra* produced from the Buddha's meditation is the phrase "Form is emptiness; emptiness also is form." "Form is emptiness" means that all phenomenal forms—trees, pencils, shouts, moods, etc.—as they really are, are empty of all the concepts by which we grasp them and fit them into our world, empty of all we project upon them. Thus there is "no form, no feeling . . . no nose, no tongue, no body," and so on. The things we project as existing under these names are mere emptiness, because they are empty of the meanings of these names and the entities the meanings imply.

The list of negations in the sutra goes on to include all sorts of things usually affirmed by Buddhist doctrine. Even the Four Noble Truths are negated ("no suffering, no origin of suffering, no cessation of suffering, no path"). Emptiness is all-inclusive. This is the great liberation, because the thing that has us trapped and stuck is the world of meanings we live in. When these are stripped away, we can abide in the pure dimension of emptiness, completely free and beyond limitation. Hence the mantra GATE GATE . . . , "Gone, gone, gone beyond, gone completely beyond—awakened mind, so be it."

But there is a deeper level to this emptiness. What we have said so far gives us the drift of the sutra's meaning. But it is too easy. As we have described it, emptiness itself becomes a concept, a projection that whites out all distinctions, like vision being blotted out by the brilliance of a flashbulb. Transcendental knowledge is not this crude conceptual emptiness. Therefore the key phrase at the beginning of the sutra went on to say, "emptiness also is form." Real emptiness takes the form of forms just as they are—without the conceptual overlay of being this or that, empty of emptiness as well. Adding this further dimension to the understanding of emptiness, perhaps it would be interesting to go back to the beginning of the sutra and take the voyage again.

THUS HAVE I HEARD. ONCE THE BLESSED ONE WAS DWELLING IN Rājagriha at Vulture Peak mountain, together with a great gathering of the saṅgha of monks and a great gathering of the saṅgha of bodhisattvas. At that time the Blessed One entered the samādhi that expresses the dharma called "profound illumination," and at the same time noble Avalokiteshvara, the bodhisattva mahāsattva, while practicing the profound prajñāpāramitā, saw in this way: he saw the five skandhas to be empty of nature.

Then, through the power of the Buddha, venerable Shāriputra said to noble Avalokiteshvara, the bodhisattva mahāsattva,

"How should a son or daughter of noble family train, who wishes to practice the profound prajñāpāramitā?"

Addressed in this way, noble Avalokiteshvara, the bodhisattva mahāsattva, said to venerable Shāriputra, "O Shāriputra, a son or daughter of noble family who wishes to practice the profound prajñāpāramitā should see in this way: seeing the five skandhas to be empty of nature. Form is emptiness; emptiness also is form. Emptiness is no other than form; form is no other than emptiness. In the same way, feeling, perception, formation, and consciousness are emptiness. Thus, Shāriputra, all dharmas are emptiness. There are no characteristics. There is no birth and no cessation. There is no impurity and no purity. There is no decrease and no increase. Therefore, Shāriputra, in emptiness, there is no form, no feeling, no perception, no formation, no consciousness; no eye, no ear, no nose, no tongue, no body, no mind; no appearance, no sound, no smell, no taste, no touch, no dharmas; no eye dhātu up to no mind dhātu, no dhātu of dharmas, no mind consciousness dhātu; no ignorance, no end of ignorance up to no old age and death, no end of old age and death; no suffering, no origin of suffering, no cessation of suffering, no path, no wisdom, no attainment, and no non-attainment. Therefore, Shāriputra, since the bodhisattvas have no attainment, they abide by means of prajñāpāramitā. Since there is no obscuration of mind, there is no fear. They transcend falsity and attain complete nirvāṇa. All the buddhas of the three times, by means of prajñāpāramitā, fully awaken to unsurpassable, true, complete enlightenment. Therefore, the great mantra of prajñāpāramitā, the mantra of great insight, the unsurpassed mantra, the unequaled mantra, the mantra that calms all suffering, should be known as truth, since there is no deception. The prajñāpāramitā mantra is said in this way:

OM GATE GATE PĀRAGATE PĀRASAṂ GATE BODHI SVĀHĀ

Thus, Shāriputra, the bodhisattva mahāsattva should train in the profound prajñāpāramitā."

Then the Blessed One arose from that samādhi and praised noble Avalokiteshvara, the bodhisattva mahāsattva, saying, "Good, good, O son of noble family; thus it is, O son of noble family, thus it is. One should practice the profound prajñāpāramitā just as you have taught and all the tathāgatas will rejoice."

When the Blessed One had said this, venerable Shāriputra and noble Avalokiteshvara, the bodhisattva mahāsattva, that whole assembly and the whole with its gods, humans, asuras, and gandharvas rejoiced and praised the words of the Blessed One.

Exchanging Oneself for Others   14

GYALWA GENDUN GYATSO

THE SECOND DALAI LAMA

 GENDUN GYATSO, THE SEC-
ond Dalai Lama (1475–1542)—and the
first to be recognized as an incarnation
of the Dalai Lama line—spent much of
his life traveling and teaching throughout Tibet. He also found time to write
commentaries on a wide variety of
Buddhist topics, both philosophical
and practice-oriented. In the present
writing he vividly describes the practice of "giving and taking,"
which is an essential element of the *lojong* ("mind training")
teaching introduced into Tibet by the great Indian pandit
Atisha Dipamkara (980/90–1055), to whom Gendun Gyatso
pays homage at the beginning of the piece. Atisha founded a
spiritual lineage called the Kadam school, which was dedicated
to training the mind so as to arouse genuine compassion for
others on a heartfelt and down-to-earth level. Atisha's lineage
was absorbed in part by the Geluk order of Tibetan Buddhism.
Thus the Dalai Lamas, the heads of the Geluk order, are its
direct heirs, and here the second Dalai Lama seems to speak
with the very voice of the great Indian bodhisattva of compassion, Atisha.

The context of the "giving and taking" practice described in detail here is the central Mahayana doctrine of relative and absolute *bodhichitta* ("mind of enlightenment"). Relative bodhichitta (here this is translated "conventional bodhi-mind") is connected with the longing for truth we discussed in the commentary on chapter 1. It is the aspiration, nurtured by limitless compassion, to attain enlightenment for the sake of helping others, as well as actually embarking on the training that will enable one to do so. The absolute mind of enlightenment is direct perception of the true nature of phenomena, which is emptiness.

The object of the ingeniously direct and nearly infallible giving-and-taking practice (which in the sequence described is actually a taking-and-giving practice) is arousing genuine compassion. It happens in several phases, each of which may only last a few minutes, or as long as it takes to complete. First one meditates briefly on one's aspiration to attain enlightenment. Then, following the cue of the *Metta Sutta* (see chapter 11), which presents the attitude of a mother as paragon, one visualizes and contemplates one's own mother in a particular way, powerfully described in our text. Then one resolves to take responsibility for her welfare, and the practice of taking and giving begins. Taking happens with the in-breath. Giving happens with the out-breath. With each in-breath and out-breath the practitioner does what he or she can to fulfill the attitude and action described.

One realizes then that in the course of incalculably many rebirths, everyone has been everyone's mother in one life or another. This enables one to extend whatever compassion one has aroused toward one's own mother to other people. And then the same taking and giving proceeds in relation to others in several successive phases: in relation to a person you dislike, a friend, and a stranger. Next the level is expanded to include not just one individual but many—all beings. Finally one does the practice in relation to many enemies.

Once the logistics and sequence of the phases of the practice become clear, Gendun Gyatso's clear and direct descriptions guide the practitioner. It should be emphasized, however, that the discipline gained from more basic meditation practices, such as mindfulness of breath (chapters 7, 8, 10), is a foundation needed for great success in practices such as giving and taking. Without such previous discipline, the practitioner's mind may easily wander uncontrollably among the juicy associations that giving and taking may evoke.

The second section of the text gives the meditation on absolute bodhichitta (or bodhi-mind). It is a concrete and practical lesson in what the Mahayana calls "twofold egolessness." The first is the absence of a real "I," the ordinary egolessness. The second is the so-called egolessness (or lack of an individual essence) of all dharmas, that is, of all phenomena. This is called the twofold egolessness, because the projection of separate, definite entities in the world and the projection of an ego are inseparably bound up with each other.

HOMAGE TO THE LOTUS FEET OF ATISHA,
Who is inseparably one with the incomparable Tsong Khapa.

Herein I set forth an easily understood garland of words briefly explaining how to meditate upon the two types of bodhi-mind, conventional and ultimate—the essence of all their teachings.

How to Meditate upon the Conventional Bodhi-Mind

Meditation upon the conventional bodhi-mind—the aspiration to attain Buddhahood oneself as the best means to benefit all sentient beings—begins with meditation upon love and compassion. Love and compassion form the basis of the meditation known as "giving and taking," the principal technique used (in the Atisha tradition) for producing the conventional bodhi-mind.

Sit upon your meditation seat in a comfortable posture and visualize your mother of this life sitting before you. Contemplate how she carried you in her womb for almost ten months, and how during this time she experienced much suffering and inconvenience for you. At your actual birth her pain was as intense as that of being crushed to death. Yet she did not mind undergoing all this misery for you, no matter how great it was; and, when you finally emerged from her womb, looking like a naked and helpless worm covered in blood and mucus, she took you lovingly in her arms and placed you to her soft flesh to give you warmth, gave you milk from her own breast, prepared food for you, cleaned the mucus from your nose and the excrement from your body, looked with a smiling countenance upon you, and at night sacrificed her own comfort and sleep for you. Throughout your childhood she would rather become ill herself than permit you to become ill, and would even rather die than permit harm to come to you. As you grew up, the things that she treasured too dearly to use herself, or to give to others, she gave to you: the best of her food she gave to you, as well as clothing both warm and soft. She was willing to do anything for you, even at public disgrace to herself. Ignoring her own happiness in this life and the causes of her happiness for future lives (i.e., good karma), she thought only of how to provide for your comfort, happiness, and well-being. But her kindness did not end there: That you have met with the spiritual guides (lamas) and now have the opportunity to study and practice the holy Dharma—and thus to accomplish peace and happiness for this life and beyond—are purely a result of her kindness.

Meditate in this way until you appreciate her more than anything else, until your heart opens to her with love and the mere thought of her brings joy to your mind. Then contemplate how this mother of yours has the burden of the sufferings of birth, old age, sickness, and death placed upon her body and mind, and that when she dies she must wander helplessly into the hereafter, perhaps even into the lower realms of existence (hell, ghost, or animal worlds.) If you meditate in this way long enough, and with sufficient concentration, you will spontaneously give birth to a sense of compassion toward her as great as that felt by parents who witness their only child being tortured in a pit of fire.

You should then think, "If I do not accept responsibility to produce the beneficial and to eradicate the harmful for my own mother, who will accept it? If I do not do something, who will?"

But exactly what harms her? Suffering and negativity do. Moreover, suffering is the immediate cause of harming her, whereas negativity is the indirect cause. Think: "Therefore it is these that I should separate from her."

Contemplate thus; and as you breathe in visualize that together with your breath you are inhaling all her present sufferings and unsatisfactory conditions, as well as the negative karma and distorted mental conditions (attachments, aversions, etc.) that are the causes of all her future suffering. These peel away from her body and mind and come to your heart in the form of a black cloud drawn in by your breath. Generate conviction that she is thereby set free from suffering and its causes.

Similarly, exactly what benefits her? Happiness and goodness (i.e., positive karma) do. Moreover, happiness immediately benefits her, whereas goodness does so indirectly, "Therefore it is these that I should give to her." Meditate thus and as you breathe out, visualize that together with your breath you are exhaling a white cloud of happiness and goodness, which enters into her heart and satiates her with a wondrous mass of happiness, virtue and goodness, and causes her to progress toward Buddhahood.

Then, just as was done above by using your mother as the object of meditation, consider how all friends and relatives, having been your mother again and again in previous lives, have shown you the same kindnesses as has your present mother. In each previous life, they, as your mother (of that life), have shown you all the kindnesses of a mother, and in that respect are every bit as deserving of your love and appreciation as is the mother of this life. Contemplate over and over how they were kind mothers, until the mere sight of any of them fills your heart with joy and appreciation.

Then consider how, enmeshed in suffering, they are barren of true happiness. Continue meditating in this way until compassion unable to bear their pitiable state arises. When both love and compassion have been generated, engage in the meditation technique called "giving and taking" as previously explained.

When this has been accomplished, visualize before you a person whom you dislike, a friend and a stranger (i.e., someone toward whom you have no emotion). Although your memories may be clouded by the continued experiences of death, the intermediate state (between death and rebirth) and rebirth, in actual fact each of them has in countless previous lives been your mother, and on these occasions has shown you the same kindnesses as has your mother of this life, benefitting you in limitless ways and protecting you against whatever threatened your well-being.

Generate love and compassion for them as before, and then use them as the object of meditation in "giving and taking."

Next meditate upon how all beings of the six realms have repeatedly been your mother, in lifetime upon lifetime. Engender love and compassion toward them, and then engage in "giving and taking": by inhalation take away all their suffering—the heat of the hot hells; the cold of the cold hells; starvation of the hungry ghosts; the merciless brutality and so forth of the animal world; the sufferings of birth, sickness, and old age, etc., of mankind; the violence of the antigods; and the subtle, all-embracing suffering of the higher gods. And, by exhalation, meditate on giving them all that could make them happy and well—cool breeze to the hot hells, warmth to cold, sustenance to the ghosts, etc.

Finally, visualize any enemies or people who have harmed you. Contemplate how, obscured by ignorance and by the effects of repeated birth, death, and transmigration, they do not recognize that they have many times been your mother, and you theirs; but, overpowered by karmic forces and by mental obscurations, they are blindly impelled to cause you harm in this life. However, if your kind mother of this life were suddenly to go crazy, verbally abuse you, and attack you physically, only if you were completely mindless would you react with anything but compassion. In the same way, the only correct response to those who harm or abuse one in this life is compassion.

Meditate like this until love and compassion arise, and then meditate upon "giving and taking"—taking the immediate and indirect causes of their anger, distortion and unhappiness and giving them the causes of peace and joy.

In brief, with the exception of the Buddhas and one's personal teachers (lamas), one should meditate upon "giving and taking" with all beings, even tenth-level Bodhisattvas, Shravaka Arhats and Pratyekabuddhas, who have the faults of subtle stains of distorted and limited perception still to be abandoned. There is no purpose, however, in visualizing "giving and taking" with the Buddhas, for they, having exhausted all their faults, have no shortcomings to be removed or qualities to be attained. As for one's personal teachers, it is improper to use the meditation of "giving and taking" with them as the object, because it is incorrect for a disciple to admit a fault in his teachers. Even if one of one's teachers seems to actually have faults, the disciple should not visualize removing them. To the Buddhas and one's teachers one can only make offerings of one's goodness and joy.

At this point in the meditation you should ask yourself, "However, do I really have the ability completely to fulfill the needs of all living beings?"

Answer: Not only does an ordinary being not have this ability, even a Bodhisattva of the tenth level does not.

Question: Then who does?

Answer: Only a fully and perfectly enlightened being, a Buddha.

Contemplate this deeply, until you gain an unfeigned experience of the aspiration to attain the state of complete Buddhahood as the supreme method of benefiting all living beings.

How to Meditate upon the Ultimate Bodhi-Mind

Sometimes, the thought of "I" suddenly arises with great force. If at those moments we look closely at how it appears, we will be able to understand, that although from the beginning this manifest "I" seems to be inherently existent within the collection of body and mind, in fact it does not exist at all in the manner that it seems, because it is a mere mental imputation.

The situation is like that of a rock or a tree seen protruding up from the peak of a hill on the horizon: From afar it may be mistaken for a human being. Yet the existence of a human in that rock or tree is only an illusion. On deeper investigation, no human being can be found in any of the individual pieces of the protruding entity, nor in its collection of parts, nor in any other aspect of it. Nothing in the protrusion can be said to be a valid basis for the name "human being."

Likewise, the solid "I" which seems to exist somewhere within the body and mind is merely an imputation. The body and mind are no more represented by the sense of "I" than is the protruding rock represented by the word "human." This "I" cannot be located anywhere within any individual piece of the body and mind, nor is it found within the body and mind as a collection, nor is there a place outside of these that could be considered to be a substantial basis of the object referred to by the name "I."

Meditate in this way until it becomes apparent that the "I" does not exist in the manner it would seem.

Similarly, all dharmas within cyclic existence and beyond are merely imputations of "this" and "that" name mentally projected upon their bases of ascription. Other than this mode of existence they have no established being whatsoever.

Meditate prolongedly upon this concept of emptiness. Then in the postmeditation periods, maintain an awareness of how oneself, samsara and nirvana are like an illusion and a dream: Although they appear to the mind, they are empty of inherent existence.

Because of this noninherent-existenceness it is possible for creative and destructive activities to produce their according results. He who gains this understanding becomes a sage abiding in knowledge of the inseparable nature, the common ground of emptiness and interdependent origination.

> This then is an easily understood explanation
> Of the glorious practices of higher being
> That lay the imprint of the two Buddhakayas.
> I urge you, therefore, to practice it,
> The pure essence of the great Mahayana.

Loving-Kindness 15

PEMA CHÖDRÖN

 PEMA CHÖDRÖN IS AN AMERICAN nun of the Kagyu order of Tibetan Buddhism, a student of the late Tibetan meditation master Chögyam Trungpa, Rinpoche. She is the chief administrator of a Buddhist monastery in Nova Scotia and travels and teaches widely. In this short piece she explains something of the nature of *maitri* (cf. chapter 11) and in so doing gives some very solid and wise advice about the Buddhist approach to the spiritual path.

THERE'S A COMMON MISUNDERSTANDING AMONG ALL THE HUman beings who have ever been born on the earth that the best way to live is to try to avoid pain and just try to get comfortable. You can see this even in insects and animals and birds. All of us are the same.

A much more interesting, kind, adventurous, and joyful approach to life is to begin to develop our curiosity, not caring whether the object of our inquisitiveness is bitter or sweet. To lead a life that goes beyond pettiness and prejudice and always wanting to make sure that everything turns out on our own terms, to lead a more passionate, full, and delightful life than that, we must realize that we can endure a lot of pain and pleasure for the sake of finding out who we are and what this world is, how we tick and how our world ticks, how the whole thing just *is*. If we're committed to comfort at any cost, as soon as we come up against the least edge of pain, we're going to run; we'll never know what's beyond that particular barrier or wall or fearful thing.

When people start to meditate or to work with any kind of spiritual discipline, they often think that somehow they're going to improve, which is a sort of subtle aggression against who they really are. It's a bit like saying, "If I jog, I'll be a much better person." "If I could only get a nicer house, I'd be a better person." "If I could meditate and calm down, I'd be a better person." Or the scenario may be that they find fault with others; they might say, "If it weren't for my husband, I'd have a perfect marriage." "If it weren't for the fact that my boss and I can't get on, my job would be just great." And "If it weren't for my mind, my meditation would be excellent."

But loving-kindness—*maitri*—toward ourselves doesn't mean getting rid of anything. Maitri means that we can still be crazy after all these years. We can still be angry after all these years. We can still be timid or jealous or full of feelings of unworthiness. The point is not to try to change ourselves. Meditation practice isn't about trying to throw ourselves away and become something better. It's about befriending who we are already. The ground of practice is you or me or whoever we are right now, just as we are. That's the ground, that's what we study, that's what we come to know with tremendous curiosity and interest.

Sometimes among Buddhists the word *ego* is used in a derogatory sense, with a different connotation than the Freudian term. As Buddhists, we might say, "My ego causes me so many problems." Then we might think, "Well, then, we're supposed to get rid of it, right? Then there'd be no problem." On the contrary, the idea isn't to get rid of ego but actually to begin to take an interest in ourselves, to investigate and be inquisitive about ourselves.

The path of meditation and the path of our lives altogether has to do with curiosity, inquisitiveness. The ground is ourselves; we're here to study ourselves and to get to know ourselves now, not later.

16   *The Bodhisattva Path*

CHÖGYAM TRUNGPA

THOUGH CHÖGYAM TRUNGPA, AS A TIBETAN Buddhist, represents a tradition that emphasizes the Vajrayana as the supreme vehicle, he personally insisted upon the Hinayana, Mahayana, and Vajrayana as indispensable successive stages of the Buddhist path. Thus he taught extensively on *lojong* (see chapter 15) and other aspects of the bodhisattva path of the Mahayana. The essence of the bodhisattva's practice and action is the six *paramitas*, or transcendental virtues, which Trungpa describes here. Rather than following the conventional style of describing the paramitas, Trungpa describes the inner psychological experience of these virtues, which he presents as aspects of the bodhisattva's spontaneous relationship to situations. For example, the orthodox description of the paramita of generosity lists the different kinds of offerings and gifts that should be made toward representatives of the Buddha Dharma and the proper motivation for making them. Trungpa describes generosity essentially as a willingness to open (toward situations and other people) that transcends irritation.

THE PATH OF THE BODHISATTVA IS FOR THOSE WHO ARE BRAVE
and convinced of the powerful reality of the buddha-nature
which exists within themselves. The word *bodhisattva* means
"he who is brave enough to walk on the path of the bodhi."
Bodhi means "awake," or "the awakened state." This is not to
say that the bodhisattva must already be fully awake; but he is
willing to walk the path of the awakened ones.

This path consists of six transcendental activities which take
place spontaneously. They are: transcendental generosity, discipline, patience, energy, meditation, and knowledge. These virtues are called the six *paramitas*, because *param* means "other
side" or "shore," "other side of the river," and *ita* means "arrived." *Paramita* means "arriving at the other side or shore,"
which indicates that the activities of the bodhisattva must have
the vision, the understanding which transcends the centralized
notions of ego. The bodhisattva is not trying to be good or
kind, but he is spontaneously compassionate.

Generosity

Transcendental generosity is generally misunderstood in the
study of the Buddhist scriptures as meaning being kind to
someone who is lower than you. Someone has this pain and
suffering, and you are in a superior position and can save
them—which is a very simple-minded way of looking down
upon someone. But in the case of the bodhisattva, generosity is
not so callous. It is something very strong and powerful: it is
communication.

Communication must transcend irritation, otherwise it will
be like trying to make a comfortable bed in a briar patch. The
penetrating qualities of external color, energy, and light will
come toward us, penetrating our attempts to communicate like
a thorn pricking our skin. We will wish to subdue this intense
irritation and our communication will be blocked.

Communication must be radiation and receiving and exchange. Whenever irritation is involved, then we are not able to see properly and fully and clearly the spacious quality of that which is coming toward us, that which is presenting itself as communication. The external world is immediately rejected by our irritation which says, "No, no, this irritates me, go away." Such an attitude is the complete opposite of transcendental generosity.

So the bodhisattva must experience the complete communication of generosity, transcending irritation and self-defensiveness. Otherwise, when thorns threaten to prick us, we feel that we are being attacked, that we must defend ourselves. We run away from the tremendous opportunity for communication that has been given to us, and we have not been brave enough even to look to the other shore of the river. We are looking back and trying to run away.

Generosity is a willingness to give, to open without philosophical or pious or religious motives, just simply doing what is required at any moment in any situation, not being afraid to receive anything. Opening could take place in the middle of a highway. We are not afraid that smog and dust or people's hatreds and passions will overwhelm us; we simply open, completely surrender, give. This means that we do not judge, do not evaluate. If we attempt to judge or evaluate our experience, if we try to decide to what extent we should open, to what extent we should remain closed, then openness will have no meaning at all and the idea of paramita, of transcendental generosity, will be in vain. Our action will not transcend anything, will cease to be the act of a bodhisattva.

The whole implication of the idea of transcendence is that we see through the limited notions, the limited conceptions, the warfare mentality of *this* as opposed to *that*. Generally, when we look at an object, we do not allow ourselves to see it properly. Automatically we see our version of the object instead of actually seeing that object as it is. Then we are quite satisfied, because we have manufactured our own version of the thing within ourselves. Then we comment on it, we judge, we take or reject; but there is no real communication going on at all.

So transcendental generosity is giving whatever you have. Your action must be completely open, completely naked. It is not for you to make judgments; it is for the recipients to make the gesture of receiving. If the recipients are not ready for your generosity, they will not receive it. If they are ready for it, they will come and take it. This is the selfless action of the bodhisattva. He is not self-conscious: "Am I making any mistakes?" "Am I being careful?" "To whom should I open?" He never takes sides. The bodhisattva will, figuratively, just lie like a corpse. Let people look at you and examine you. You are at their disposal. Such noble action, such complete action, action that does not contain any hypocrisy, any philosophical or religious judgment at all. That is why it is transcendental. That is why it is paramita. It is beautiful.

Discipline

And if we proceed further and examine the paramita of "morality" or "discipline," the *shila* paramita, we find that the same principles apply. That is, shila, or discipline, is not a matter of binding oneself to a fixed set of laws or patterns. For if a bodhisattva is completely selfless, a completely open person, then he will act according to openness, will not have to follow rules; he will simply fall into patterns. It is impossible for the bodhisattva to destroy or harm other people, because he embodies transcendental generosity. He has opened himself completely and so does not discriminate between *this* and *that*. He just acts in accordance with what *is*. From another person's point of view—if someone were observing the bodhisattva—he always appears to act correctly, always seems to do the right thing at the right time. But if we were to try to imitate him, it would be impossible to do so, because his mind is so precise, so accurate that he never makes mistakes. He never runs into unexpected problems, never creates chaos in a destructive way. He just falls into patterns. Even if life seems to be chaotic, he just falls in, participates in the chaos and somehow things sort themselves out. The bodhisattva is able to cross the river so to speak, without falling into its turbulence.

If we are completely open, not watching ourselves at all, but being completely open and communicating with situations as they are, then action is pure, absolute, superior. However, if we attempt to achieve pure conduct through effort, our action will be clumsy. However pure it may be, still there will be clumsiness and rigidity involved. In the case of the bodhisattva his whole action is flowing, there is no rigidity at all. Everything just fits into place, as if someone had taken years and years to figure out the whole situation. The bodhisattva does not act in a premeditated way; he just communicates. He starts from the generosity of openness and falls into the pattern of the situation. It is an often-used metaphor that the bodhisattva's conduct is like the walk of an elephant. Elephants do not hurry; they just walk slowly and surely through the jungle, one step after another. They just sail right along. They never fall, nor do they make mistakes. Each step they take is solid and definite.

Patience

The next act of the bodhisattva is patience. Actually you cannot really divide the six activities of the bodhisattva into strictly separate practices. One leads into and embodies the next. So in the case of the paramita of patience, this action is not a matter of trying to control oneself, trying to become a hard worker, trying to be an extremely forbearing person, disregarding one's physical or mental weakness, going on and on and on until one completely drops dead. But patience also involves skillful means, as with discipline and generosity.

Transcendental patience never expects anything. Not expecting anything, we do not get impatient. However, generally in our lives we expect a lot, we push ourselves, and this kind of action is very much based on impulse. We find something exciting and beautiful and we push ourselves very hard towards it, and sooner or later we are pushed back. The more we push forward, the more we will be pushed back, because impulse is such a strong driving force without wisdom. The action of impulse is like that of a person running without eyes to see, like that of a blind man trying to reach his destination. But the action of the bodhisattva never provokes a reaction. The bodhisattva can accommodate himself to any situation because he never desires or is fascinated by anything. The force behind transcendental patience is not driven by premature impulse nor by anything else of that nature. It is very slow and sure and continuous, like the walk of an elephant.

Patience also feels space. It never fears new situations, because nothing can surprise the bodhisattva—nothing. Whatever comes—be it destructive, chaotic, creative, welcoming, or inviting—the bodhisattva is never disturbed, never shocked, because he is aware of the space between the situation and himself. Once one is aware of the space between the situation and oneself, then anything can happen in that space. Whatever occurs does so in the midst of space. Nothing takes place "here" or "there" in terms of relationship or battle. Therefore transcendental patience means that we have a flowing relationship with the world, that we do not fight anything.

Energy

And then we could go to the next stage, the paramita of energy, *virya*, which is the kind of energy that immediately leads us into situations so that we never miss a chance, never miss an opportunity. In other words, it is joy, joyous energy, as Shantideva points out in his *Bodhicharyavatara*. This energy is joy, rather than the kind of energy with which we work hard because we feel we must. It is joyous energy because we are completely interested in the creative patterns of our lives. One's whole life is opened by generosity, activated by morality, strengthened by patience, and now one arrives at the next stage, that of joy. One never sees situations as uninteresting or stagnant at all, because the bodhisattva's view of life is extremely open-minded, intensely interested. He never evaluates; though that does not mean that he becomes a complete blank. It does not mean that he is absorbed into a "higher consciousness," the "highest state of samadhi," so that he cannot differentiate day from night or breakfast from lunch. It does not mean he becomes vague or wooly-minded. Rather, he actually sees verbalized and conceptualized values as they are, and then he sees beyond concept and evaluation. He sees the sameness of these little distinctions that we make. He sees situations from a panoramic point of view and therefore takes a great deal of interest in life as it is. So the bodhisattva does not strive at all; he just lives.

He takes a vow when he enters the bodhisattva path that he
will not attain enlightenment until he has helped all sentient
beings to attain the awakened state of mind or buddhahood
before him. Beginning with such a noble act of giving, of opening, of sacrifice, he continues to follow this path, taking tremendous interest in everyday situations, never tiring of working
with life. This is virya, working hard with joy. There is tremendous energy in realizing that we have given up trying to become
the Buddha, that now we have the time to really live life, that
we have gone beyond neurotic speed.

Interestingly, although the bodhisattva has taken a vow not
to attain enlightenment, because he is so precise and accurate,
he never wastes one second. He always lives life thoroughly and
fully, and the result is that, before he realizes where he is, he
has attained enlightenment. But his unwillingness to attain enlightenment continues, strangely enough, even after he has
reached Buddhahood. Then compassion and wisdom really
burst out, reinforcing his energy and conviction. If we never tire
of situations, our energy is joyous. If we are completely open,
fully awake to life, there is never a dull moment. This is virya.

Meditation

The next paramita is *dhyana,* or meditation. There are two
types of dhyana. The first is that of the bodhisattva, where because of his compassionate energy, he experiences continual
panoramic awareness. *Dhyana* literally means "awareness," being in a state of "awake." But this does not only mean the practice of meditation in a formal sense. The bodhisattva never
seeks a trance state, bliss, or absorption. He is simply awake to
life situations as they are. He is particularly aware of the continuity of meditation with generosity, morality, practice, and energy. There is a continual feeling of "awake."

The other type of dhyana is the concentration practice of the
realm of the gods. The main difference between that type of
meditation and the meditation of the bodhisattva is that the
bodhisattva does not dwell upon anything, although he deals
with actual physical life situations. He does not set up a central
authority in his meditation, does not watch himself acting or

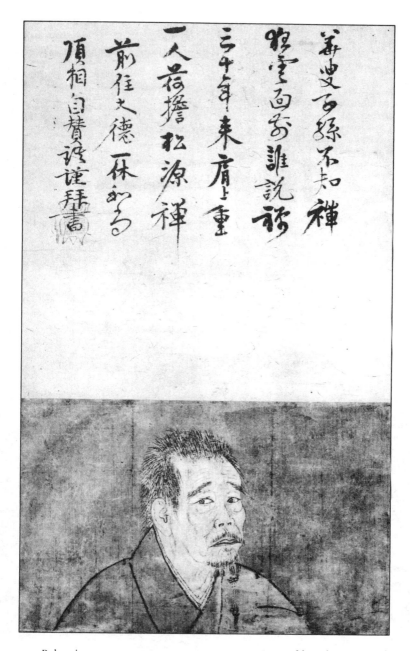

13. Bokusai, THE ZEN PRIEST IKKYU OSHO. Japan, fifteenth century, ink and paper. Tokyo National Museum.

The Japanese Zen master Ikkyu Sojun (1394–1481) was renowned for his deep realization, his calligraphy and poetry, and his eccentric, uncompromising behavior. This informal portrait is believed to have been executed by his close student Bokusai. The rough features and penetrating eyes present a startling intensity, which is matched by the vibrant energy of Ikkyu's own calligraphy above.

14. Miyamoto Musashi, HOTEI WATCHING A COCK FIGHT. Japan, seventeenth century, ink and paper. Fukuoka City Art Museum.

A special feature of Zen painting is the use of bold brushwork that disregards conventional artistry. The famous swordsman Miyamoto Musashi (1582–1645) works in this manner to portray the legendary Zen vagabond Hotei totally absorbed in watching a pair of sparring roosters. The painting suggests the basis for the close connection between Zen and the martial arts—it is the freedom and power that come from the ability to live in the moment.

15. Ryoanji garden, Kyoto. Japan, fifteenth century. Photo by John C. Huntington.

The Japanese term for the Zen rock garden is *kara senzui*, or "dry landscape." The sparsest of its kind is the garden of Ryoanji, which consists of only fifteen stones set into an expanse of raked sand. Ryoanji garden invites the viewer to experience a meditative reverie on emptiness. At the heart of the arts of Zen lies the ability to communicate, by simple means, the Mahayana teaching that "form is emptiness, emptiness is form."

16.   Ito Jakuchu, VEGETABLE PARINIRVANA. Japan, late eighteenth
century, ink on paper. Kyoto National Museum.

The great radish in the center of *Vegetable Parinirvana* represents Shakyamuni Buddha recumbent upon his deathbed, while the circle of disheveled
fruits and vegetables stands for the mourners. Jakuchu's family were
wealthy Kyoto greengrocers, and the painting was probably made as an offering upon the death of a close relative.

17.   PRAJNAPARAMITA. Indonesia, about 1300 CE, stone. Jakarta, Museum Nasional.
Photo by Dirk Bakker.

Prajnaparamita, or transcendent wisdom, is the wisdom that sees emptiness. It is described as
"the mother of all the Buddhas" and is personified in Vajrayana art as a bodhisattva in female
form. With its serene features and crisp carving, this large image of Prajnaparamita has com-
pelling power. According to oral tradition it was executed as a funerary monument to Dedes,
the first queen of the Singasari dynasty of Eastern Java.

meditating, so that his action is always meditation and his meditation is always action.

Knowledge

The next paramita is *prajna,* or "knowledge." Prajna is traditionally symbolized by a sharp, two-edged sword which cuts through all confusion. Even if the bodhisattva has perfected the other five paramitas, lacking prajna the other actions are incomplete. It is said in the sutras that the five paramitas are like five rivers flowing into the ocean of prajna. It also says in the sutras that the *chakravartin,* or universal emperor, goes to war at the head of four different armies. Without the emperor to lead them, the armies have no direction. In other words, prajna is the intelligence, the basic pattern into which all these other virtues lead and dissolve. It is that which cuts through the conceptualized versions of bodhisattva action—generosity, discipline, and all the rest. The bodhisattva might perform his actions methodically and properly, but without knowledge, without the sword that cuts through doubt and hesitation his action is not really transcendental at all. Thus prajna is intelligence, the all-seeing eye, the opposite of the ego's watching itself doing everything.

The bodhisattva transmutes the watcher or ego into discriminating knowledge, prajna paramita. *Pra* means "super," *jna* means "knowing": superknowledge, complete, accurate knowledge which sees everything. Consciousness fixed on "this" and "that" has been cut through, which produces the two-fold knowledge, the prajna of knowing and the prajna of seeing.

The prajna of knowing deals with the emotions. It is the cutting through of conflicting emotions—the attitudes that one has toward oneself—thereby revealing what one is. The prajna of seeing is the transcendence of primitive preconceptions of the world. It is seeing situations as they are. Therefore the prajna of seeing allows for dealing with situations in as balanced a way as possible. Prajna completely cuts through any kind of awareness which has the slightest inclination toward separating "that" and "this." This is the reason why the blade is two-edged. It does not just cut in *this* direction, but in *that* one as well. The bodhisattva no longer experiences the irritating quality that comes from distinguishing between *this* and *that*. He just sails through situations without needing to check back. So all the six paramitas are interdependent.

The Sutra Called Flawless Purity

A Dialogue with the
Laywoman Gangottara

TRANSLATED BY GARMA C. C. CHANG

THIS SHORT SUTRA FROM ONE OF THE OLDEST collections of Mahayana sutras, the *Ratnakuta* (the "Heap of Jewels"), further explores the meaning of emptiness. If phenomena are empty of any essence, then the whole dualistic mind that wants to apprehend them as real so as to possess or shun them, together with the world of apparently real things it creates, has really never come into existence. Fundamentally, it is unborn, yet it appears like a magic display. Since it is unborn, it also never dies. Here that inapprehensible (beyond the grasp of conceptual mind) dimension is referred to as nirvana.

The setting of the sutra is the Jeta Grove outside of the city of Shravasti, north of the Ganges River in central India. This is the site of one of the first great monasteries built for the Buddha and his community, donated by the great patron Anathapindada. The Buddha is being incisively interrogated on his own ground by the fearless laywoman Gangottara, who obviously already has a superb command of his teaching (though tending slightly to the nihilistic side). Though an unflinching debater she addresses him respectfully as the Tathagata, which essentially means "he who has gone beyond."

THUS HAVE I HEARD. ONCE THE BUDDHA WAS DWELLING IN THE garden of Anathapindada, in the Jeta Grove near Shravasti. At that time, a laywoman named Gangottara came from her dwelling in Sravasti to see the Buddha. She prostrated herself with her head at the Buddha's feet, withdrew to one side, and sat down.

The World-Honored One asked Gangottara, "Where do you come from?"

The laywoman asked the Buddha, "World-Honored One, if someone were to ask a magically produced being where he came from, how should the question be answered?"

The World-Honored One told her, "A magically produced being neither comes nor goes, neither is born nor perishes; how can one speak of a place from which he comes?"

Then the laywoman asked, "Is it not true that all things are illusory, like magic?"

The Buddha said, "Yes, indeed. What you say is true."

Gangottara asked, "If all things are illusory, like magic, why did you ask me where I came from?"

The World-Honored One told her, "A magically produced being does not go to the miserable planes of existence, nor to heaven; nor does he attain nirvana. Gangottara, is that also true of you?"

The laywoman replied, "As I see it, if my own body were different from a magically produced one, then I could speak of going to the good or miserable planes of existence, or of attaining nirvana. I see no difference, though, between my body and a magically produced one, so how can I speak of going to the good or miserable planes, or of attaining nirvana?

"Furthermore, World-Honored One, nirvana's very nature is such that it is not reborn in the good or miserable planes, nor does it experience parinirvana. I perceive that the same is true of my own nature."

The Buddha asked, "Do you not seek the state of nirvana?"

Gangottara asked in turn, "If this question were put to one who had never come into being, how should it be answered?"

The Buddha replied, "That which has never come into being is nirvana itself."

Gangottara asked, "Are not all things identical with nirvana?"

The Buddha replied, "So they are, so they are."

"World-Honored One, if all things are identical with nirvana, why did you ask me, 'Do you not seek the state of nirvana?'

"Furthermore, World-Honored One, if a magically produced being asked another magically produced being, 'Do you not seek the state of nirvana?' what would the answer be?"

The World-Honored One told her, "A magically produced being has no mental attachments [and thus seeks nothing]."

Gangottara inquired, "Does the Tathagata's very question stem from some mental attachment?"

The World-Honored One told her, "I raised the question because there are in this assembly good men and good women who can be brought to maturity. I am free of mental attachments. Why? Because the Tathagata knows that even the names of things are inapprehensible, let alone the things themselves or those who seek nirvana."

Gangottara said, "If so, why all the accumulation of good roots for the attainment of enlightenment?"

[The Buddha replied,] "Neither Bodhisattvas nor their good roots can be apprehended, because in the Bodhisattvas' minds there is no discriminative thought as to whether they are accumulating good roots or not."

Gangottara asked, "What do you mean by 'no discriminative thought'?"

The World-Honored One answered, "The absence of discriminative thought cannot be understood or grasped by means of thinking. Why? Because in the state [of no discriminative thought], even the mind is inapprehensible, let alone the mental functions. This state, in which the mind is inapprehensible, is called inconceivable. It cannot be grasped or realized; it is neither pure nor impure. Why so? Because, as the Tathagata always teaches, all things are as empty and unimpeded as space."

Gangottara inquired, "If all things are like empty space, why does the World-Honored One speak of form, feeling, conception, impulse, and consciousness; the [eighteen] elements; the [twelve] entrances; the twelve links of dependent origination;

the defiled and the undefiled; the pure and the impure; samsara and nirvana?"

The Buddha told Gangottara, "When I speak of a 'self,' for example, although I express the concept by a word, actually the nature of a 'self' is inapprehensible. I speak of form, but in reality the nature of form is also inapprehensible, and so it is with the other [dharmas], up to nirvana. Just as we cannot find water in mirages, so we cannot find a nature in form, and so it is with the others, up to nirvana.

"Gangottara, only a person who cultivates pure conduct in accordance with the Dharma, perceiving that nothing can be apprehended, deserves to be called a real cultivator of pure conduct. Since the arrogant say that they have apprehended something, they cannot be said to be firmly established in genuine pure conduct. Such arrogant people will be terrified and doubtful when they hear this profound Dharma. They will be unable to liberate themselves from birth, old age, sickness, death, worry, sorrow, suffering, and distress.

"Gangottara, after my parinirvana, there will be some people able to spread this profound Dharma, which can stop the rounds of samsara. However, some fools, because of their evil views, will hate those Dharma-masters, and will contrive to harm them. Such fools will fall to the hells for that."

Gangottara asked, "You speak of 'this profound Dharma which can stop the rounds of samsara.' What do you mean by 'stop the rounds of samsara'?"

The World-Honored One replied, "To stop the rounds of samsara is [to penetrate] reality, the realm of the inconceivable. Such a Dharma cannot be damaged or destroyed. Hence, it is called the Dharma that can stop the rounds of samsara."

Then the World-Honored One smiled graciously and emitted from his forehead blue, yellow, red, white, and crystalline lights. The lights illuminated all the numerous lands, reaching as high as the Brahma Heaven, then returned and entered the top of the Buddha's head.

Seeing this, the Venerable Ananda thought to himself, "The Tathagata, the Worthy One, the Supremely Enlightened One, does not smile without a reason." He rose from his seat, uncovered his right shoulder, knelt on his right knee, and joined his palms toward the Buddha, inquiring, "Why did the Buddha smile?"

The Buddha replied, "I recall that, in the past, a thousand Tathagatas also taught this Dharma here, and each of those assemblies was also led by a laywoman named Gangottara. After hearing this Dharma preached, the laywoman and all the assembly left the household life. [In time,] they entered the nirvana without residue."

Ananda asked the Buddha, "What name should be given to this sutra and how should we accept and uphold it?"

The Buddha said, "This sutra is called 'Flawless Purity,' and you should accept and uphold it by that name."

During the preaching of this sutra, seven hundred monks and four hundred nuns were liberated from defilements forever and their minds were set free.

At that time, the gods of the Realm of Desire magically produced various kinds of wonderful celestial flowers and scattered them upon the Buddha, saying, "Rare indeed is this laywoman, who can converse fearlessly with the Tathagata on equal terms. She must have served and made offerings to countless Buddhas, and planted good roots of every kind in their presence."

After the Buddha had finished speaking this sutra, the laywoman Gangottara and all the gods, humans, asuras, gandharvas, and so forth were jubilant over the Buddha's teaching. They accepted it with faith, and began to follow it with veneration.

18   *Looking at Living Beings*

TRANSLATED BY CHARLES LUK

THIS SELECTION IS THE SEVENTH CHAPTER OF the *Vimalakirti-Nirdesha Sutra* (Discourse-of-Vimalakirti Sutra), an important Mahayana work thought to have been composed in the second century C.E., early on in the development of the Mahayana. A wealthy lay disciple *(upasaka)* of the Buddha's, Vimalakirti, who follows the Mahayana way of the bodhisattva, is sick in bed. The Buddha asks his monastic disciples to go and see how Vimalakirti is faring. All refuse because they are intimidated by the brilliance of Vimalakirti's spiritual realization. Finally the Buddha's great disciple Manjushri agrees to go, and the others follow. Even the greatest of these disciples, attached as they still are to the way of the arhat, find themselves no more than students when they encounter the Mahayana wisdom of the great bodhisattva householder.

At the beginning of this chapter, Vimalakirti uses many metaphors to explain to Manjushri that living beings should be seen as illusory. Manjushri then asks how one should be kind to living beings. One might expect that it is not necessary to be kind to illusions, but Vimalakirti enumerates many ways to be kind to illusory living beings. More teachings unfold in a kind of regression as Manjushri continues to question the householder about the basis for each thing he says. Finally the question is about the root cause of inverted thinking. Vimalakirti answers "nonabiding," by which he means failing to abide in transcendental knowledge of emptiness and thus entering into duality.

Then a goddess appears and is engaged in conversation by another great monastic disciple of the Buddha's, Shariputra, who is known for his indomitable intellect but here finds himself being instructed. In this passage we have the explicit contrast of the bodhisattva's transcendental view with the outlook of the *shravaka* (one following the Hinayana way of the arhat). The shravaka view, though taking the ego to be unreal, regards the rest of conventional reality (such as time and space) as real. Because of its elevation of the householder and its expression of the view based on emptiness, the *Vimalakirti-nirdesha Sutra* became a landmark in the development of the Mahayana.

Though the Mahayana sutras champion the absolute vision of emptiness, they never advocate contempt for conventional or relative reality. The bodhisattva vows to liberate all sentient beings, an inexhaustible number of which remain caught up in the conventional everyday outlook. In order to work with these beings, no matter how clear his perception of the absolute view of emptiness, the bodhisattva must continue to deal skillfully and appropriately with the relative world. And in fact, the bodhisattva's pure vision and unobstructed nondualistic approach makes it possible to do this extraordinarily well.

MANJUSHRI ASKED VIMALAKIRTI: "HOW SHOULD A BODHI-sattva look at living beings?"

Vimalakirti replied: "A bodhisattva should look at living beings like an illusionist does at the illusory men (he has created); and like a wise man looking at the moon's reflection in water; at his own face in a mirror; at the flame of a burning fire; at the echo of a calling voice; at flying clouds in the sky; at foam in a liquid; at bubbles on water; at the (empty) core of a banana tree; at a flash of lightning; at the (nonexistent) fifth element (beside the four that make the human body); at the sixth aggregate (beside the five that make a sentient being); at the seventh sense datum (beside the six objects of sense); at the thirteenth entrance (beside the twelve involving the six organs and six sense data); at the nineteenth realm of sense (beside the eighteen dhātus, or fields of sense); at form in the formless world;

at the (nonexistent) sprout of a charred grain of rice; at a body seen by a shrota-apanna (who has wiped out the illusory body to enter the holy stream); at the entry of an anagamin (or a nonreturning shravaka) into the womb of a woman (for re-birth); at an arhat still preserving the three poisons (of desire, anger and stupidity which he has eliminated forever); at a bo-dhisattva realizing the patient endurance of the uncreate who is still greedy, resentful and breaking the prohibitions; at a bud-dha still suffering from klesha (troubles); at a blind man seeing things; at an adept who still breathes air in and out while in the state of nirvanic imperturbability; at the tracks of birds flying in the air; at the progeny of a barren woman; at the suffering of an illusory man; at a sleeping man seeing he is awake in a dream; at a devout man realizing nirvana who takes a bodily form for (another) reincarnation; and at a smokeless fire.

"This is how a bodhisattva should look at living beings."

Thereat, Manjushri asked Vimalakirti: "When a bodhisattva so meditates, how should he practice kindness (maitri)?

Vimalakirti replied: "When a bodhisattva has made this meditation, he should think that he ought to teach living beings to meditate in the same manner; this is true kindness. He should practice causeless (nirvanic) kindness, which prevents creativeness; unheated kindness, which puts an end to klesha (troubles and causes of trouble); impartial kindness, which cov-ers all the three periods of time (which means that it is eternal involving past, future, and present); passionless kindness, which wipes out disputation; nondual kindness, which is beyond sense organs within and sense data without; indestructible kindness, which eradicates all corruptibility;[1] stable kindness, which is a characteristic of the undying self-mind; pure and clean kindness which is spotless like dharmata; boundless kindness, which is all-pervasive like space; the kindness of the arhat stage, which destroys all bondage; the bodhisattva kindness, which gives comfort to living beings; the tathagata kindness, which leads to the state of thatness; the buddha kindness, which enlightens all living beings; spontaneous kindness, which is causeless; bodhi kindness, which is of one flavor (i.e., uniform and unmixed wisdom); unsurpassed kindness, which cuts off all desires; mer-

---

[1] Indestructible kindness is a characteristic of the self-nature, which is incor-ruptible.

ciful kindness, which leads to the Mahayana (path); untiring
kindness because of deep insight into the void and nonexistent
ego; Dharma-bestowing (dana) kindness, which is free from regret and repentance; precepts (shila) upholding kindness to
convert those who have broken the commandments; patient
(kshanti) kindness, which protects both the self and others;
zealous (virya) kindness to liberate all living beings; serene
(dhyana) kindness, which is unaffected by the five senses; wise
(prajna) kindness, which is always timely; expedient (upaya)
kindness to appear at all times for converting living beings; un-
hidden kindness because of the purity and cleanness of the
straightforward mind; profound minded kindness, which is free
from discrimination; undeceptive kindness, which is faultless;
and joyful kindness, which bestows the buddha joy (in
nirvana).

"Such are the specialties of bodhisattva kindness."

Manjushri asked Vimalakirti: "What should be his compassion (karuna)?"

Vimalakirti replied: "His compassion should include sharing
with all living beings all the merits he has won."

Manjushri asked: "What should be his joy (mudita)?"

Vimalakirti replied: "He should be filled with joy on seeing
others win the benefit of the Dharma with no regret whatsoever."

Manjushri asked "What should he relinquish (upeksha)?"

Vimalakirti replied: "In his work of salvation he should expect nothing (i.e., no gratitude or reward) in return."

Manjushri asked: "On what should he rely in his fear of birth
and death?"

Vimalakirti replied: "He should rely on the power of the
Tathagata's moral merits."

Manjushri asked: "What should he do to win support from
the power of the Tathagata's moral merits?"

Vimalakirti replied: "He should liberate all living beings in
order to win support from the power of the Tathagata's moral
merits."

Manjushri asked: "What should he wipe out in order to liberate living beings?"

Vimalakirti replied: "When liberating living beings he should
wipe out their klesha (troubles and causes of troubles)."

Manjushri asked: "What should he do to wipe out klesha?"

Vimalakirti replied: "He should uphold right mindfulness."[2]

Manjushri asked: "What should he do to uphold right mindfulness?"

Vimalakirti replied: "He should advocate the unborn and the undying."

Manjushri asked: "What is the unborn and what is the undying?"

Vimalakirti replied: "The unborn is evil that does not arise and the undying is good that does not end."

Manjushri asked: "What is the root of good and evil?"

Vimalakirti replied: "The body is the root of good and evil."

Manjushri asked: "What is the root of the body?"

Vimalakirti replied: "Craving is the root of the body."

Manjushri asked: "What is the root of craving?"

Vimalakirti replied: "Baseless discrimination is the root of craving."

Manjushri asked: "What is the root of baseless discrimination?"

Vimalakirti replied: "Inverted thinking is the root of discrimination."

Manjushri asked: "What is the root of inverted thinking?"

Vimalakirti replied: "Nonabiding is the root of inverted thinking."

Manjushri asked: "What is the root of nonabiding?"

Vimalakirti replied: "Nonabiding is rootless. Manjushri, from this nonabiding root all things arise."

A goddess who had watched the gods listening to the Dharma in Vimalakirti's room appeared in bodily form to shower flowers on the bodhisattvas and the chief disciples of the Buddha (in their honor). When the flowers fell on the bodhisattvas, they fell to the ground, but when they fell on the chief disciples, they stuck to their bodies and did not drop in spite of all their efforts to shake them off.

Thereat, the goddess asked Shariputra why he strove to shake the flowers off. Shariputra replied: "I want to shake off these flowers which are not in the state of suchness." The goddess said: "Do not say these flowers are not in the state of suchness. Why? Because they do not differentiate, and it is you (alone) who give rise to differentiation. If you (still) differentiate after

---

[2] Right mindfulness retains the true and keeps from the false.

leaving home in your quest of Dharma, this is not the state of suchness, but if you no longer give rise to differentiation, this will be the state of suchness. Look at the bodhisattvas whose bodies do not retain the flowers; this is because they have put an end to differentiation. This is like a man taking fright who invites trouble for himself from evil (people). So if a disciple fears birth and death, then form, sound, smell, taste and touch can trouble him, but if he is fearless he is immune from all the five sense data. (In your case) it is because the force of habit still remains that these flowers cleave to your body but if you cut it off, they will not stick to it."

Shariputra asked: "How long have you been in this room?" The goddess replied: "My stay in this room is just like the Venerable Elder's liberation."[3] Shariputra asked: "Do you then mean that you have stayed here for a long time?" The goddess retorted: "Does your liberation also involve time?"[4] Shariputra kept silent and did not reply. The goddess then asked: "Why is the wise elder silent on this point?" Shariputra replied: "He who wins liberation does not express it in words; hence I do not know what to say."[5] The goddess said: "Spoken and written words reveal liberation. Why? For liberation is neither within nor without nor in between, and words also are neither inside nor outside nor in between. Therefore, Shariputra, liberation cannot be preached without using words. Why? Because all things point to liberation."[6]

---

[3] Shariputra was surprised by the goddess's eloquence and thought she must have been there for some time to listen to Vimalakirti's teaching, thus implying the element of time in his question. The goddess taught him to wipe out the element of time in his quest of Mahayana and said that her stay in the absolute state was just what his own liberation should be, that is, beyond time and space.

[4] Shariputra misunderstood the goddess's teaching and asked if she had stayed there for a considerable time, like his own liberation in the shravaka stage he had realized long ago. So the goddess retorted by asking if his own liberation implied time which is bondage instead of liberation. Thus the goddess wiped out the element of time.

[5] Shariputra was called "Shariputra, the Wise" because he had won great wisdom which distinguished him from the other chief disciples of the Buddha in the shravaka stage.

[6] Time was wiped out in the preceding lines; here space is wiped out as well to expose the absolute.

The three dogmas of the middle, or Madhyamika, school are: the immaterial noumenon, the material phenomenon, and the "mean" or the unifier which places each in the other and all in all. The doctrine opposes the rigid categories of existence (the material) and non-existence (the im-

Shariputra asked: "Do you then mean that there is no need to keep from carnality, hatred and stupidity to win liberation?"

The goddess replied: "In the presence of those who are proud (of their superior knowledge) the Buddha said it is important to keep from carnality, hatred and stupidity in the quest of liberation; but where they are absent, He said that the underlying nature of carnality, hatred and stupidity (i.e., the self-nature) is identical with liberation."[7]

Shariputra exclaimed: "Excellent, goddess, excellent, what have you gained and experienced that gives you such an eloquence?"

The goddess replied: "The fact that I neither gain nor experience anything gives me this eloquence. Why is it so? Because he who (claims to) have won and experienced (something) is arrogant in the eye of the Buddha Dharma."

Shariputra asked: "Which of the three vehicles[8] is your aim?"

The goddess replied: "When I preach the shravaka Dharma to convert people, I appear as a shravaka; when I expound the (twelve) links in the chain of existence I appear as a pratyeka-buddha; and when I teach great compassion to convert them, I appear as a (teacher of) Mahayana. Shariputra, like those entering a campa[9] grove who smell only the fragrance of campas to the exclusion of all odors, those entering this room smell only the fragrance of Buddha merits and no longer like the aroma of achievements by shravakas and pratyeka-buddhas.

Shariputra, when Indra, Brahma, the four deva kings of the

material) and denies the two extremes in the interests of a middle or supreme way which is absolute being above and beyond all dualities, relativities and contraries.

Shariputra spoke of the immaterial noumenon according to which liberation is beyond spoken and written words; hence his speechlessness. The goddess preached the "mean" according to which neither liberation nor words can be found within, without and in-between. Nevertheless, "liberation" is also a word which cannot be dropped when we speak of liberation. She meant that the immaterial cannot be revealed without using the material for both are neither unity nor diversity, pointing to the "mean" which is true liberation.

[7] According to the *Lotus Sutra,* there were some five thousand disciples who wrongly thought they had realized liberation and so refused to listen to this important sermon. But where there were no such arrogant people, the Buddha revealed that the underlying nature of sins is but liberation.

[8] The three vehicles by which shravakas, pratyeka-buddhas, and bodhisattvas attain their goals.

[9] Campa: a yellow fragrant flower in India.

four heavens (guardians of the world), heavenly dragons, ghosts and spirits, etc. entered the room and heard this upasaka (Vimalakirti) expound the right Dharma, they all took delight in smelling the fragrance of Buddha merits and developed the Mahayana mind before returning to their worlds.

"Shariputra, I have stayed here for twelve years during which I have never heard the Dharmas of shravakas and pratyeka-buddhas but only the doctrine of great kindness (maitri) and great compassion (karuna) of the bodhisattvas and the inconceivable Buddha Dharma.

"Shariputra, in this room there are always eight unusual manifestations:

"Firstly, this room is illuminated by a golden light which is the same by day and by night and does not depend on either sunlight or moonlight to light it up;

"Secondly, he who enters it is immune from all troubles caused by defilements;

"Thirdly, this room is visited by Indra, Brahma, the four deva kings of the four heavens, and bodhisattvas from other realms;

"Fourthly, the never-receding Dharma of the six paramitas is always expounded in it;

"Fifthly, the most melodious heavenly music intoning countless Dharma doors (to enlightenment) is heard in it;

"Sixthly, this room contains the four canons (of sutras, vinaya, shastras, and miscellaneous scriptures) full of inexhaustible precious treasures for those who are (spiritually) poor;

"Seventhly, when the venerable upasaka thinks of Shakyamuni Buddha, Amitabha Buddha, Akshobhya Buddha, the Buddha of Precious Virtues, the Buddha of Precious Flame, the Buddha of Precious Moonshine, the Buddha of Precious Majesty, the Invincible Buddha, the Buddha of the Lion's Roar, the Buddha of All-Perfection, and countless other Buddhas in the ten directions, they all come to expound the secrets of the esoteric Buddha Dharma, after which they return to their realms;

"Eighthly, all majestic heavenly palaces and all pure lands of Buddhas appear in this room.

"Shariputra, after witnessing these eight remarkable things in this room, who still seeks the shravaka Dharma?"

Shariputra asked: "Why do not you change your female bodily form?"

The goddess replied: "For the last twelve years I have been looking in vain for a female bodily form; so what do you want me to change? This is like an illusionist who creates an illusory woman; is it correct to ask him to change this unreal woman?"

Shariputra said: "No, because it is not a real body; into what then can it be changed?"

The goddess said: "All phenomena (including forms) are also unreal. So why have you asked me to change my unreal female body?"

Thereat, she used her supernatural powers to change Shariputra into a heavenly goddess and herself into a man similar to Shariputra, and asked him: "Why do not you change your female form?"

Shariputra replied: "I do not know why I have turned into a goddess."

The goddess said: "Shariputra, if you can change your female body, all women should also be able to turn into men. Like Shariputra who is not a woman but appears in female bodily form, all women are the same and though they appear in female form, they are fundamentally not women. Hence the Buddha said: 'All things are neither male nor female'."

Thereat, the goddess again used her supernatural powers to change Shariputra back to his (original) male body, and asked: "Where is your female body now?"

Shariputra replied: "The form of a woman neither exists nor is nonexistent."

The goddess then declared: "Likewise, all things are fundamentally neither existing nor nonexistent, and that which neither exists nor is nonexistent is proclaimed by the Buddha."[10]

Shariputra asked: "When will you leave (die) here and where will you be reborn?"

The goddess replied: "I shall be reborn like a buddha by transformation."

Shariputra interjected: "The Buddha's transformation body implies neither birth nor death."

The goddess said: "Likewise all living beings (fundamentally) are subject to neither death nor birth.[11]

[10] Reality, or the absolute as proclaimed by the Buddha, is neither existing nor nonexistent because it is absolute and is beyond all dualities, relativities, and contraries.

[11] This reveals the changeless underlying nature of all living beings.

Shariputra asked: "When will you realize supreme enlightenment?"

The goddess replied: "I shall realize supreme enlightenment when Shariputra returns to the worldly way of life."[12]

Shariputra retorted: "There is no such thing as myself (a holy man at the shravaka stage) returning to the worldly way of life."

The goddess said: "There is also no such thing as myself realizing enlightenment. Why? Because bodhi (enlightenment) is not an objective which can be realized.[13]

Shariputra retorted: "There are buddhas as countless as sand grains in the Ganges who have realized and will win supreme enlightenment; what will you say of them?"

The goddess said: "The three periods of time (the past, future and present) are spoken of (to the common) as being in line with worldly thinking, but this does not mean that bodhi (which is timeless or eternal) is tied to the past, future and present." She then asked Shariputra: "Shariputra, have you realized arhatship?"

Shariputra replied: "I have realized it because I hold no concept of winning anything."

The goddess said: "Likewise, all buddhas and great bodhisattvas achieved their goals because they were free from the idea of winning supreme enlightenment."

Thereat, Vimalakirti said to Shariputra: "This goddess has made offerings to ninety-two lakhs of Buddhas. She is able to play with the bodhisattva transcendental powers, has fulfilled all her vows, has realized the patient endurance of the uncreate, and has reached the never-receding bodhisattva stage. In fulfillment of a vow, she appears at will (everywhere) to teach and convert living beings."

---

[12] To reveal that fundamentally there is no difference between the holy and the worldly, i.e., to cut short all discriminating.
[13] To wipe out the dualism of subject and object.

19 The Enlightenment of Hui-neng

TRANSLATED BY WONG MOU-LAM

THIS STORY—THE AUTOBIOGRA-phy of Hui-neng—comprises the first chapter of the *Sutra of Hui Neng,* also known as the "Sutra from the High Seat [Platform] of the Dharma Treasury" and called the Platform Sutra for short. This sutra contains some of the most profound passages in Zen litera-ture. In chapter 12, we heard from Seng-ts'an, the third Ch'an (Zen) patriarch, or lineage holder. Hui-neng (638–713) is the sixth patriarch of the same lineage, and here we learn how he came to be that. His story affords us a precious intimate look at the transmission of the mind lineage of enlightenment from teacher to disciple in a flash of realization. The *prajna* spoken of here is none other than the *prajnaparamita* we encountered earlier (e.g., in chapter 13)—the transcendental knowing that perceives the nature of emptiness. The Ch'an presentation of it, as here, always conveys the particular flavor of immediate ex-perience.

ONCE, WHEN THE PATRIARCH HAD ARRIVED AT PAO-LIN MON-
astery, Prefect Wei of Shao-chou and other officials went there
to ask him to deliver public lectures on Buddhism in the hall of
Ta-fan temple in the city [Canton].

In due course, there were assembled [in the lecture hall] Prefect Wei, government officials, and Confucian scholars, about
thirty each, and *bhikshus, bhikshunis,* Taoists, and laymen to the
number of about one thousand. After the patriarch had taken
his seat, the congregation in a body paid him homage and asked
him to preach on the fundamental laws of Buddhism, whereupon His Holiness delivered the following address:

Learned Audience, our essence of mind [literally, self-na-
ture], which is the seed or kernel of enlightenment [*bodhi*], is
pure by nature, and by making use of this mind alone we can
reach buddhahood directly. Now let me tell you something
about my own life and how I came into possession of the esoteric teaching of the Dhyana [Zen] school.

My father, a native of Fan-yang, was dismissed from his official post and banished to be a commoner in Hsin-chou in
Kwangtung. I was unlucky in that my father died when I was
very young, leaving my mother poor and miserable. We moved
to Kuang-chou [Canton] and were then in very bad circumstances.

I was selling firewood in the market one day, when one of
my customers ordered some to be brought to his shop. Upon
delivery being made and payment received, I left the shop, outside of which I found a man reciting a sutra. As soon as I heard
the text of this sutra my mind at once became enlightened.
Thereupon I asked the man the name of the book he was reciting and was told that it was the *Diamond Sutra.* I further inquired whence he came and why he recited this particular sutra.
He replied that he came from Tung-shan monastery in the
Huang-mei district of Ch'i-chou; that the abbot in charge of
this temple was Hung-jen, the fifth patriarch; that there were
about one thousand disciples under him; and that when he
went there to pay homage to the patriarch, he attended lectures

on this sutra. He further told me that His Holiness used to encourage the laity as well as the monks to recite this scripture, as by doing so they might realize their own essence of mind, and thereby reach buddhahood directly.

It must be due to my good karma in past lives that I heard about this, and that I was given ten taels for the maintenance of my mother by a man who advised me to go to Huang-mei to interview the fifth patriarch. After arrangements had been made for her, I left for Huang-mei, which took me less than thirty days to reach.

I then went to pay homage to the patriarch, and was asked where I came from and what I expected to get from him. I replied, "I am a commoner from Hsin-chou of Kwangtung. I have traveled far to pay you respect and I ask for nothing but buddhahood."

"You are a native of Kwangtung, a barbarian? How can you expect to be a buddha?"

I replied: "Although there are northern men and southern men, north and south make no difference to their buddha-nature. A barbarian is different from Your Holiness physically, but there is no difference in our buddha-nature."

He was going to speak further to me, but the presence of other disciples made him stop short. He then ordered me to join the crowd to work.

"May I tell Your Holiness," said I, "that *prajna* [transcendental wisdom] often rises in my mind. When one does not go astray from one's own essence of mind, one may be called the 'field of merits.' I do not know what work Your Holiness would ask me to do."

"This barbarian is too bright," he remarked. "Go to the stable and speak no more." I then withdrew myself to the backyard and was told by a lay brother to split firewood and to pound rice.

More than eight months after, the patriarch saw me one day and said, "I know your knowledge of Buddhism is very sound, but I have to refrain from speaking to you lest evildoers should do you harm. Do you understand?"

"Yes, sir, I do," I replied: "To avoid people taking notice of me, I dare not go near your hall."

The patriarch one day assembled all his disciples and said to them, "The question of incessant rebirth is a momentous one.

Day after day, instead of trying to free yourselves from this bitter sea of life and death, you seem to go after tainted merits
only [i.e., merits that cause rebirth]. Yet merits will be of no
help if your essence of mind is obscured. Go and seek for *prajna*
in your own mind and then write me a stanza about it. He who
understands what the essence of mind is will be given the robe
[the insignia of the patriarchate] and the Dharma [i.e., the esoteric teaching of the Dhyana school], and I shall make him the
sixth patriarch. Go away quickly. Delay not in writing the
stanza, as deliberation is quite unnecessary and of no use. The
man who has realized the essence of mind can speak of it at
once, as soon as he is spoken to about it; and he cannot lose
sight of it, even when engaged in battle."

Having received this instruction, the disciples withdrew and
said to one another, "It is of no use for us to concentrate our
mind to write the stanza and submit it to His Holiness, since
the patriarchate is bound to be won by Shen-hsiu, our instructor. And if we write perfunctorily, it will only be a waste of
energy." Upon hearing this, all of them made up their minds
not to write and said, "Why should we take the trouble? Hereafter, we will simply follow our instructor, Shen-hsiu, wherever
he goes, and look to him for guidance."

Meanwhile, Shen-hsiu reasoned thus with himself: "Considering that I am their teacher, none of them will take part in the
competition. I wonder whether I should write a stanza and submit it to His Holiness. If I do not, how can the patriarch know
how deep or superficial my knowledge is? If my object is to get
the dharma, my motive is a pure one. If I were after the patriarchate, then it would be bad. In that case, my mind would be
that of a worldling and my action would amount to robbing
the patriarch's holy seat. But if I do not submit the stanza, I
shall never have a chance of getting the dharma. A very difficult
point to decide, indeed!"

In front of the patriarch's hall there were three corridors, the
walls of which were to be painted by a court artist named Lu-
chen with pictures from the *Lankavatara-sutra* depicting the
transfiguration of the assembly, and with scenes showing the
genealogy of the five patriarchs, for the information and veneration of the public.

When Shen-hsiu had composed his stanza he made several
attempts to submit it to the patriarch, but as soon as he went

near the hall his mind was so perturbed that he sweated all over. He could not screw up courage to submit it, although in the course of four days he made altogether thirteen attempts to do so.

Then he suggested to himself, "It would be better for me to write it on the wall of the corridor and let the patriarch see it for himself. It he approves it, I shall come out to pay homage, and tell him that it is done by me; but if he disapproves it, then I shall have wasted several years in this mountain in receiving homage from others that I by no means deserve! In that case, what progress have I made in learning Buddhism?"

At twelve o'clock that night he went secretly with a lamp to write the stanza on the wall of the south corridor, so that the patriarch might know what spiritual insight he had attained. The stanza read:

> Our body is the bodhi tree,
> And our mind a mirror bright.
> Carefully we wipe them hour by hour,
> And let no dust alight.

As soon as he had written it he left at once for his room, so nobody knew what he had done. In his room he again pondered: "When the patriarch sees my stanza tomorrow and is pleased with it, I shall be ready for the dharma; but if he says that it is badly done, it will mean that I am unfit for the Dharma, owing to the misdeeds in previous lives that thickly becloud my mind. It is difficult to know what the patriarch will say about it!" In this vein he kept on thinking until dawn, as he could neither sleep nor sit at ease.

But the patriarch knew already that Shen-hsiu had not entered the door of enlightenment, and that he had not known the essence of mind.

In the morning, he sent for Lu-chen, the court artist, and went with him to the south corridor to have the walls there painted with pictures. By chance, he saw the stanza. "I am sorry to have troubled you to come so far," he said to the artist. "The walls need not be painted now, as the sutra says, 'All forms or phenomena are transient and illusive.' It will be better to leave the stanza here, so that people may study it and recite it. If they put its teaching into actual practice, they will be saved from the misery of being born in these evil realms of existence. The merit gained by one who practices it will be great indeed!"

He then ordered incense to be burned, and all his disciples to pay homage to it and to recite it, so that they might realize the essence of mind. After they had recited it, all of them exclaimed, "Well done!"

At midnight, the patriarch sent for Shen-hsiu to come to the hall, and asked him whether the stanza was written by him or not.

"It was, sir," replied Shen-hsiu. "I dare not be so vain as to expect to get the patriarchate, but I wish Your Holiness would kindly tell me whether my stanza shows the least grain of wisdom."

"Your stanza," replied the patriarch, "shows that you have not yet realized the essence of mind. So far you have reached the door of enlightenment, but you have not yet entered it. To seek for supreme enlightenment with such an understanding as yours can hardly be successful.

"To attain supreme enlightenment, one must be able to know spontaneously one's own nature or essence of mind, which is neither created nor can it be annihilated. From *kshana* to *kshana* [thought moment to thought moment], one should be able to realize the essence of mind all the time. All things will then be free from restraint [i.e., emancipated]. Once the *Tathata* [suchness, another name for the essence of mind] is known, one will be free from delusion forever; and in all circumstances one's mind is absolute truth. If you can see things in such a frame of mind you will have known the essence of mind, which is supreme enlightenment.

"You had better go back to think it over again for a couple of days, and then submit me another stanza. If your stanza shows that you have entered the door of enlightenment, I will transmit to you the robe and the Dharma."

Shen-hsiu made obeisance to the patriarch and left. For several days, he tried in vain to write another stanza. This upset his mind so much that he was as ill at ease as if he were in a nightmare, and he could find comfort neither in sitting nor in walking.

Two days after, it happened that a young boy who was passing by the room where I was pounding rice recited loudly the stanza written by Shen-hsiu. As soon as I heard it, I knew at once that the composer of it had not yet realized the essence of mind. For although I had not been taught about it at that time, I already had a general idea of it.

"What stanza is this?" I asked the boy.

"You barbarian," he replied, "don't you know about it? The patriarch told his disciples that the question of incessant rebirth was a momentous one, that those who wished to inherit his robe and dharma should write him a stanza, and that the one who had an understanding of the essence of mind would get them and be made the sixth patriarch. Elder Shen-hsiu wrote this formless stanza on the wall of the south corridor and the patriarch told us to recite it. He also said that those who put its teaching into actual practice would attain great merit, and be saved from the misery of being born in the evil realms of existence."

I told the boy that I wished to recite the stanza too, so that I might have an affinity with its teaching in future life. I also told him that although I had been pounding rice there for eight months I had never been to the hall, and that he would have to show me where the stanza was to enable me to make obeisance to it.

The boy took me there and I asked him to read it to me, as I am illiterate. A petty officer of the Chiang-chou district named Chang Tih-yung, who happened to be there, read it out to me. When he had finished reading I told him that I also had composed a stanza, and asked him to write it for me. "Extraordinary indeed," he exclaimed, "that you also can compose a stanza!"

"Don't despise a beginner," said I, "if you are a seeker of supreme enlightenment. You should know that the lowest class may have the sharpest wit, while the highest may be in want of intelligence. If you slight others, you commit a very great sin."

"Dictate your stanza," said he. "I will take it down for you. But do not forget to deliver me, should you succeed in getting the dharma!"

My stanza read:

> There is no bodhi tree,
> Nor stand of a mirror bright.
> Since all is void,
> Where can the dust alight?

When he had written this, all disciples and others who were
present were greatly surprised. Filled with admiration, they said
to one another, "How wonderful! No doubt we should not
judge people by appearance. How can it be that for so long we
have made a bodhisattva incarnate work for us?"

Seeing that the crowd was overwhelmed with amazement, the
patriarch rubbed off the stanza with his shoe, lest jealous ones
should do me injury. He expressed the opinion, which they
took for granted, that the author of this stanza had also not yet
realized the essence of mind.

Next day the patriarch came secretly to the room where the
rice was pounded. Seeing that I was working there with a stone
pestle, he said to me, "A seeker of the path risks his life for the
dharma. Should he not do so?" Then he asked, "Is the rice
ready?"

"Ready long ago," I replied, "only waiting for the sieve." He
knocked the mortar thrice with his stick and left.

Knowing what his message meant, in the third watch of the
night I went to his room. Using the robe as a screen so that
none could see us, he expounded the *Diamond Sutra* to me.
When he came to the sentence, "One should use one's mind in
such a way that it will be free from any attachment," I at once
became thoroughly enlightened, and realized that all things in
the universe are the essence of mind itself.

"Who would have thought," I said to the patriarch, "that the
essence of mind is intrinsically pure! Who would have thought
that the essence of mind is intrinsically free from becoming or
annihilation! Who would have thought that the essence of mind
is intrinsically self-sufficient! Who would have thought that the
essence of mind is intrinsically free from change! Who would
have thought that all things are the manifestation of the essence
of mind!"

Knowing that I had realized the essence of mind, the patriarch said, "For him who does not know his own mind there is
no use learning Buddhism. On the other hand, if he knows his
own mind and sees intuitively his own nature, he is a hero, a
teacher of gods and men, a buddha."

Thus, to the knowledge of no one, the dharma was transmitted to me at midnight, and consequently I became the inheritor
of the teaching of the Sudden school as well as of the robe and
the begging bowl.

"You are now the sixth patriarch," said he. "Take good care of yourself, and deliver as many sentient beings as possible. Spread and preserve the teaching, and don't let it come to an end. Take note of my stanza:

Sentient beings who sow the seeds of enlightenment
In the field of causation will reap the fruit of buddhahood.
Inanimate objects void of buddha-nature
Sow not and reap not.

He further said, "When the patriarch Bodhidharma first came to China, most Chinese had no confidence in him, and so this robe was handed down as a testimony from one patriarch to another. As to the dharma, this is transmitted from heart to heart, and the recipient must realize it by his own efforts. From time immemorial it has been the practice for one buddha to pass to his successor the quintessence of the dharma, and for one patriarch to transmit to another the esoteric teaching from heart to heart. As the robe may give cause for dispute, you are the last one to inherit it. Should you hand it down to your successor, your life would be in imminent danger. Now leave this place as quickly as you can, lest some one should do you harm."

"Whither should I go?" I asked.

"At Huai you stop and at Hui you seclude yourself," he replied.

Upon receiving the robe and the begging bowl in the middle of the night, I told the patriarch that, being a Southerner, I did not know the mountain tracks, and that it was impossible for me to get to the mouth of the river [to catch a boat]. "You need not worry," said he. "I will go with you."

He then accompanied me to Chiu-chiang, and there ordered me into a boat. As he did the rowing himself, I asked him to sit down and let me handle the oar.

"It is only right for me to carry you across," he said [an allusion to the sea of birth and death which one has to go across before the shore of nirvana can be reached].

To this I replied, "While I am under illusion, it is for you to get me across; but after enlightenment, I should cross it by myself. [Although the phrase "to go across" is the same, it is used differently in each case]. As I happen to be born on the frontier, even my speaking is incorrect in pronounciation, [but in spite of this] I have had the honor to inherit the dharma from you. Since I am now enlightened, it is only right for me to cross the sea of birth and death myself by realizing my own essence of mind."

"Quite so, quite so," he agreed. "Beginning from you the Dhyana school will become very popular. Three years after your departure from me I shall leave this world. You may start on your journey now. Go as fast as you can toward the south. Do not preach too soon, as Buddhism is not so easily spread."

After saying good-bye, I left him and walked toward the south. In about two months' time, I reached Ta-yü Mountain. There I noticed that several hundred men were in pursuit of me with the intention of robbing me of my robe and begging bowl.

Among them there was a monk named Hui-ming, whose lay surname was Ch'en. He was a general of the fourth rank in lay life. His manner was rough and his temper hot. Of all the pursuers, he was the most vigilant in search of me. When he was about to overtake me, I threw the robe and the begging bowl on a rock, saying, "This robe is nothing but a symbol. What is the use of taking it away by force?" [I then hid myself.]

When he got to the rock, he tried to pick them up, but found he could not. Then he shouted out, "Lay brother, lay brother [for the patriarch had not yet formally joined the Order], I come for the dharma, not for the robe."

Whereupon I came out from my hiding place and squatted on the rock. He made obeisance and said, "Lay brother, preach to me, please."

"Since the object of your coming is the dharma," said I, "refrain from thinking of anything and keep your mind blank. I will then teach you." When he had done this for a considerable time, I said, "When you are thinking of neither good nor evil, what is at that particular moment, venerable sir, your real nature [literally original face]?"

As soon as he heard this he at once became enlightened. But he further asked, "Apart from those esoteric sayings and esoteric ideas handed down by the patriarchs from generation to generation, are there any other esoteric teachings?"

"What I can tell you is not esoteric," I replied. "If you turn your light inwardly, you will find what is esoteric within you."

"In spite of my staying in Huang-mei," said he, "I did not

realize my self-nature. Now, thanks to your guidance, I know it as a water drinker knows how hot or how cold the water is. Lay brother, you are now my teacher."

I replied, "If that is so, then you and I are fellow disciples of the fifth patriarch. Take good care of yourself."

In answering his question whither he should go thereafter, I told him to stop at Yüan and to take up his abode in Meng. He paid homage and departed.

Sometime after I reached Ts'ao-ch'i. There the evildoers again persecuted me and I had to take refuge in Szu-hui, where I stayed with a party of hunters for a period as long as fifteen years.

Occasionally I preached to them in a way that befitted their understanding. They used to put me to watch their nets, but whenever I found living creatures therein I set them free. At mealtimes I put vegetables in the pan in which they cooked their meat. Some of them questioned me, and I explained to them that I would eat the vegetables only, after they had been cooked with the meat.

One day I bethought myself that I ought not to pass a secluded life all the time, and that it was high time for me to propagate the law. Accordingly, I left there and went to Fa-hsin temple in Canton.

At that time Bhikshu Yin-tsung, master of the Dharma, was lecturing on the Mahaparinirvana-sutra in the temple. It happened that one day, when a pennant was blown about by the wind, two *bhikshus* entered into a dispute as to what it was that was in motion, the wind or the pennant. As they could not settle their difference I submitted to them that it was neither, and that what actually moved was their own mind. The whole assembly was startled by what I said, and Bhikshu Yin-tsung invited me to take a seat of honor and questioned me about various knotty points in the sutras.

Seeing that my answers were precise and accurate, and that they showed something more than book knowledge, he said to me, "Lay brother, you must be an extraordinary man. I was told long ago that the inheritor of the fifth patriarch's robe and Dharma had come to the South. Very likely you are the man."

To this I politely assented. He immediately made obeisance and asked me to show the assembly the robe and the begging bowl which I had inherited.

He further asked what instructions I had when the fifth patriarch transmitted to me the Dharma. "Apart from a discussion on the realization of the essence of mind," I replied, "he gave me no other instruction, nor did he refer to dhyana and emancipation."

"Why not?" he asked.

"Because that would mean two ways," I replied. "And there cannot be two ways in Buddhism. There is one way only."

He asked what was the only way. I replied, "The *Mahaparinirvana-sutra,* which you expound, explains that buddha-nature is the only way. For example, in that sutra King Kao Kuei-teh, a bodhisattva, asked Buddha whether or not those who commit the four acts of gross misconduct or the five deadly sins, and those who are heretics, and so forth, would eradicate their element of goodness and their buddha-nature. Buddha replied, 'There are two kinds of elements of goodness, the eternal and the noneternal. Since buddha-nature is neither eternal nor noneternal, therefore their element of goodness is not eradicated.' Now Buddhism is known as having no two ways. There are good ways and evil ways, but since buddha-nature is neither, therefore Buddhism is known as having no two ways. From the point of view of ordinary folks, the component parts of a personality [*skandhas*] and factors of consciousness (*dhatus*) are two separate things, but enlightened men understand that they are not dual in nature. Buddha-nature is nonduality."

Bhikshu Yin-tsung was highly pleased with my answer. Putting his two palms together as a sign of respect, he said, "My interpretation of the sutra is as worthless as a heap of debris, while your discourse is as valuable as genuine gold." Subsequently he conducted the ceremony of hair cutting for me [i.e., the ceremony of initiation into the order] and asked me to accept him as my pupil.

Thenceforth, under the bodhi tree I preached the teaching of the Tung-shan school [the school of the fourth and the fifth patriarchs, who lived in Tung-shan].

Since the time when the Dharma was transmitted to me in Tung-shan, I have gone through many hardships and my life often seemed to be hanging by a thread. Today, I have had the honor of meeting you in this assembly, and I must ascribe this to our good connection in previous kalpas [cyclic periods], as well as to our common accumulated merits in making offerings to various buddhas in our past reincarnations; otherwise, we should have had no chance of hearing the above teaching of the Sudden school, and thereby laying the foundation of our future success in understanding the Dharma.

This teaching was handed down from the past patriarchs, and it is not a system of my own invention. Those who wish to hear the teaching should first purify their own minds, and after hearing it they should each clear up their own doubts in the same way as the sages did in the past.

At the end of the address, the assembly rejoiced, made obeisance, and departed.

To Forget the Self   20

DOGEN ZENJI

TRANSLATED BY HAKUYU TAIZAN MAEZUMI

DOGEN ZENJI, OR EIHEI DO-
gen (1200–1253), was a great early
Zen master and is considered by
many to have been the greatest of all.
Japanese Buddhists of all traditions
venerate Dogen as a great bodhisattva. He brought the Soto (Chin.,
Ts'ao-tung) lineage of Zen to Japan.

After studying with Japanese mas-
ters, Dogen traveled to China. He became enlightened on the
spot when his Chinese master Ju-ching told him he had to
"drop body and mind." Afterward he went to his master, who
confirmed that he had indeed dropped body and mind and become enlightened. The grateful Dogen prostrated himself before his master in gratitude. "That's dropping dropped," said
Ju-ching.

The following is an excerpt from the *Shobogenzo* (Treasury
of the Eye of True Dharma). It is from a famous chapter called
the "Genjokoan" (Enlightenment as Everyday Life), which deals
with the connection between meditation practice and enlightenment. It is unparalleled in its profound and poetic expression
of the nondualistic experience of awakened mind.

SEEING FORMS WITH THE WHOLE BODY AND MIND,
hearing sounds with the whole body and mind, one
understands them intimately.
Yet it is not like a mirror with reflections, nor like water
under the moon—
When one side is realized, the other side is dark.

To study the buddha way is to study the self.
To study the self is to forget the self.
To forget the self is to be enlightened by the ten thousand
dharmas.
To be enlightened by the ten thousand dharmas is to free
one's body and mind and those of others.
No trace of enlightenment remains, and this traceless
enlightenment is continued forever.

When one first seeks the truth, one separates oneself far
from its environs.
When one has already correctly transmitted the truth to
oneself, one is one's original self at that moment.
When riding on a boat, if one watches the shore one may
assume that the shore is moving.
But watching the boat directly, one knows that it is the
boat that moves.
If one examines the ten thousand dharmas with a
deluded body and mind, one will suppose that one's
mind and nature are permanent.
But if one practices intimately and returns to the true self,
it will be clear that the ten thousand dharmas are
without self.

Firewood turns into ash and does not turn into firewood
again.
But do not suppose that the ash is after and the firewood
is before.
We must realize that firewood is in the state of being

firewood and has its before and after. Yet having this
before and after, it is independent of them.
Ash is in the state of being ash and has its before and
after.
Just as firewood does not become firewood again after it
is ash, so after one's death one does not return to life
again.
Thus, that life does not become death is a confirmed
teaching of the buddha-dharma; for this reason, life is
called the non-born.
That death does not become life is a confirmed teaching
of the buddha-dharma; therefore, death is called the
non-extinguished.
Life is a period of itself.
Death is a period of itself.
For example, they are like winter and spring.
We do not think that winter becomes spring, nor do we
say that spring becomes summer.

Gaining enlightenment is like the moon reflecting in the
water.
The moon does not get wet, nor is the water disturbed.
Although its light is extensive and great, the moon is
reflected even in a puddle an inch across.
The whole moon and the whole sky are reflected in a
dew-drop in the grass, in one drop of water.
Enlightenment does not disturb the person, just as the
moon does not disturb the water.

A person does not hinder enlightenment, just as a
dewdrop does not hinder the moon in the sky.
The depth of the drop is the height of the moon.
As for the duration of the reflection, you should examine
the water's vastness or smallness,
And you should discern the brightness or dimness of the
heavenly moon.

When the truth does not fill our body and mind, we
think that we have enough.
When the truth fills our body and mind, we realize that
something is missing.

For example, when we view the four directions from a boat on the ocean where no land is in sight, we see only a circle and nothing else.

No other aspects are apparent.

However, this ocean is neither round nor square, and its qualities are infinite in variety. It is like a palace. It is like a jewel. It just seems circular as far as our eyes can reach at the time.

The ten thousand dharmas are likewise like this.

Although ordinary life and enlightened life assume many aspects, we only recognize and understand through practice what the penetrating power of our vision can reach.

In order to appreciate the ten thousand dharmas, we should know that although they may look round or square, the other qualities of oceans and mountains are infinite in variety; furthermore, other universes lie in all quarters.

It is so not only around ourselves but also right here, and in a single drop of water.

When a fish swims in the ocean, there is no limit to the water, no matter how far it swims.

When a bird flies in the sky, there is no limit to the air, no matter how far it flies.

However, no fish or bird has ever left its element since the beginning.

When the need is large, it is used largely.

When the need is small, it is used in a small way.

Thus, no creature ever comes short of its own completeness.

Wherever it stands, it does not fail to cover the ground.

If a bird leaves the air, it will die at once.

If a fish leaves the water, it will die at once.

Know, then, that water is life.

Know that air is life.

Life is the bird and life is the fish.

Beyond these, there are further implications and ramifications.

In this way, there are practice and enlightenment, mortality and immortality.

Now if a bird or a fish tries to reach the limit of its
element before moving in it, this bird or this fish will
not find its way or its place.

Attaining this place, one's daily life is the realization of
ultimate reality [*genjokoan*]. Attaining this way, one's
daily life is the realization of ultimate reality
[*genjokoan*].

Since this place and this way are neither large nor small,
neither self nor other, neither existing previously nor
just arising now, they therefore exist thus.

Thus, if one practices and realizes the buddha way, when
one gains one dharma, one penetrates one dharma;
when one encounters one action, one practices one
action.

Since the place is here and the way leads everywhere, the
reason the limits of the knowable are unknowable is
simply that our knowledge arises with, and practices
with, the absolute perfection of the buddha-dharma.

Do not practice thinking that realization must become
the object of one's knowledge and vision and be
grasped conceptually.

Even though the attainment of realization is immediately
manifest, its intimate nature is not necessarily realized.
Some may realize it and some may not.

Priest Pao-ch'e of Ma-ku shan was fanning himself. A
monk approached and asked, "Sir, the nature of the wind
is permanent, and there is no place it does not reach. Why,
then, must you still fan yourself?"

"Although you understand that the nature of wind is
permanent," the master replied, "you do not understand
the meaning of its reaching everywhere."

"What is the meaning of its reaching everywhere?"
asked the monk.

The master just fanned himself. The monk bowed with
deep respect.

This is the enlightened experience of buddha-dharma
and the vital way of its correct transmission. Those who
say we should not use a fan because wind is permanent,

and so we should know the existence of wind without using a fan, know neither permanency nor the nature of wind.

Because the nature of wind is eternally present, the wind of Buddhism actualizes the gold of the earth and ripens the cheese of the long river.

THE ZEN OXHERDING PICTURES

KAKUAN

TRANSLATED BY NYOGEN SENZAKI

AND PAUL REPS

THE ENLIGHTENMENT FOR WHICH ZEN AIMS, for which Zen exists, comes of itself. As consciousness, one moment it does not exist, the next it does. But physically we walk in the element of time even as we walk in mud, dragging our feet and our true nature.

So even Zen must compromise and recognize progressive steps of awareness leading closer to the very instant of enlightenment.

That is what this chapter is about. In the twelfth century the Chinese master Kakuan drew the pictures of the ten bulls, basing them on earlier Taoist bulls, and wrote the comments in prose and verse translated here. His version was pure Zen, going deeper than earlier versions, which had ended with the nothingness of the eighth picture. It has been a constant source of inspiration to students ever since, and many illustrations of Kakuan's bulls have been made through the centuries.

The illustrations reproduced here are modern versions by the noted Kyoto woodblock artist Tomikichiro Tokuriki. His ox-herding pictures are as delightfully direct and timelessly meaningful as Kakuan's original pictures must have been.

I. The Search for the Bull

In the pasture of this world, I endlessly push aside the tall
  grasses in search of the bull.
Following unnamed rivers, lost upon the interpenetrating
  paths of distant mountains,
My strength failing and my vitality exhausted, I cannot find
  the bull.
I only hear the locusts chirring through the forest at night.

COMMENT: The bull never has been lost. What need is there
to search? Only because of separation from my true nature, I
fail to find him. In the confusion of the senses I lose even his
tracks. Far from home, I see many crossroads, but which way is
the right one I know not. Greed and fear, good and bad, entan-
gle me.

2. Discovering the Footprints

Along the riverbank under the trees, I discover footprints!
Even under the fragrant grass I see his prints.
Deep in remote mountains they are found.
These traces no more can be hidden than one's nose, looking
heavenward.

COMMENT: Understanding the teaching, I see the footprints
of the bull. Then I learn that, just as many utensils are made
from one metal, so too are myriad entities made of the fabric
of self. Unless I discriminate, how will I perceive the true from
the untrue? Not yet having entered the gate, nevertheless I have
discerned the path.

3. Perceiving the Bull

I hear the song of the nightingale.
The sun is warm, the wind is mild, willows are green along
   the shore,
Here no bull can hide!
What artist can draw that massive head, those majestic
   horns?

COMMENT: When one hears the voice, one can sense its source. As soon as the six senses merge, the gate is entered. Wherever one enters one sees the head of the bull! This unity is like salt in water, like color in dyestuff. The slightest thing is not apart from self.

4. Catching the Bull

I seize him with a terrific struggle.
His great will and power are inexhaustible.
He charges to the high plateau far above the cloud-mists,
Or in an impenetrable ravine he stands.

COMMENT: He dwelt in the forest a long time, but I caught
him today! Infatuation for scenery interferes with his direction.
Longing for sweeter grass, he wanders away. His mind still is
stubborn and unbridled. If I wish him to submit, I must raise
my whip.

5. *Taming the Bull*

The whip and rope are necessary,
Else he might stray off down some dusty road.
Being well trained, he becomes naturally gentle.
Then, unfettered, he obeys his master.

COMMENT: When one thought arises, another thought follows. When the first thought springs from enlightenment, all subsequent thoughts are true. Through delusion, one makes everything untrue. Delusion is not caused by objectivity; it is the result of subjectivity. Hold the nose-ring tight and do not allow even a doubt.

6. Riding the Bull Home

Mounting the bull, slowly I return homeward.
The voice of my flute intones through the evening.
Measuring with hand-beats the pulsating harmony, I direct
*   the endless rhythm.*
Whoever hears this melody will join me.

COMMENT: This struggle is over; gain and loss are assimilated. I sing the song of the village woodsman, and play the
tunes of the children. Astride the bull, I observe the clouds
above. Onward I go, no matter who may wish to call me back.

7. The Bull Transcended

Astride the bull, I reach home.
I am serene. The bull too can rest.
The dawn has come. In blissful repose,
Within my thatched dwelling I have abandoned the whip
 and rope.

COMMENT: All is one law, not two. We only make the bull a temporary subject. It is as the relation of rabbit and trap, of fish and net. It is as gold and dross, or the moon emerging from a cloud. One path of clear light travels on throughout endless time.

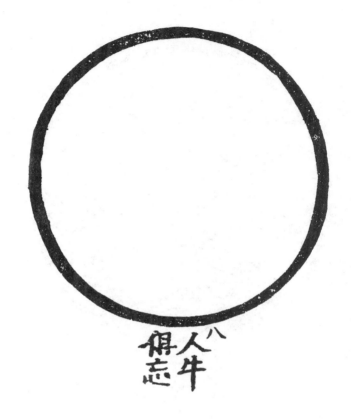

8. Both Bull and Self Transcended

Whip, rope, person, and bull—all merge in No-Thing.
This heaven is so vast no message can stain it.
How may a snowflake exist in a raging fire?
Here are the footprints of the patriarchs.

COMMENT: Mediocrity is gone. Mind is clear of limitation. I seek no state of enlightenment. Neither do I remain where no enlightenment exists. Since I linger in neither condition, eyes cannot see me. If hundreds of birds strew my path with flowers, such praise would be meaningless.

9. Reaching the Source

Too many steps have been taken returning to the root and
the source.
Better to have been blind and deaf from the beginning!
Dwelling in one's true abode, unconcerned with that
without—
The river flows tranquilly on and the flowers are red.

COMMENT: From the beginning, truth is clear. Poised in silence, I observe the forms of integration and disintegration.
One who is not attached to "form" need not be "reformed."
The water *is* emerald, the mountain *is* indigo, and I see that
which *is* creating and that which *is* destroying.

10. *In the World*

Barefooted and naked of breast, I mingle with the people of
the world.
My clothes are ragged and dust-laden, and I am ever
blissful.
I use no magic to extend my life;
Now, before me, the dead trees become alive.

COMMENT: Inside my gate, a thousand sages do not know
me. The beauty of my garden is invisible. Why should one
search for the footprints of the patriarchs? I go to the market
place with my wine bottle and return home with my staff. I visit
the wineshop and the market, and everyone I look upon becomes enlightened.

TAKUAN SOHO

TAKUAN SOHO (1573–1645) WAS AN important master of the Rinzai (Chin. Lin-chi) school of Zen. The name Takuan, which he gave himself, means "pickled radish." He was not only a meditation master but applied his Zen also to poetry, painting, *shodo* (the way of writing), and *chado* (the way of tea). What matters most for our present selection, an excerpt from *The Mysterious Record of Immovable Wisdom,* is that he was the master of the famous swordsman Yagyu Munenori. Here Takuan explains to the swordsman what he means when he says that "the mind that does not stop at all is called immovable wisdom."

The Affliction of Abiding in Ignorance

THE TERM *IGNORANCE* MEANS THE ABSENCE OF ENLIGHTENment. Which is to say, delusion.

Abiding place means the place where the mind stops.

In the practice of Buddhism, there are said to be fifty-two stages, and within these fifty-two, the place where the mind stops at one thing is called the *abiding place*. Abiding signifies stopping, and *stopping* means the mind is being detained by some matter, which may be any matter at all.

To speak in terms of your own martial art, when you first notice the sword that is moving to strike you, if you think of meeting that sword just as it is, your mind will stop at the sword in just that position, your own movements will be undone, and you will be cut down by your opponent. This is what *stopping* means.

Although you see the sword that moves to strike you, if your mind is not detained by it and you meet the rhythm of the advancing sword; if you do not think of striking your opponent and no thoughts or judgments remain; if the instant you see the swinging sword your mind is not the least bit detained and you move straight in and wrench the sword away from him; the sword that was going to cut you down will become your own, and, contrarily, will be the sword that cuts down your opponent.

In Zen this is called "grabbing the spear and, contrariwise, piercing the man who had come to pierce you." The spear is a weapon. The heart of this is that the sword you wrest from your adversary becomes the sword that cuts him down. This is what you, in your style, call "No-Sword."

Whether by the strike of the enemy or your own thrust, whether by the man who strikes or the sword that strikes, whether by position or rhythm, if your mind is diverted in any way, your actions will falter, and this can mean that you will be cut down.

If you place yourself before your opponent, your mind will be taken by him. You should not place your mind within yourself. Bracing the mind in the body is something done only at the inception of training, when one is a beginner.

The mind can be taken by the sword. If you put your mind in the rhythm of the contest, your mind can be taken by that as well. If you place your mind in your own sword, your mind can be taken by your own sword. Your mind stopping at any of these places, you become an empty shell. You surely recall such situations yourself. They can be said to apply to Buddhism.

In Buddhism, we call this stopping of the mind *delusion*.
Thus we say, "The affliction of abiding in ignorance."

The Immovable Wisdom of All Buddhas

Immovable means unmoving.

Wisdom means the wisdom of intelligence.

Although wisdom is called immovable, this does not signify
any insentient thing, like wood or stone. It moves as the mind
is wont to move: forward or back, to the left, to the right, in
the ten directions and to the eight points; and the mind that
does not stop at all is called *immovable wisdom*.

Fudō Myōō grasps a sword in his right hand and holds a
rope in his left hand.[1] He bares his teeth and his eyes flash with
anger. His form stands firmly, ready to defeat the evil spirits
that would obstruct the Buddhist Law. This is not hidden in
any country anywhere. His form is made in the shape of a pro-
tector of Buddhism, while his embodiment is that of immovable wisdom. This is what is shown to living things.

Seeing this form, the ordinary man becomes afraid and has
no thoughts of becoming an enemy of Buddhism. The man
who is close to enlightenment understands that this manifests
immovable wisdom and clears away all delusion. For the man
who can make his immovable wisdom apparent and who is able
to physically practice this mental dharma as well as Fudō Myōō,
the evil spirits will no longer proliferate. This is the purpose of
Fudō Myōō's tidings.

What is called Fudō Myōō is said to be one's unmoving mind
and an unvacillating body. *Unvacillating* means not being detained by anything.

Glancing at something and not stopping the mind is called
immovable. This is because when the mind stops at something,
as the breast is filled with various judgments, there are various
movements within it. When its movements cease, the stopping
mind moves, but does not move at all.

If ten men, each with a sword, come at you with swords

---

[1] Fudō Myōō is literally "Immovable Enlightened King" (Skt. Achala). One
of the Five Wisdom Deities, in Zen Buddhism he is considered to manifest
the true nature of all living things.

slashing, if you parry each sword without stopping the mind at each action, and go from one to the next, you will not be lacking in a proper action for every one of the ten.

Although the mind act ten times against ten men, if it does not halt at even one of them and you react to one after another, will proper action be lacking?

But if the mind stops before one of these men, though you parry his striking sword, when the next man comes, the right action will have slipped away.

Considering that the Thousand-Armed Kannon has one thousand arms on its one body, if the mind stops at the one holding a bow, the other nine hundred and ninety-nine will be useless.[2] It is because the mind is not detained at one place that all the arms are useful.

As for Kannon, to what purpose would it have a thousand arms attached to one body? This form is made with the intent of pointing out to men that if their immovable wisdom is let go, even if a body have a thousand arms, every one will be of use.

When facing a single tree, if you look at a single one of its red leaves, you will not see all the others. When the eye is not set on any one leaf, and you face the tree with nothing at all in mind, any number of leaves are visible to the eye without limit. But if a single leaf holds the eye, it will be as if the remaining leaves were not there.

One who has understood this is no different from the Kannon with a thousand arms and a thousand eyes.

The ordinary man simply believes that it is blessed because of its thousand arms and its thousand eyes. The man of half-baked wisdom, wondering how anybody could have a thousand eyes, calls it a lie and gives in to slander. But if now one understands a little better, he will have a respectful belief based on principle and will not need the simple faith of the ordinary man or the slander of the other, and he will understand that Buddhism, with this one thing, manifests its principle well.

[2] Kannon, a bodhisattva, the Buddhist Goddess of Mercy (Skt. Avalokiteshvara). Originally depicted as a male, in one of the common forms of representation she has a thousand eyes and a thousand hands.

Zen Mind, Beginner's Mind

SHUNRYU SUZUKI

SHUNRYU SUZUKI (1905–1971) WAS a Japanese Zen master of the Soto school who moved to the United States in 1958. He founded Zen Center in San Francisco and Zen Mountain Center in Tassajara, California, the first Soto monastery in the West. Suzuki Roshi had a quality of impeccable, spotless awareness. Any reader, whether familiar with Zen or not, can gain a luminous experience of this spotless awareness simply by reading a few pages of his talks to his students. The selection given here is on the right practice of *zazen,* or sitting meditation. It is a direct and lucid journey to the heart of actual practice, which is the beginning and conclusion of Zen.

Beginner's Mind

PEOPLE SAY THAT PRACTICING ZEN IS DIFFICULT, BUT THERE IS a misunderstanding as to why. It is not difficult because it is hard to sit in the cross-legged position, or to attain enlightenment. It is difficult because it is hard to keep our mind pure and our practice pure in its fundamental sense. The Zen school developed in many ways after it was established in China, but at the same time, it became more and more impure. But I do not want to talk about Chinese Zen or the history of Zen. I am interested in helping you keep your practice from becoming impure.

In Japan we have the phrase *shoshin,* which means "beginner's mind." The goal of practice is always to keep our beginner's mind. Suppose you recite the *Prajna Paramita Sutra* only once. It might be a very good recitation. But what would happen to you if you recited it twice, three times, four times, or more? You might easily lose your original attitude towards it. The same thing will happen in your other Zen practices. For a while you will keep your beginner's mind, but if you continue to practice one, two, three years or more, although you may improve some, you are liable to lose the limitless meaning of original mind.

For Zen students the most important thing is not to be dualistic. Our "original mind" includes everything within itself. It is always rich and sufficient within itself. You should not lose your self-sufficient state of mind. This does not mean a closed mind, but actually an empty mind and a ready mind. If your mind is empty, it is always ready for anything; it is open to everything. In the beginner's mind there are many possibilities; in the expert's mind there are few.

If you discriminate too much, you limit yourself. If you are too demanding or too greedy, your mind is not rich and self-sufficient. If we lose our original self-sufficient mind, we will lose all precepts. When your mind becomes demanding, when you long for something, you will end up violating your own precepts: not to tell lies, not to steal, not to kill, not to be immoral, and so forth. If you keep your original mind, the precepts will keep themselves.

In the beginner's mind there is no thought, "I have attained something." All self-centered thoughts limit our vast mind. When we have no thought of achievement, no thought of self, we are true beginners. Then we can really learn something. The beginner's mind is the mind of compassion. When our mind is compassionate, it is boundless. Dogen-zenji, the founder of our school, always emphasized how important it is to resume our boundless original mind. Then we are always true to ourselves, in sympathy with all beings, and can actually practice.

So the most difficult thing is always to keep your beginner's mind. There is no need to have a deep understanding of Zen. Even though you read much Zen literature, you must read each sentence with a fresh mind. You should not say, "I know what Zen is," or "I have attained enlightenment." This is also the real secret of the arts: always be a beginner. Be very very careful about this point. If you start to practice zazen, you will begin to appreciate your beginner's mind. It is the secret of Zen practice.

Posture

Now I would like to talk about our zazen posture. When you sit in the full lotus position, your left foot is on your right thigh, and your right foot is on your left thigh. When we cross our legs like this, even though we have a right leg and a left leg, they have become one. The position expresses the oneness of duality: not two, and not one. This is the most important teaching: not two, and not one. Our body and mind are not two and not one. If you think your body and mind are two, that is wrong; if you think that they are one, that is also wrong. Our body and mind are both two *and* one. We usually think that if something is not one, it is more than one; if it is not singular, it is plural. But in actual experience, our life is not only plural, but also singular. Each one of us is both dependent and independent.

After some years we will die. If we just think that it is the end of our life, this will be the wrong understanding. But, on the other hand, if we think that we do not die, this is also wrong. We die, and we do not die. This is the right understanding. Some people may say that our mind or soul exists forever, and it is only our physical body which dies. But this is not exactly right, because both mind and body have their end. But at the same time it is also true that they exist externally. And even though we say mind and body, they are actually two sides of one coin. This is the right understanding. So when we take this posture it symbolizes this truth. When I have the left foot on the right side of my body, and the right foot on the left side of my body, I do not know which is which. So either may be the left or the right side.

The most important thing in taking the zazen posture is to keep your spine straight. Your ears and your shoulders should be on one line. Relax your shoulders, and push up towards the ceiling with the back of your head. And you should pull your chin in. When your chin is tilted up, you have no strength in your posture; you are probably dreaming. Also to gain strength in your posture, press your diaphragm down towards your *hara,* or lower abdomen. This will help you maintain your physical and mental balance. When you try to keep this posture, at first you may find some difficulty breathing naturally, but when you get accustomed to it you will be able to breathe naturally and deeply.

Your hands should form the "cosmic mudra." If you put your left hand on top of your right, middle joints of your middle fingers together, and touch your thumbs lightly together (as if you held a piece of paper between them), your hands will make a beautiful oval. You should keep this universal mudra with great care, as if you were holding something very precious in your hand. Your hands should be held against your body, with your thumbs at about the height of your navel. Hold your arms freely and easily, and slightly away from your body, as if you held an egg under each arm without breaking it.

You should not be tilted sideways, backwards, or forwards. You should be sitting straight up as if you were supporting the sky with your head. This is not just form or breathing. It expresses the key point of Buddhism. It is a perfect expression of your Buddha nature. If you want true understanding of Buddhism, you should practice this way. These forms are not a means of obtaining the right state of mind. To take this posture itself is the purpose of our practice. When you have this posture, you have the right state of mind, so there is no need to try to attain some special state. When you try to attain something, your mind starts to wander about somewhere else. When you do not try to attain anything, you have your own body and mind right here. A Zen master would say, "Kill the Buddha!" Kill the Buddha if the Buddha exists somewhere else. Kill the Buddha, because you should resume your own Buddha nature.

Doing something is expressing our own nature. We do not exist for the sake of something else. We exist for the sake of ourselves. This is the fundamental teaching expressed in the forms we observe. Just as for sitting, when we stand in the zendo we have some rules. But the purpose of these rules is not to make everyone the same, but to allow each to express his own self most freely. For instance, each one of us has his own way of standing, so our standing posture is based on the proportions of our own bodies. When you stand, your heels should be as far apart as the width of your own fist, your big toes in line with the centers of your breasts. As in zazen, put some strength in your abdomen. Here also your hands should express your self. Hold your left hand against your chest with fingers encircling your thumb, and put your right hand over it. Holding your thumb pointing downward, and your forearms parallel to the floor, you feel as if you have some round pillar in your grasp—a big round temple pillar—so you cannot be slumped or tilted to the side.

The most important point is to own your own physical body. If you slump, you will lose your self. Your mind will be wandering about somewhere else; you will not be in your body. This is not the way. We must exist right here, right now! This is the key point. You must have your own body and mind. Everything should exist in the right place, in the right way. Then there is no problem. If the microphone I use when I speak exists somewhere else, it will not serve its purpose. When we have our body and mind in order, everything else will exist in the right place, in the right way.

But usually, without being aware of it, we try to change something other than ourselves, we try to order things outside us. But it is impossible to organize things if you yourself are not in order. When you do things in the right way, at the right time, everything else will be organized. You are the "boss." When the boss is sleeping, everyone is sleeping. When the boss does something right, everyone will do everything right, and at the right time. That is the secret of Buddhism.

So try always to keep the right posture, not only when you practice zazen, but in all your activities. Take the right posture when you are driving your car, and when you are reading. If you read in a slumped position, you cannot stay awake long. Try. You will discover how important it is to keep the right posture. This is the true teaching. The teaching which is written on paper is not the true teaching. Written teaching is a kind of food for your brain. Of course it is necessary to take some food for your brain, but it is more important to be yourself by practicing the right way of life.

That is why Buddha could not accept the religions existing at his time. He studied many religions, but he was not satisfied with their practices. He could not find the answer in asceticism or in philosophies. He was not interested in some metaphysical existence, but in his own body and mind, here and now. And when he found himself, he found that everything that exists has Buddha nature. That was his enlightenment. Enlightenment is not some good feeling or some particular state of mind. The state of mind that exists when you sit in the right posture is, itself, enlightenment. If you cannot be satisfied with the state of mind you have in zazen, it means your mind is still wandering about. Our body and mind should not be wobbling or wandering about. In this posture there is no need to talk about the right state of mind. You already have it. This is the conclusion of Buddhism.

Breathing

When we practice zazen our mind always follows our breathing. When we inhale, the air comes into the inner world. When we exhale, the air goes out to the outer world. The inner world is limitless, and the outer world is also limitless. We say "inner world" or "outer world," but actually there is just one whole world. In this limitless world, our throat is like a swinging door. The air comes in and goes out like someone passing through a swinging door. If you think, "I breathe," the "I" is extra. There is no you to say "I." What we call "I" is just a swinging door which moves when we inhale and when we exhale. It just moves; that is all. When your mind is pure and calm enough to follow this movement, there is nothing: no "I," no world, no mind nor body; just a swinging door.

So when we practice zazen, all that exists is the movement of the breathing, but we are aware of this movement. You should not be absent-minded. But to be aware of the movement does not mean to be aware of your small self, but rather of your universal nature, or Buddha nature. This kind of awareness is very important, because we are usually so one-sided. Our usual understanding of life is dualistic: you and I, this and that, good and bad. But actually these discriminations are themselves the awareness of the universal existence. "You" means to be aware of the universe in the form of you, and "I" means to be aware of it in the form of I. You and I are just swinging doors. This kind of understanding is necessary. This should not even be called understanding; it is actually the true experience of life through Zen practice.

So when you practice zazen, there is no idea of time or space. You may say, "We started sitting at a quarter to six in this room." Thus you have some idea of time (a quarter to six), and some idea of space (in this room). Actually what you are doing, however, is just sitting and being aware of the universal activity. That is all. This moment the swinging door is opening in one direction, and the next moment the swinging door will be opening in the opposite direction. Moment after moment each one of us repeats this activity. Here there is no idea of time or space. Time and space are one. You may say, "I must do something this afternoon," but actually there is no "this afternoon." We do things one after the other. That is all. There is no such time as "this afternoon" or "one o'clock" or "two o'clock." At one o'clock you will eat your lunch. To eat lunch is itself one o'clock. You will be somewhere, but that place cannot be separated from one o'clock. For someone who actually appreciates our life, they are the same. But when we become tired of our life we may say, "I shouldn't have come to this place. It may have been much better to have gone to some other place for lunch. This place is not so good." In your mind you create an idea of place separate from an actual time.

Or you may say, "This is bad, so I should not do this." Actually, when you say, "I should not do this," you are doing not-doing in that moment. So there is no choice for you. When you separate the idea of time and space, you feel as if you have some choice, but actually, you have to do something, or you have to do not-doing. Not-to-do something is doing something. Good and bad are only in your mind. So we should not say, "This is good," or "This is bad." Instead of saying bad, you should say, "not-to-do"! If you think, "This is bad," it will create some confusion for you. So in the realm of pure religion there is no confusion of time and space, or good or bad. All that we should

233

do is just do something as it comes. *Do* something! Whatever it is, we should do it, even if it is not-doing something. We should live in this moment. So when we sit we concentrate on our breathing, and we become a swinging door, and we do something we should do, something we must do. This is Zen practice. In this practice there is no confusion. If you establish this kind of life you have no confusion whatsoever.

Tozan, a famous Zen master, said, "The blue mountain is the father of the white cloud. The white cloud is the son of the blue mountain. All day long they depend on each other, without being dependent on each other. The white cloud is always the white cloud. The blue mountain is always the blue mountain." This is a pure, clear interpretation of life. There may be many things like the white cloud and blue mountain: man and woman, teacher and disciple. They depend on each other. But the white cloud should not be bothered by the blue mountain. The blue mountain should not be bothered by the white cloud. They are quite independent, but yet dependent. This is how we live, and how we practice zazen.

When we become truly ourselves, we just become a swinging door, and we are purely independent of, and at the same time, dependent upon everything. Without air, we cannot breathe. Each one of us is in the midst of myriads of worlds. We are in the center of the world always, moment after moment. So we are completely dependent and independent. If you have this kind of experience, this kind of existence, you have absolute independence; you will not be bothered by anything. So when you practice zazen, your mind should be concentrated on your breathing. This kind of activity is the fundamental activity of the universal being. Without this experience, this practice, it is impossible to attain absolute freedom.

Control

To live in the realm of Buddha nature means to die as a small being, moment after moment. When we lose our balance we die, but at the same time we also develop ourselves, we grow. Whatever we see is changing, losing its balance. The reason everything looks beautiful is because it is out of balance, but its background is always in perfect harmony. This is how every-thing exists in the realm of Buddha nature, losing its balance against a background of perfect balance. So if you see things without realizing the background of Buddha nature, everything appears to be in the form of suffering. But if you understand the background of existence, you realize that suffering itself is how we live, and how we extend our life. So in Zen sometimes we emphasize the imbalance or disorder of life.

Nowadays traditional Japanese painting has become pretty formal and lifeless. That is why modern art has developed. An-cient painters used to practice putting dots on paper in artistic disorder. This is rather difficult. Even though you try to do it, usually what you do is arranged in some order. You think you can control it, but you cannot; it is almost impossible to ar-range your dots out of order. It is the same with taking care of your everyday life. Even though you try to put people under some control, it is impossible. You cannot do it. The best way to control people is to encourage them to be mischievous. Then they will be in control in its wider sense. To give your sheep or cow a large, spacious meadow is the way to control him. So it is with people: first let them do what they want, and watch them. This is the best policy. To ignore them is not good; that is the worst policy. The second worst is trying to control them. The best one is to watch them, just to watch them, without trying to control them.

The same way works for you yourself as well. If you want to obtain perfect calmness in your zazen, you should not be both-ered by the various images you find in your mind. Let them come, and let them go. Then they will be under control. But this policy is not so easy. It sounds easy, but it requires some special effort. How to make this kind of effort is the secret of practice. Suppose you are sitting under some extraordinary cir-cumstances. If you try to calm your mind you will be unable to sit, and if you try not to be disturbed, your effort will not be the right effort. The only effort that will help you is to count your breathing, or to concentrate on your inhaling and exhal-ing. We say concentration, but to concentrate your mind on something is not the true purpose of Zen. The true purpose is to see things as they are, to observe things as they are, and to let everything go as it goes. This is to put everything under con-trol in its widest sense. Zen practice is to open up our small mind. So concentrating is just an aid to help you realize "big mind," or the mind that is everything. If you want to discover the true meaning of Zen in your everyday life, you have to understand the meaning of keeping your mind on your breathing and your body in the right posture in zazen. You should follow the rules of practice and your study should become more subtle and careful. Only in this way can you experience the vital freedom of Zen.

Dogen-zenji said, "Time goes from present to past." This is absurd, but in our practice sometimes it is true. Instead of time progressing from past to present, it goes backwards from present to past. Yoshitsune was a famous warrior who lived in medieval Japan. Because of the situation of the country at that time, he was sent to the northern provinces, where he was killed. Before he left he bade farewell to his wife, and soon after she wrote in a poem, "Just as you unreel the thread from a spool, I want the past to become present." When she said this, actually she made past time present. In her mind the past became alive and *was* the present. So as Dogen said, "Time goes from present to past." This is not true in our logical mind, but it is in the actual experience of making past time present. There we have poetry, and there we have human life.

When we experience this kind of truth it means we have found the true meaning of time. Time constantly goes from past to present and from present to future. This is true, but it is also true that time goes from future to present and from present to past. A Zen master once said, "To go eastward one mile is to go westward one mile." This is vital freedom. We should acquire this kind of perfect freedom.

But perfect freedom is not found without some rules. People, especially young people, think that freedom is to do just what they want, that in Zen there is no need for rules. But it is absolutely necessary for us to have some rules. But this does not mean always to be under control. As long as you have rules, you have a chance for freedom. To try to obtain freedom without being aware of the rules means nothing. It is to acquire this perfect freedom that we practice Zen.

Mind Waves

When you are practicing zazen, do not try to stop your thinking. Let it stop by itself. If something comes into your mind, let it come in, and let it go out. It will not stay long. When you try to stop your thinking, it means you are bothered by it. Do not be bothered by anything. It appears as if something comes from outside your mind, but actually it is only the waves of your mind, and if you are not bothered by the waves, gradually they will become calmer and calmer. In five or at most ten minutes, your mind will be completely serene and calm. At that time your breathing will become quite slow, while your pulse will become a little faster.

It will take quite a long time before you find your calm, serene mind in your practice. Many sensations come, many thoughts or images arise, but they are just waves of your own mind. Nothing comes from outside your mind. Usually we think of our mind as receiving impressions and experiences from outside, but that is not a true understanding of our mind. The true understanding is that the mind includes everything; when you think something comes from outside it means only that something appears in your mind. Nothing outside yourself can cause any trouble. You yourself make the waves in your mind. If you leave your mind as it is, it will become calm. This mind is called big mind.

If your mind is related to something outside itself, that mind is a small mind, a limited mind. If your mind is not related to anything else, then there is no dualistic understanding in the activity of your mind. You understand activity as just waves of your mind. Big mind experiences everything within itself. Do you understand the difference between the two minds: the mind which includes everything, and the mind which is related to something? Actually they are the same thing, but the understanding is different, and your attitude towards your life will be different according to which understanding you have.

That everything is included within your mind is the essence of mind. To experience this is to have religious feeling. Even though waves arise, the essence of mind is pure; it is just like clear water with a few waves. Actually water always has waves. Waves are the practice of the water. To speak of waves apart from water or water apart from waves is a delusion. Water and waves are one. Big mind and small mind are one. When you understand your mind in this way, you have some security in your feeling. As your mind does not expect anything from outside, it is always filled. A mind with waves in it is not a disturbed mind, but actually an amplified one. Whatever you experience is an expression of big mind.

The activity of big mind is to amplify itself through various experiences. In one sense our experiences coming one by one are always fresh and new, but in another sense they are nothing but a continuous or repeated unfolding of the one big mind. For instance, if you have something good for breakfast, you will say, "This is good." "Good" is supplied as something experienced some time long ago, even though you may not remember when. With big mind we accept each of our experiences as if recognizing the face we see in a mirror as our own. For us there is no fear of losing this mind. There is nowhere to come or to go; there is no fear of death, no suffering from old age or sickness. Because we enjoy all aspects of life as an unfolding of big mind, we do not care for any excessive joy. So we have imperturbable composure, and it is with this imperturbable composure of big mind that we practice zazen.

Mind Weeds

When the alarm rings early in the morning, and you get up, I think you do not feel so good. It is not easy to go and sit, and even after you arrive at the zendo and begin zazen you have to encourage yourself to sit well. These are just waves of your mind. In pure zazen there should not be any waves in your mind. While you are sitting these waves will become smaller and smaller, and your effort will change into some subtle feeling.

We say, "Pulling out the weeds we give nourishment to the plant." We pull the weeds and bury them near the plant to give it nourishment. So even though you have some difficulty in your practice, even though you have some waves while you are sitting, those waves themselves will help you. So you should not be bothered by your mind. You should rather be grateful for the weeds, because eventually they will enrich your practice. If you have some experience of how the weeds in your mind change into mental nourishment, your practice will make remarkable progress. You will feel the progress. You will feel how they change into self-nourishment. Of course it is not so difficult to give some philosophical or psychological interpretation of our practice, but that is not enough. We must have the actual experience of how our weeds change into nourishment.

Strictly speaking, any effort we make is not good for our practice because it creates waves in our mind. It is impossible, however, to attain absolute calmness of our mind without any effort. We must make some effort, but we must forget ourselves in the effort we make. In this realm there is no subjectivity or objectivity. Our mind is just calm, without even any awareness. In this unawareness, every effort and every idea and thought will vanish. So it is necessary for us to encourage ourselves and to make an effort up to the last moment, when all effort disappears. You should keep your mind on your breathing until you are not aware of your breathing.

We should try to continue our effort forever, but we should not expect to reach some stage when we will forget all about it. We should just try to keep our mind on our breathing. That is our actual practice. That effort will be refined more and more while you are sitting. At first the effort you make is quite rough and impure, but by the power of practice the effort will become purer and purer. When your effort becomes pure, your body and mind become pure. This is the way we practice Zen. Once you understand your innate power to purify ourselves and our surroundings, you can act properly, and you will learn from those around you, and you will become friendly with others. This is the merit of Zen practice. But the way of practice is just to be concentrated on your breathing with the right posture and with great, pure effort. This is how we practice Zen.

24 *Emptiness*

DAININ KATAGIRI

DAININ KATAGIRI (1928–1990) came to the United States from Japan in 1963 and became the first abbot of the Minnesota Zen Meditation Center in Minneapolis in 1972. The following excerpt from one of his talks to his American students provides the needed antidote for any tendency to regard the Buddhist teaching of emptiness nihilistically ("Since everything is an empty illusion, why should I make any effort?") or eternalistically ("Everything I do is a monument to good or evil that will change things forever"). Beyond that, it is the antidote to thinking that the Buddhist notion of emptiness, however accurate, is just abstract philosophy that doesn't really apply to life. And beyond all sense of ills and cures, this talk on emptiness given by Katagiri Roshi communicates his flawless humility and penetrating vision of things as they are. There is never any doubt that he is talking about life as it really is.

THE BUDDHIST TEACHING OF EMPTINESS IS QUITE DIFFICULT TO understand, but this teaching is very important for us. Emptiness is that which enables us to open our eyes to see directly what being is. If after careful consideration we decide to do something that we believe is the best way, from the beginning to the end we should do our best. We must respect our capability, our knowledge, without comparing ourselves with others, and then use our knowledge and capability and think about how to act. Very naturally a result will occur. We should take responsibility for the results of what we have done, but the final goal is that we shouldn't be obsessed with the result, whether good or evil or neutral. This is called emptiness. This is the most important meaning of emptiness.

When I became a monk I had no idea about the practical aspects of Buddhism or about life at the temple or about life as a Buddhist. My master told me very often that I was a person who was blessed with good fortune. I didn't understand exactly, but from my life at that time I could feel a little bit that I was fortunate. When the village people came to the temple and offered something to us, they didn't say, "This is a present for the teacher," they always said, "This is for Dainin Katagiri," for me.

My teacher, Daichō Hayashi Roshi, became a monk at the age of ten. He had practiced and studied very hard since his childhood under the guidance of a famous teacher of those days, at a monastery. Finally Hayashi Roshi became a very famous preacher, traveling all over Japan to preach about Buddhism to the Japanese people. And then he was given a wonderful, big temple in Nara, a very nice old city next to Kyoto.

Hayashi Roshi was very concerned about his teacher, who had been criticized and asked to leave his temple by the people he served, after he used money for his own personal needs that had been given to him to rebuild the temple after it had burned. My master found a small temple and made a place for his teacher there so he could take care of him. That is the temple of which I am now the abbot. By chance, at this same time, my teacher found his mother, whom he had not seen for many,

many years. He couldn't leave her alone, because she was very old, so he brought her to this temple too. After his teacher died he was very concerned about how to care for his mother, who was now alone at the small temple. He had to decide whether to take his mother to the big temple in Nara or whether he should go to the small temple and live with her. Finally he decided to leave the big temple and he moved to the small temple and lived with his mother. It was fortunate that he did, because that big temple in Nara burned up right after he left.

At that time Hayashi Roshi was a very famous teacher and many people wanted to be his disciple. He had had six disciples, but when I became a monk under him, he had no disciples left. Actually one person was left but he was in a mental hospital, and then several months later, that disciple died. So all his disciples were gone. Some of them died, some committed suicide, some ran away from the temple, one disciple fought with the master and was put in jail. And then only I was left, but unfortunately I also went away, and came to the United States. So he died at his temple by himself.

He continued to plant good seeds, helping people, preaching about Buddhism, but his life was not lucky. In a sense it was a little bit sad and pensive, but he enjoyed himself. He said to me, "You are really a person who is blessed with good fortune. Sometimes you take my good fortune. I am jealous." Of course he said this with a smile. I asked my teacher, if he believed that he was an unlucky person, why did he practice Buddhism? Even though he did good things still he was an unlucky person, so why did he continue to practice? He said, "The karmic retribution of good and evil occurs at three different periods in time. One is the retribution experienced in one's present life, second is retribution experienced in the life following one's death, and third is retribution experienced in subsequent lives." The karmic retribution will continue from past, present, future, life after life; someday, somewhere, it occurs. This is the understanding of karmic retribution in Buddhism. He also said to me, "Dōgen Zenji says that if you discontinue practicing the Buddha Way you lose merit." I was very impressed by his answer. This was why he wanted to continue to practice the Buddha Way.

There is the law of causation and we shouldn't ignore it. If we do something good, there will be a good result. If we do something wrong, a wrong result will occur. This is the law of causation. But, actually, even though there is the law of causation, human life doesn't seem to follow this law, because, just like my master, sometimes we do good things, but we are not lucky people, and the results are not good. So apparently there are two possible results following the law of causation: a good cause will bring a good result and a good cause will not bring a good result. We have to understand both. But we are always tossed away by these two ways. If we see our life according to "good cause will not bring a good result," it is easy to allow our life to become decadent and not to care about a sense of morality. If we see people who are still lucky even though they have done something wrong in the past, we become skeptical and are unable to trust anybody. This way of looking at life is pretty hard to take care of, so it is necessary that we understand the law of causation within the overall picture of human life. It tells us to "watch out," to be cautious about our actions.

According to the law of causation, karmic retribution or results occur in the present life, or in the life following this one or in subsequent lives. My master didn't like his unfortunate life. He would have liked to be more fortunate. But he was not, he was unlucky. He did something good every day, but the results were not often good. Was there something that compelled him to be an unfortunate person? Maybe it was the result of his previous life, or his lives before his previous life. We don't know. But if we look at our life with straightforward stability, we can do something good every day. Whatever happens, all we have to do is to continue to sow good seeds. For whom? For when? For you, for all sentient beings, for this time, or that time, for the life after the next life, for future generations, all we have to do is sow good seeds. This is the practice for us.

The important point is that we shouldn't be obsessed or bogged down with the results that we see, feel and experience. All results, whether good, evil or neutral, must be completely accepted. All we have to do is sow good seeds day after day, without leaving any trace of good seeds, without creating any attachment. This is why my teacher, until his death, just continued to practice and help people. This is the meaning of emptiness. We cannot attach to either idea about the law of causation, that a good cause will bring a good result, or that a good cause will not bring a good result, because everything is changing constantly. Within this situation the point is how we can live in peace and harmony for the good of people and of future generations, life after life.

Emptiness doesn't mean to destroy our life or to ignore responsibility or a sense of morality, or our knowledge or our capability. We should use our knowledge, our capability, our career, whatever we can offer, to do our best to accomplish what we have decided to do. Results come up very naturally if we do our best. They can be a good hint, showing us what to do next, so we should completely accept them. This is emptiness. This is how to live, how to handle our daily human life.

But in daily living there are lots of distractions, both criticism and admiration. These things are distractions for us because it's pretty easy to be obsessed with them. If people admire us we are completely infatuated with that admiration. If someone gives us criticism we are completely tossed away and it's pretty hard to spring back. Always there is something that we are obsessed with, and we are stuck there. This is not emptiness. It's very hard, but this is daily living, so we cannot escape from this. The question is, how should we handle the admiration, criticism and judgment, good or bad, right or wrong? In daily living it's pretty difficult to do our best in order to accomplish what we have decided to do, because between the time we have made the decision and the time when we start to act, many things come up. Sometimes, before we start to act we are already tossed away. So it's pretty hard. This is why we have to know the overall picture of human life, which is very tangled with complications.

For this, zazen is a very simple practice. Zazen, itself, teaches us how to handle our daily living. We should think carefully about zazen, using our body and mind, using our knowledge, our perceptions, our emotions, everything. Then, after deciding to do zazen, just do it. If we do our best to accomplish this practice, according to the suggestions and information that the ancestors have given us, immediately we can see the result. Good zazen, good concentration, delusions, the beautiful face of Avalokiteshvara, angry *arhats,* many things come up. These are results in the realm of zazen. But these results are something we have to accept completely, because they are coming from our decision, our life. We are changing day after day, so whatever results come up, we have to take responsibility for them and accept them. But our zazen must be empty, so don't be obsessed with these results. All we have to do is do our best to accomplish our zazen after thinking carefully about what zazen is and then deciding to do it. Immediately results come up whether we like it or not, but these things are just within us. Nothing is given by others outside of us. These things are given by ourselves. When we realize this, it's a little easier to concentrate, to sit down without being tossed away by these results. It's a very clear human life; we can see who we are, how we have handled our life in the past, how we are handling our life now, and how we will handle our life in the future. In zazen we can see anywhere. These pictures of life in zazen are good hints for how to deal with life moving toward the future. If we see something we have to correct, we should just correct it. If we correct it and then believe we are correct, immediately we are off balance again. Then we have to correct again. Always there is something happening. This is zazen. This is why zazen is exactly life. The important thing is to accept completely those things that happen. If you see something you have to correct, correct it. If there is nothing to do, just do nothing. Whatever happens, from beginning to end, just continue to do your best to do zazen. That's all you have to do. In zazen there is regulation of mind; regulation of mind is having no sign of becoming buddha. This is emptiness.

Whatever happens, don't create attachment. "Don't create attachment" doesn't mean to ignore attachment. There is already attachment. The important point is to understand how to use attachment without creating too much trouble. If you see trouble, confine the trouble to a minimum, understanding what attachment is. Consider carefully what to do, using your knowledge and capability. This is already attachment. Without attachment, how can we do anything? Attachment is desire. Broadly speaking, without desire, how can we survive in this world? Using our knowledge, we consider carefully what to do next. And then whatever we decide to do, let's just do it, do our best to accomplish it from the beginning to the end. That's all we have to do. Immediately, see the result and accept it. Just continue to sow good seeds from moment to moment. This is zazen, which is called *shikantaza*, in which all delusions, doubts, distractions drop off. This kind of zazen is exactly Buddhist faith.

Buddhist faith is not an idea. It is practical action, something we have to actualize. Even though we can explain what Buddhist faith is, what zazen is, through and through, finally there is a little bit we cannot explain. This is the core of zazen or of faith. This is the core of being. Zazen, nose, mouth, ears, whatever it is, this is something we have to actualize in our daily living through our body and mind. Religious faith can become something dangerous that hurts people, so we have to polish our knowledge, polish our perceptions through and through. Then this is Buddhist faith, which is based on emptiness.

Engaged Buddhism   25

THICH NHAT HANH

THICH NHAT HANH—POET, ZEN master, and chairman of the Vietnamese Buddhist Peace Delegation during the Vietnam War—lives in exile in France. In this selection, he makes it clear how individual meditation practice is at the same time service to society. This is based on the central teaching of the *Avatamsaka Sutra* (Flower Ornament Sutra), on the interrelatedness of all things, which the sutra calls the "net of Indra" (Indra being the king of the gods in Indian mythology). The teaching of interdependence arose directly out of the Buddha's account of his own enlightenment experience and became known as *pratitya-samutpada* (the "interdependent or conditional origination" of all things; see introduction to Part Three).

MEDITATION IS NOT TO GET OUT OF SOCIETY, TO ESCAPE FROM society, but to prepare for a reentry into society. We call this "engaged Buddhism." When we go to a meditation center, we may have the impression that we leave everything behind—family, society, and all the complications involved in them—and come as an individual in order to practice and to search for peace. This is already an illusion, because in Buddhism there is no such thing as an individual.

Just as a piece of paper is the fruit, the combination of many elements that can be called non-paper elements, the individual is made of non-individual elements. If you are a poet, you will see clearly that there is a cloud floating in this sheet of paper. Without a cloud there will be no water; without water, the trees cannot grow; and without trees, you cannot make paper. So the cloud is in here. The existence of this page is dependent on the existence of a cloud. Paper and cloud are so close. Let us think of other things, like sunshine. Sunshine is very important because the forest cannot grow without sunshine, and we humans cannot grow without sunshine. So the logger needs sunshine in order to cut the tree, and the tree needs sunshine in order to be a tree. Therefore you can see sunshine in this sheet of paper. And if you look more deeply, with the eyes of a bodhisattva, with the eyes of those who are awake, you see not only the cloud and the sunshine in it, but that everything is here: the wheat that became the bread for the logger to eat, the logger's father—everything is in this sheet of paper.

The *Avatamsaka Sutra* tells us that you cannot point to one thing that does not have a relationship with this sheet of paper. So we say, "A sheet of paper is made of non-paper elements." A cloud is a non-paper element. The forest is a non-paper element. Sunshine is a non-paper element. The paper is made of all the non-paper elements to the extent that if we return the non-paper elements to their sources, the cloud to the sky, the sunshine to the sun, the logger to his father, the paper is empty. Empty of what? Empty of a separate self. It has been made by all the non-self elements, non-paper elements, and if all these non-paper elements are taken out, it is truly empty, empty of an independent self. Empty, in this sense, means that the paper is full of everything, the entire cosmos. The presence of this tiny sheet of paper proves the presence of the whole cosmos.

In the same way, the individual is made of non-individual elements. How do you expect to leave everything behind when you enter a meditation center? The kind of suffering that you carry in your heart, that is society itself. You bring that with you, you bring society with you. You bring all of us with you. When you meditate, it is not just for yourself, you do it for the whole society. You seek solutions to your problems not only for yourself, but for all of us.

Leaves are usually looked upon as the children of the tree. Yes, they are children of the tree, born from the tree, but they are also mothers of the tree. The leaves combine raw sap, water, and minerals, with sunshine and gas, and convert it into a variegated sap that can nourish the tree. In this way, the leaves become the mother of the tree. We are all children of society, but we are also mothers. We have to nourish society. If we are uprooted from society, we cannot transform it into a more livable place for us and for our children. The leaves are linked to the tree by a stem. The stem is very important.

I have been gardening in our community for many years, and I know that sometimes it is difficult to transplant cuttings. Some plants do not transplant easily, so we use a kind of vegetable hormone to help them be rooted in the soil more easily. I wonder whether there is a kind of powder, something that may be found in meditation practice that can help people who are uprooted be rooted again in society. Meditation is not an escape from society. Meditation is to equip oneself with the capacity to reintegrate into society, in order for the leaf to nourish the tree.

PART FOUR

The Tantric

Teachings

Introduction

IF   WE   TAKE   THE   BUDDHA   DHARMA   AS   A
whole, it is made up of the Hinayana, Mahayana, and Vajrayana. The third major vehicle, the Vajrayana, is also called
Tantra and is associated with a genre of scriptures known as
tantras. (It is not directly related to the aspect of Hinduism
that is also known as Tantra.) Like the sutras of the Hinayana
and Mahayana, the tantras are attributed to the Buddha, but
tradition tells us that, to teach most of them, he took forms
other than that of the historical buddha, Shakyamuni.

We have seen that the Hinayana holds up the arhat as an
ideal, while the Mahayana aspires to the state of the bodhisattva. The Vajrayana, in its turn, is inspired by the figure of
the siddha, a master whose spiritual realization is so profound that he has power over the phenomenal world, such
as, for example, the power to fly or stop the movement of
the sun. Another traditional characteristic of the siddha is the
spurning of convention and conventional morality. Accord-

ing to tradition, there were eighty-four "great siddhas" *(ma-hasiddhas)* in India during the time of the first great flourishing of the tantric teachings (eighth-twelfth centuries).

The Vajrayana incorporates and depends upon all the teachings of the Hinayana and Mahayana, and, most especially, it depends upon the practitioner's being accomplished in the meditative practices of the Hinayana and Mahayana. But the Vajrayana goes further. For example, while fully accepting the Mahayana doctrine of emptiness, the Vajrayana adds a deeper dimension to it. The tantric critique of the Mahayana view centering on emptiness is that it is too much oriented toward transcending this world. Tantra sees the power, profundity, and vastness of the absolute truth as fully and completely manifest in the phenomenal world, the world of the senses. It speaks of the unity of the absolute and relative truths. And thus it also speaks of the unity of emptiness with luminosity, which is the vivid, precise, and powerful quality of phenomenal display.

Vajrayana is the vehicle or path connected with the "indestructible." (*Vajra* in Sanskrit means "adamantine" or "indestructible.") What is indestructible is the basic nature of things as they are. Nothing can destroy the basic nature of things, because nothing departs from it. Because this vajra nature can never become anything else, it is said to be unborn. Also because it can never become anything else, it is tantra, which means "continuity."

The principal meditative practice in the Vajrayana is that of "sacred outlook," or "seeing appearances as pure." This means seeing all phenomena nakedly in their vajra nature. The main technique used in the Vajrayana for developing this way of seeing entails identifying with deities who represent vajra nature and repeating their sacred utterances, called *mantras*, and emulating their gestures, called *mudras*. These deities are regarded not as actually existing but as expressions of the nature of what is.

CHÖGYAM TRUNGPA

TRUNGPA RINPOCHE WAS THE ELEVENTH IN-
carnation of the Trungpa line of Tibetan gurus and originally
the abbot of a group of monasteries in eastern Tibet. After coming to the West, he studied comparative religion at Oxford and
later founded meditation centers throughout North America
and Europe. In this chapter, after emphasizing the continuity of
the Hinayana, Mahayana, and Vajrayana, he raises the question
of what could be the starting point for Tantra within the practitioner's experience. It turns out that confusion and ambiguity
are the starting point, the "seed syllable." In Vajrayana liturgy,
a seed syllable is a Sanskrit syllable, often represented by a single letter, that stands for the essence of a particular deity and
actually gives birth to the deity. Thus, very unexpectedly, confusion—the very thing we might have hoped spiritual practice
would rid us of—turns out to be the potent seed of the awakened state of mind.

THE TANTRIC TEACHINGS OF BUDDHISM ARE EXTREMELY SA-
cred and, in some sense, inaccessible. Tantric practitioners of
the past have put tremendous energy and effort into the study
of tantra. Now we are bringing tantra to North America, which
is a landmark in the history of Buddhism.

A tantric revolution took place in India many centuries ago. The wisdom of that tradition was handed down orally from generation to generation by the great mahasiddhas, or tantric masters. Therefore, tantra is known as the ear-whispered, or secret, lineage. However, secrecy does not imply that tantra is like a foreign language. It is not as though our parents speak two languages but only teach us English so that they can use Chinese or Yiddish when they want to keep a secret from us. Rather, tantra introduces us to the actuality of the phenomenal world. It is one of the most advanced, sharp, and extraordinary perceptions that has ever developed. It is unusual and eccentric; it is powerful, magical, and outrageous; but it is also extremely simple.

In order to understand the phenomenon of tantra, or tantric consciousness, we should be quite clear that we are not talking about tantra as a vague spiritual process. Tantra, or vajrayana Buddhism, is extremely precise, and it is unique. We cannot afford to jumble the vajrayana into a spiritual or philosophical stew. Instead, we should discuss tantra technically, spiritually, and personally—in a very exact sense—and we should discuss what the uniqueness of the tantric tradition has to offer to sentient beings.

The future of Buddhism depends on continuing to discover what the Buddha experienced and on sharing such experience with others. So there is a need to identify ourselves personally with tantric experience, rather than regarding tantra as one more spiritual trip.

Fundamentally, the vajrayana comes out of a complete understanding and comprehension of both hinayana and mahayana Buddhism. The development of the three *yanas*—hinayana, mahayana, and vajrayana—is one continuous process. In fact, the word *tantra,* or *gyü* in Tibetan, means "continuity." There is a continuous thread running through the Buddhist path, which is our personal experience and our commitment to the Buddhist teachings. Usually we think of a thread as starting somewhere. But according to the Buddhist teachings, the thread has no beginning, and therefore there is continuity. In fact, such a thread does not even exist, but at the same time, it is continuous.

At this point we are not yet in a position to discuss what tantra is. Since the continuity of tantra is based on personal experience we first need to understand the person who is having the experience. That is, we need to know who is studying tantra: who is it, or what is it? So, to begin with, we have to go back to the beginning, and find out who is perceiving tantra, that is, who is the *tantrika*, or tantric practitioner.

We could say that some people are tantric by nature. They are inspired in their lives; they realize that some reality is taking place in the true sense, and they feel that the experience of energy is relevant to them. They may feel threatened by energy or they may feel a lack of energy, but they have a personal interest in the world: the visual world, the auditory world, the world of the senses altogether. They are interested in how things work and how things are perceived. That sense of enormous interest, that interest in perceptions, is tantric by nature. However, one problem with inspired, future tantric practitioners is that they are often *too* fascinated by the world of the senses. There is something lacking: although they are inspired, they may not have made a genuine connection to the world of the senses, which presents problems in understanding true tantra. Still, they could be regarded as tantric fetuses, or potential members of the tantric family.

When we begin to explore who the tantric practitioner actually is, our inquiry takes us further and further back, right to the basis of Buddhist practice, which is the hinayana teachings. From this point of view, hinayana *is* tantra. One of the inspiring glimpses or experiences of the hinayana practitioner is the absence of self, which is also the absence of God. When we realize that there is no individual being or personality who is perceiving external entities, the situation becomes open. We don't have to limit things by having a conceptualized divine being, traditionally known as God. We are simply examining who we are. In examining who we are, we find, according to both the hinayana and the tantric observation, that we are nobody—rather, nonbody. We might ask, "How is that possible? I have a name. I have a body. I eat. I sleep. I lead my life. I wear clothes." But that is precisely the point: we misunderstand ourselves, our nonexistent selves. Because we eat, we sleep, we live and we have a name, we presume that something must be there. That common misunderstanding took place a long time ago, and it still takes place constantly, every single moment. Just because we have a name doesn't mean we have a self. How do we realize that? Because if we do not use such reference points as our name or our clothing, if we stop saying, "I eat, I sleep, I do such and such," then there is a big gap.

In a similar fashion, we often use reference points to show that we do not exist. We say we do *not* exist because of something else. We might say, "I do not exist because I am penniless." There is something wrong with that logic, because we still have a penny to be less of. However, this does not mean that we should try to destroy relative reference points. As an extreme example, during the 1960s some people made hysterical attempts not to exist. By destroying references and credentials such as draft cards and birth certificates, they hoped to become invisible. But creating their draft-cardlessness was still a statement of deliberate individuality, and it was still fighting over the question of existence by struggling not to exist.

In the Buddhist tradition, discovering nonexistence, or egolessness, has nothing to do with destroying relative reference points. Whether we try to maintain such reference points or destroy them, we still have the same problem. The Buddhist approach is not to use any reference points at all—none whatsoever. Then we are not finding out whether we exist or not, but we are simply looking at ourselves directly, without any reference points—without even looking, we could say. That may be very demanding, but let it be so. Let us get to the heart of the matter.

When we attempt to see ourselves without reference points, we may find ourselves in a situation of not knowing what to do. We may feel completely lost, and we may think that what we are trying to do is very strange indeed: "I can't even begin. How can I do anything?" Then we might have an inkling of beginning at the beginning. Having to relate with the bewilderment of not knowing how to deal with ourselves without using reference points is getting closer to the truth. At the same time, we have not found the root of reality, if there is one at all.

We cannot find the beginning of the tantric thread unless we come to the conclusion that we do not exist. We might try to work out our nonexistence logically. However, the conclusion that we do not exist has to be experiential, and it also has to be beyond our stupidity and confusion. Our confusion at this point is not knowing how to begin. From that, we can start to feel the beginninglessness of the thread, and its endlessness as well. So we are getting somewhere, but we still might feel rather stupid, like jellyfish or robots. There is no sense of discovery at all, and the whole thing seems rather flat.

According to the tantric tradition, the only way to find our way out of that confusion, or our way in, is by having a sense of humor about our predicament. We are trying to find ourselves, but we are not able to do so, and we feel enormously flat and heavy and in the way. Something is being a nuisance, but we cannot put our finger on exactly what it is. Nevertheless, something, somewhere, is being a nuisance. Or is it? If we view this with humor, we begin to find that even the flatness, the lack of inspiration, the solidity, and the confusion are dancing constantly. We need to develop a sense of excitement and dance rather than just trying to feel better. When we begin to dance with our humor, our apparent stupidity becomes somewhat uplifted. However, we do not know for sure whether we are just looking at ourselves humorously while our stupidity grows heavier all the time, or whether we might actually be able to cure ourselves. There is still something that is uncertain, completely confused, and very ambiguous.

At that point, we finally could start to relate with the ambiguity. In the tantric tradition, discovering that ambiguity is called "discovering the seed syllable." Ambiguity is called a "seed syllable" when it becomes a starting point rather than a source of problems. When we accept uncertainty as the working base, then we begin to discover that we do not exist. We can experience and appreciate the ambiguity as the source of confusion as well as the source of humor. The discovery of nonexistence comes from experiencing both the energy of humor and the heavy "thingness" or form of confusion. But form or thingness does not prove the existence of energy, and energy does not prove the existence of form. So there is no confirmation, just ambiguity. Therefore, we still find ourselves at a loss. However, at this point that feeling of being lost has the quality of freedom rather than the quality of confusion.

This experience of ambiguity is a personal experience rather than an analytical experience. We begin to realize that actually we do not exist. We do not exist because of our existence: that is the punchline of our ambiguity. And the world exists because of our nonexistence. We do not exist; therefore the world exists. There is an enormous joke behind the whole thing, a big joke.

We might ask, "Who is playing such a joke on us?" It is difficult to say. We do not know who it is at all. We are so uncertain that we might not even have a question mark to put at the end of our sentence. Nevertheless, that is our purpose in studying tantra: to find out who is the questioner, who set this question up altogether, if anyone at all.

The beginner's point of view is to realize nonexistence, to understand nonexistence, and to experience nonexistence. It is very important for us to realize that sight, smell, colors, emotions, formlessness, and form are all expressions of no-beginning, nonexistence, egolessness. Such nonexistence has to be experienced personally rather than analytically or philosophically. That personal experience is extremely important. In order for us to get into tantra properly, in order to become good tantra students, we have to go through the experience of nonexistence, however frustrating, confusing, or irritating it may seem. Otherwise, what we do will be completely fruitless.

The Temptress and the Monk

REGINALD A. RAY

THOSE WHO IN THE VAJRAYANA replaced the arhats of the Hinayana, and the bodhisattvas of the Mahayana, as ideal exemplars of the spiritual path, were the siddhas. The siddhas' outstanding characteristic was their possession of the "supreme and ordinary *siddhis*," or spiritual powers. The supreme siddhi is enlightenment itself, and the ordinary siddhis are a host of miraculous powers manifesting mastery over the phenomenal world. Tradition records the existence of eighty-four great siddhas, or *mahasiddhas*, who lived in India between the eighth and twelfth centuries. These wild figures, who included men and women of all social backgrounds, mocked, from the pinnacle of their realization, conventionality in all its forms, particularly the plodding conventionalized spirituality of established monasticism. The essence of their message and example is that the highest spiritual truth is independent of any and all relative conditions, and thus can be manifested and realized instantaneously in any circumstances.

Here Dr. Ray, a professor of Buddhist studies at the Naropa Institute in Boulder, Colorado, gives us the tale of a reluctant fledgling siddha, who is wrested willy-nilly from the nest of convention by the force of the unveiled nature of ultimate reality itself, personified as the wisdom goddess Vajrayogini.

AN INDIAN BUDDHIST COULD FOLLOW ANY ONE OF THREE LIFE-style options: he or she could be a layperson, a monastic living in a community of monks or nuns, or a meditating *yogin* dwelling and practicing in solitude. Tantric or Vajrayana Buddhism originally, and to some extent throughout its history, represented primarily the third option: it was essentially a nonmonastic, esoteric tradition practiced by meditators in solitary retreat. In the texts, Tantric yogins are depicted as carrying out their practice in isolated caves, inaccessible mountaintops, and remote valleys. They also practiced in another place remote from "civilization," the cremation ground, populated by beasts of prey, hostile spirits, and the living dead, feared by the Indian populace but a favorite haunt of *yogins*.

There is little if any evidence of the Vajrayana until it appears on the stage of Indian history in the seventh century. At this time, it is in the process of undergoing a transition from being a strictly secret and esoteric tradition of *yogins* living in the wilds, to developing as a movement of increasing popularity among both monastics and the laity. No one knows when the Vajrayana originally developed, but the Tibetan historian Lama Taranatha (seventeenth century) articulates the general Tibetan view that the Vajrayana goes back to the time of the Buddha as his most esoteric, highest, and most sacred instruction.

In one sense, the Vajrayana is no different from the other contemplative traditions of Indian Buddhism—Theravada forest traditions, early Mahayana, Dhyana (Ch'an, Zen)—where the emphasis is placed on intensive meditation, a close relationship with one's guru, and striving for enlightenment in the present life. But the methods used by the Vajrayana are in some ways distinctive. Meditation is set within a liturgical context. One receives meditation instructions and permission to practice from one's guru in the form of empowering ceremonies (*abhisekas*). Buddhahood is embodied in various male and female buddhas with whom one seeks to identify oneself. Women, feminine symbolism, and female deities (understood as buddhas or *yidams*) such as Vajrayogini are accorded particular respect as special embodiments of wisdom. It is regarded as a great blessing when a deity manifests itself in person, and particularly the greatest tantric saints (*siddhas*) are said to have received teachings in this way. And men and women practice together, particular in *ganachakras*, or "tantric feasts," in which realization is actualized and celebrated with meditation, singing, and dancing. Among Buddhist traditions, the Vajrayana is sometimes especially unconventional, and its saints have no hesitation in demonstrating the often ego-centered and self-serving character of conventional morality and religion. There is an outrageous, sometimes shocking character to the Vajrayana, embodied in its saints, which reflects, so its adherents say, the outrage of enlightenment itself and its insult to the human ego.

In the eighth century, a line of kings belonging to the Pala dynasty assumed power in northeastern India. The Palas appear to have been devotees of the Vajrayana, propagating tantric Buddhism and building monasteries in which it was especially venerated and studied. As the Vajrayana began to become a concern of monks and monasteries, it inevitably underwent changes. Most important, the Vajrayana, at least as practiced in the monasteries, tended to become a subject of erudition and commentary, and to some extent lost its forest character. Monastic scholars collected tantric texts, and the contents of the growing tantric corpus were catalogued and categorized. In the traditional scholastic manner, the texts were studied, their contents were debated, and learned commentaries and subcommentaries were written on them. In many cases, however, this was as far as it went, and evidently there were many who did not actually put the tantric teachings into practice at all.

Abhayakaragupta, a very learned and famous monk from North India who lived in the eleventh century, was one of those who studied but did not practice the Vajrayana. His fame as a scholar was in fact quite widespread in the India of his day. The following story, recounted by Lama Taranatha, vividly illustrates the deterioration of Vajrayana spirituality in a monastic context as well as the power of the tradition to reawaken its adherents to genuine practice and realization.

Abhayakaragupta was from the south of India. His father was a kshatriya (warrior caste) and his mother a brahmin (priestly caste). From an early age, he demonstrated a remarkable scholarly ability and avidly pursued the study of texts of all sorts, including the Vedas, the larger Vedic literature, logic, and grammar and philology. He subsequently mastered the textual traditions as well as the tantras of the non-Buddhist schools. He seems to have been a meticulous person, as brahmins were expected to be, following the rules which enjoined the avoidance of people and situations that would bring defilement, including low-caste persons and substances such as cow flesh and alcohol.

One day he had shut himself in a garden and was reciting mantras when a beautiful maiden appeared before him. She said, "I am a chandala [outcaste] girl, and I want to practice with you." Abhayakaragupta, ever the fastidious brahmin, replied, "That is not possible. I am a high-caste person, and I would be disgraced."

The maiden left, but when Abhayakaragupta looked, he saw that the doors were still locked from the inside. This caused some doubt in his mind, and he wondered whether this was not some unusual girl he had encountered. In his uncertainty, he brought the matter to a Buddhist *yogin* that he knew. The yogin replied, "It is most unfortunate that you did not accept her invitation, for that was the deity Vajrayogini, the female buddha. She would have conferred realization [*siddhi*] upon you." Vajrayogini had invited Abhayakaragupta to relinquish his attachment to his high-caste status, offering spiritual awakening in return. The *yogin* friend then continued, "Your inner, spiritual affiliation is clearly with the Buddhists, and you should go to the east and become a Buddhist."

Abhayakaragupta went to Bengal and followed the suggestion of the *yogin*. However, instead of entering the path of meditation in emulation of his friend, he received ordination as a Buddhist monk *(bhikshu)* and took up the path of study. He became thoroughly trained in all the sutras and tantras, and became known as an exceptionally learned bhikshu. In addition, he received numerous tantric empowerments from many different teachers. He was known as a scholarly expert in the Vajrayana, although he did not practice it.

On another occasion, he was in the courtyard of a temple when a young maiden appeared carrying a piece of cow flesh, dripping with blood. She urged this on him, saying, "I am a chandala girl. I have killed this expressly for you. Eat it." Her invitation was a deep affront not only to Abhayakaragupta the

brahmin, but also to the monk. For a brahmin, killing a cow is
regarded as a heinous crime, and eating beef is polluting in the
extreme. Moreover, according to the Buddhist monastic rules,
monks are prohibited from eating anything killed specifically
for them. Abhayakaragupta replied accordingly, "I am a *bhikshu*
from a pure caste. How can I eat the flesh of a cow killed for
me?" The chandala maiden then disappeared from the courtyard. Taranatha remarks that once again, Abhayakaragupta had
refused the invitation of Vajrayogini and turned away the realization she offered him, preferring instead to maintain his elevated social standing as a brahmin and a fully ordained monk.

Taranatha tells us that although at this time Abhayakaragupta
was a great scholar, his heart remained unfulfilled, for he had
not received the inner teachings of realization. So he set forth
and wandered everywhere throughout the land, going to various masters to receive oral instructions on meditation. He finally ended up at the monastic university of Nalanda. There he
became very learned in the monastic literature of the most important Buddhist schools, much of the scholastic writings, and
the tantric texts. He also mastered the six fields of knowledge,
including mathematics, metaphysics, and logic. He finally went
to a tantric teacher, received all the teachings on the Vajrayana,
and took the teacher as his primary guru, receiving meditation
instruction from him.

Abhayakaragupta then went to the monastery of his teacher
and meditated on the instructions that he had received. One
night on the eighth day of the month while he was meditating,
there appeared in his practice cell a maiden who looked just like
the servant who drew water for his teacher. From a small basket, she took many objects for a tantric feast liturgy. She said,
"I have been sent by your teacher. I am to perform a *ganachakra* with you."

He replied, "I have never done this practice before."

She said, "Fine. Let's do one now." Yet the scholar, because
of his preconceptions and scruples, refused to join with her in
the tantric feast. The maiden said, "You know three hundred
tantras and have received the very best oral instructions on
them. How can you possibly have doubts about the actual practice?" Saying this, she gathered up the feast materials and went
away. Suddenly, it became darker, and when Abhayakaragupta
inspected the doors to his practice cell, he saw that these

doors—which he himself had locked from the inside—were still locked.

The next morning, he asked his guru, "Did you send your servant girl to me yesterday evening to conduct a feast liturgy?"

His teacher replied, "You have so many doubts and concepts, I would not have done such a thing. What did you see?" Abhayakaragupta then told him the story of what occurred. The guru said, "Vajrayogini offered you the attainment of realization, but you would not accept it."

Then Abhayakaragupta despaired and, rejecting food for seven days, made supplications to Vajrayogini. On the seventh night, in a dream, he saw an old woman. Knowing that she was Vajrayogini, he offered confession and supplications. Then she became Vajrayogini in actuality and said to him, "Throughout many lives, you have recited my mantra and made offerings to me. This time, I offered you *siddhi* on three separate occasions, but you were unwilling to accept it. Because of this, you will not attain supreme realization in this life."

Vajrayogini then set Abhayakaragupta to composing texts and teaching others and predicted that he would attain realization after death. After that, adopting the *yogin*'s way of life, he stayed in various cremation grounds meditating. He later meditated at a certain hermitage given to him by the wife of one of the Pala kings and one of his periods of *samadhi*, Taranatha reports, lasted six months. As a result of his accomplishment in meditation, he acquired many supernormal powers enabling him to help others, including the ability to raise the dead, quell natural disasters, and protect people from adversity, all in accord with the teachings of the tantras. When he composed texts, it is said, he no longer spoke on his own accord, but was filled by the presence of Vajrayogini, who taught through him. So miraculous was his teaching that when he spoke, flowers would sometimes fall from the sky.

This story shows clearly the unconventional and yogic character of Vajrayana Buddhism. Abhayakaragupta comes to understand that the Vajrayana is not a matter of seemly behavior or accumulated knowledge. Rather, its primary value is the direct and personal experience of realization, and it presents a raw and rugged challenge to any kind of status-seeking or clinging to convention. Moreover, it is relentless: even as a non-Buddhist, Abhayakaragupta is sought out, so to speak, and touched by Vajrayogini. In his pride, pretention, and ignorance, he wants to study from a safe distance: nevertheless, the tradition works on him. Finally, he comes face to face with the tragedy of his own ego: to maintain his caste and monastic status and his self-image, he has thrown away his heart's desire. The truth finally seeps through his defenses, and once he is able to accept the terrible truth, he is ultimately able to open himself to, and become a vehicle for, genuine wisdom, compassion, and power. All of this illustrates the general Tibetan belief that Vajrayana Buddhism is particularly effective for those especially plagued by the defilements of ignorance and ego-clinging. The greatest *siddhas* or saints are often precisely those who begin with the greatest defilements.

28   *The Union of Joy and Happiness*

TILOPA (989–1069) WAS ONE of the most famous of the eighty-four Indian mahasiddhas. He was a cowherd as a boy, but with the help of a spiritual teacher who took an interest in him, Tilopa performed a miracle that defeated an enemy army, and he thus became the king of the small kingdom in which he lived. After a time, he became disgusted with worldly life and, ceding the throne to his son, went off and became a monk. One day he was studying the *prajnaparamita* teachings (see chapter 13) when he had a vision in which a woman with a mustache appeared and told him he must abandon monkhood and seek the truth behind what he was studying. She gave him certain initiations and instructions, which he followed. Thereafter, over a period of years he attended upon a number of gurus and made great spiritual progress. He finally attained complete realization after twelve years during which he earned his living by crushing sesame seeds for oil during the day and acting as a procurer for a prostitute at night. His activity after his enlightenment was characterized by bizarre and antisocial behavior, including countless miracles. Through his unaccountable and occasionally repugnant actions, he tricked many wayward individuals into awakening to the folly or harm of their ways and adopting a wholesome approach to life. Not rarely he cured their spiritual blindness altogether, leading them to enlightenment. According to one story, he brought the inhabitants of an entire region to spiritual illumination by singing them songs of insight while seated high in the air. He is counted as the first human being in the Mahamudra lineage, the transmission of which he is said to have received from Vajrayogini, a semiwrathful female deity into whose celestial castle he rudely forced his way.

The stanzas that follow are the oral instructions on Mahamudra that Tilopa gave to his disciple Naropa (1016–1100) on the banks of the Ganges River. Tilopa dwelled there for many years, living off fish entrails discarded by fishermen. Thus his iconography shows him sitting in a meditative posture, holding a fish and clad only in a loincloth.

Mahamudra ("great seal") is one of the highest meditative teachings of the Vajrayana. It has been preserved in the Tibetan Vajrayana lineages, particularly the Kagyu, of which Tilopa is considered to be the founder. In this selection we see clearly the continuity between Mahamudra and the Mahayana. A certain amount of what is said here could have been uttered by Huineng (chapter 19). However, there is more. Tilopa speaks of emptiness, but when he gets to the heart of the matter he talks of the luminous nature of mind. This is something like a positive quality of the emptiness. Instead of emphasizing meditation, Tilopa speaks of nonmeditation, because the unity of emptiness and luminosity that is the nature of mind is spontaneously present in all experience and need not be sought. This is the "great seal" borne by all phenomena.

— HOMAGE TO THE COEMERGENT WISDOM![1]

Mahamudra cannot be shown;
But for you who are devoted to the guru, who have
    mastered the ascetic practices

[1] Coemergent Wisdom: the primordial wisdom, born simultaneously with ignorance, just as nirvana and samsara must come simultaneously into being.

And are forebearing in suffering, intelligent Naropa,
Take this to heart, my fortunate student.

Kye-ho!

Look at the nature of the world,
Impermanent like a mirage or dream;
Even the mirage or dream does not exist.
Therefore, develop renunciation and abandon worldly
    activities.

Renounce servants and kin, causes of passion and
    aggression.
Meditate alone in the forest, in retreats, in solitary places.
Remain in the state of nonmeditation.
If you attain nonattainment, then you have attained
    mahamudra.

The dharma of samsara is petty, causing passion and
    aggression.
The things we have created have no substance; therefore,
    seek the substance of the ultimate.
The dharma of mind cannot see the meaning of
    transcendent mind.
The dharma of action cannot discover the meaning of
    nonaction.

If you would attain the realization of transcendent mind
    and nonaction,
Then cut the root of mind and let consciousness remain
    naked.
Let the polluted waters of mental activities clear.
Do not seek to stop projections, but let them come to
    rest of themselves.
If there is no rejecting or accepting, then you are
    liberated in the mahamudra.

When trees grow leaves and branches,
If you cut the roots, the many leaves and branches wither.
Likewise, if you cut the root of mind,
The various mental activities will subside.

The darkness that has collected in thousands of kalpas
    one torch will dispel.

Likewise, one moment's experience of luminous mind
Will dissolve the veil of karmic impurities.

Men of lesser intelligence who cannot grasp this,
Concentrate your awareness and focus on the breath.
Through different eye-gazes and concentration practices,
Discipline your mind until it rests naturally.

If you perceive space,
The fixed ideas of center and boundary dissolve.
Likewise, if mind perceives mind,
All mental activities will cease, you will remain in a state
    of nonthought,
And you will realize the supreme *bodhicitta*.

Vapors arising from the earth become clouds and then
    vanish into the sky;
It is not known where the clouds go when they have
    dissolved.
Likewise, the waves of thoughts derived from mind
Dissolve when mind perceives mind.

Space has neither color nor shape;
It is changeless, it is not tinged by black or white.
Likewise, luminous mind has neither color nor shape;
It is not tinged by black or white, virtue or vice.

The sun's pure and brilliant essence
Cannot be dimmed by the darkness that endures for a
    thousand kalpas.
Likewise, the luminous essence of mind
Cannot be dimmed by the long kalpas of samsara.

Though it may be said that space is empty,
Space cannot be described.
Likewise, though it may be said that mind is luminous,
Naming it does not prove that it exists.
Space is completely without locality.
Likewise, mahamudra mind dwells nowhere.

Without change, rest loose in the primordial state;
There is no doubt that your bonds will loosen.
The essence of mind is like space;
Therefore, there is nothing which it does not encompass.

Let the movements of the body ease into genuineness,
Cease your idle chatter, let your speech become an echo,
Have no mind, but see the dharma of the leap.

The body, like a hollow bamboo, has no substance.
Mind is like the essence of space, having no place for
     thoughts.
Rest loose your mind; neither hold it nor permit it to
     wander.
If mind has no aim, it is mahamudra.
Accomplishing this is the attainment of supreme
     enlightenment.

The nature of mind is luminous, without object of
     perception.
You will discover the path of Buddha when there is no
     path of meditation.
By meditating on nonmeditation you will attain the
     supreme *bodhi*.

This is the king of views—it transcends fixing and
     holding.[2]
This is the king of meditations—without wandering
     mind.

This is the king of actions—without effort.
When there is no hope and fear, you have realized the
     goal.

The unborn *alaya* is without habits and veils.
Rest mind in the unborn essence; make no distinctions
     between meditation and post-meditation.
When projections exhaust the dharma of mind,
One attains the king of views, free from all limitations.

Boundless and deep is the supreme king of meditations.
Effortless self-existence is the supreme king of actions.
Hopeless self-existence is the supreme king of the
     fruition.

In the beginning mind is like a turbulent river.
In the middle it is like the river Ganges, flowing slowly.
In the end it is like the confluence of all rivers, like the
     meeting of son and mother.

[2] Holding: holding on to projections. Fixing: believing in the existence of a
projector.

18.   Tibetan monks making a Kalachakra sand mandala. From the film *Little Buddha*.

A mandala is a diagram of totality that is employed in Vajrayana practice and ritual. These monks are creating a finely wrought mandala from colored sand in preparation for an empowerment ceremony of the Kalachakra cycle of teachings. After the practitioners have been entered into the world of the mandala, the sand will be discarded in a river. The living tradition of Tibetan Buddhism offers opportunities to witness the making of art from ephemeral materials such as butter, dough, or sand.

19.   Borobudur, aerial view. Indonesia, ninth century, stone. Photo by Luca Invernizzi Tettoni.

The largest Buddhist monument in Asia is Borobudur in Central Java. Its symbolism is complex and mysterious. At the center is a stupa that is surrounded by seventy-two small stupas and reached by an ambulatory encircling the monument on four levels. But Borobudur also seems to be a Vajrayana mandala executed on a vast scale that permits the visitor literally to enter and ascend to the center.

20. Taktsang Monastery. Bhutan. Photo by Steven Powers.

The monastery of Taktsang, whose name means "tiger's nest," hugs the wall of a mountain overlooking Paro Valley in Bhutan. Taktsang is a revered holy place which pilgrims reach via a steep ascent from the valley. Especially sacred is the meditation cave of Guru Padmasambhava, which is enshrined in the lower building. For centuries great meditators have kept the practicing lineages of Buddhism alive at retreat sites such as this.

21. The Potala, Lhasa. Tibet, seventeenth century. Photo courtesy of the Newark Museum. Photo by Ovshe Norzunov, a Russian Kalmyck who visited Lhasa, ca. 1900.

In the harsh climate of the Himalayas, Buddhist architecture took on a fortresslike character. The Potala in Lhasa is the traditional seat of the Dalai Lama. Its majestic setting and impressive solidity are evident in this photograph taken around 1900. Tibetan monasteries built on this huge scale once housed tens of thousands of monks and upheld an illustrious tradition of Buddhist scholarship.

22. Appliqué *thangka* of Guru Padmasambhava on display at Tashichodzong, Bhutan. Photo by Ernst Haas. Courtesy of the Ernst Haas Studio, New York, New York.

A distinctive tradition of Himalayan Buddhism is the making of huge *thangkas* of appliquéd cloth, which are unrolled on ceremonial occasions. This one is shown hanging at Tashichodzong in Thimphu during the coronation of the king of Bhutan in 1974. The *thangka* represents Guru Padmasambhava, the Indian *yogin* who meditated at Taktsang in the eighth century. He is venerated as the bringer of Vajrayana Buddhism to Tibet and neighboring regions.

23. DAMPA SANGYE. Central Tibet, 1350–1400 CE, bronze with inlaid copper and silver. Los Angeles County Museum of Art. From the Nasli and Alice Heeramaneck Collection, Museum Associates Purchase.

Padampa (or Dampa) Sangye was an Indian master of the eleventh century who brought to Tibet the teachings of Chöd, a Buddhist yogic practice. In this small sculpture he assumes an unusual squatting position that is reminiscent of a yoga posture. Padampa Sangye's mastery over the forces of the body is further suggested by his staring eyes and sharply delineated features. The wealth of portrait sculpture in Tibetan art reflects the Vajrayana emphasis upon the lineage of teachers through which teachings are transmitted.

24. VAJRASATTVA AND CONSORT. Tibet, eighteenth century, bronze. Courtesy of the Board of Trustees of the Victoria and Albert Museum, London.

This sculpture is an example of the imagery of *yab-yum*, or "father-mother," which presents the meditational deities of Vajrayana in embrace with their consorts. The male figure represents compassion; the female, wisdom. Their union refers to the inseparability of these spiritual qualities within enlightened mind. In the Vajrayana tradition, certain teachings and images are revealed only to those prepared to grasp their true meaning.

The followers of Tantra, the *Prajnaparamita*,
The Vinaya, the Sutras, and other religions—
All these, by their texts and philosophical dogmas,
Will not see the luminous mahamudra.

Having no mind, without desires,
Self-quieted, self-existing,
It is like a wave of water.
Luminosity is veiled only by the rising of desire.

The real vow of *samaya* is broken by thinking in terms of
    precepts.
If you neither dwell, perceive, nor stray from the
    ultimate,
Then you are the holy practitioner, the torch which
    illumines darkness.

If you are without desire, if you do not dwell in extremes,
You will see the dharmas of all the teachings.

If you strive in this endeavor, you will free yourself from
    samsaric imprisonment.
If you meditate in this way, you will burn the veil of
    karmic impurities.
Therefore, you are known as "the Torch of the Doctrine."

Even ignorant people who are not devoted to this
    teaching
Could be saved by you from constantly drowning in the
    river of samsara.

It is a pity that beings endure such suffering in the lower
    realms.
Those who would free themselves from suffering should
    seek a wise guru.
Being possessed by the *adhishthana*,[3] one's mind will be
    freed.

If you seek a *karma mudra*,[4] then the wisdom of the
    union of joy and emptiness will arise.
The union of skillful means and knowledge brings
    blessings.

---

[3] *Adhishthana:* blessings; the atmosphere created by the guru.
[4] *Karma mudra:* one's consort in the practice of the third initiation (*abhisheka*).

Bring it down and give rise to the mandala.
Deliver it to the places and distribute it throughout the
　　body.

If there is no desire involved, then the union of joy and
　　emptiness will arise.
Gain long life, without white hairs, and you will wax like
　　the moon.
Become radiant, and your strength will be perfect.
Having speedily achieved the relative *siddhi*s, one should
　　seek the absolute siddhis.
May this pointed instruction in mahamudra remain in
　　the hearts of fortunate beings.

TRANSLATED BY KARMA TSULTRIM PALMO

MILAREPA (1052–1135) IS PER-
haps the best known of all the great Tibetan meditators. A youth marked by
hardship and catastrophe proved to be
nothing compared with the rigors and sorrows he experienced while training under
his guru Marpa (1012–1097). When his
training was complete, he meditated for
years in solitude in caves in the snow-cov-
ered mountains. Despite the cold, because of his endurance and
his mastery of the yoga of inner heat (Skt. *chandali*; Tib.
tummo), he wore only a single white cotton cloth. Hence his
name Milarepa, the "Cotton-Clad One." As his realization
grew, many disciples found their way to him, even in the remote mountain fastnesses. He expressed his enlightenment in
many spontaneous songs, said to number one hundred thousand. A few of them follow.

The Ultimate View, Meditation, Conduct, and Result

The view is the wisdom of emptiness.
Meditation is luminosity without clinging.

Conduct is continuous and without attachment.
The result is stainless and naked.

The view, which is the wisdom of emptiness,
Is in danger of straying when it is only a "verbal" view.
If certainty about the meaning does not arise,
Words alone won't liberate one from clinging to a self.
Therefore, strong certainty is important.

Meditation, which is luminosity without clinging,
Is in danger of straying when it is only "resting."
If wisdom does not arise from within,
Stable resting alone lacks a liberating quality.
Wisdom does not arise within dullness or agitation.
Therefore, undistracted mindfulness is important.

Conduct, which is continuous and without attachment,
Is in danger of straying when it is only a pretense.
If it does not arise as an aid for the view and meditation,
Yogic conduct becomes an aid for the eight worldly
    values.
Therefore, to have no attachments and no obscurations is
    important.

The result, which is stainless and naked,
Is in danger of wearing the clothes of conceptual
    characteristics.
If confusion is not destroyed from within,
To meditate with merely a mental aspiration is of little
    benefit.
Therefore, it is important to destroy confusion.

The Way to Carry the Four Activities onto the Path

Rechungpa, my son, listen and pay attention.
I, your father, Milarepa,
Sometimes meditate while sleeping and sleeping.
When I meditate while sleeping and sleeping,
I have the oral instructions for ignorance to arise as
    luminosity.
I have these; others do not.
If all had these, I would be happy.

I, your father, Milarepa,
Sometimes meditate while eating and eating.

When I meditate while eating and eating,
I have the oral instructions for regarding food and drink
    as a *ganachakra*.
I have these; all do not.
If all had these, I would be happy.

I, your father, Milarepa,
Sometimes meditate while walking and walking.
When I meditate while walking and walking,
I have the oral instructions for regarding walking and
    sitting as circumambulation.
I have these; others do not.
If all had these, I would be happy.

I, your father, Milarepa,
Sometimes meditate while doing and doing things.
When I meditate while doing and doing things,
I have the oral instructions for liberating all actions into
    dharmata.
I have these; all do not.
If all had these, I would be happy.

Rechungpa, son, practice like this.
Megom, wake up and cook the soup.

Five Ways of Resting Naturally Settled

Rest in a natural way like a small child.
Rest like an ocean without waves.
Rest within clarity like a candle flame.
Rest without self-concerns like a human corpse.
Rest unmoving like a mountain.

The View, Meditation, Conduct, and Result, Which Are Beyond the Intellect

The view is to look at reality, which is beyond the
    intellect.
Meditation is to rest in a state of nondistraction.
Conduct is to sustain unceasingly whatever naturally
    occurs.
The result is to abandon hopes, fears, and conventional
    terms.

The Eight Kinds of Wonderful Happiness

At the feet of the jetsün nirmanakaya, who is like a wish-
fulfilling jewel,
A precious chakravartin,
The supreme lamp that clears away the darkness of
ignorance—
To Marpa the translator, I bow down.

The lofty red rock sky fortress
Is the gathering place of the four classes of *dakinis*.
In this place, which has delighted this old person,
I sing a song of my joyful experiences.
All students gathered here, who are endowed
With intelligence, wisdom, and exertion in meditation,
please listen.

This mountain retreat, a place that fosters no bias or
partiality,
Is the guide for sustaining the experiences of *samadhi*.
Is there anyone here who possesses this path?
Someone who recognizes their own body as a monastery
is happy.
That the innate mind is pure, like space, is wonderful. E
MA HO.

Stable, unchanging faith
Is the guide for abandoning *samsara*.
Is there anyone here who possesses this path?
Someone who has liberated *samsara* and *nirvana* in their
own places is happy.
That the four *kayas* are complete within mind is
wonderful. E MA HO.

To meet with what appears to the six sense
consciousnesses
Is the guide for adverse conditions to arise as the path.
Is there anyone here who possesses this path?
Someone who has brought desires to the state of
exhaustion is happy.
To cut the connection to the perceived and perceiver is
wonderful. E MA HO.

The genuine lama of the lineage
Is the guide for dispelling the darkness of ignorance.
Is there anyone here who possesses this path?
Someone who relies upon the lama as the buddha is
    happy.
To recognize the essence of the innate mind is wonderful.
    E MA HO.

Cotton clothes, which are never too cold or too warm,
Are the guide for wandering in snow mountains.
Is there anyone here who possesses this path?
Someone who has no fear of heat or cold is happy.
To sleep naked in the snow is wonderful. E MA HO.

The instructions for mixing, combined with those for
    powa,
Are the guide for conquering fears of the *bardo.*
Is there anyone here who possesses this path?
Someone who does not distinghish between this life and
    the next is happy.
To arrive within the expanse of *dharmata* is wonderful.
    E MA HO.

The profound path of the skilled means of the hearing
    lineage
Is the guide for separating the impurities from the pure
    essence of mind.
Is there anyone here who possesses this path?
Someone whose physical and mental bliss expands is
    happy.
To bring the life force into the avadhuti is wonderful.
    E MA HO.

The *yogin* who is advanced in compassion and emptiness
Is the guide for cutting through conventions and
    elaborations.
Is there anyone here who possesses this path?
Someone who is surrounded by a realized retinue is
    happy.
To attract *nirmanakayas* as a retinue is wonderful.
E MA HO.

This little song of experience, about the eight kinds of
    happiness
That are this old person's delight,

Has been sung from a *yogin*'s joyfulness
To enhance the practice of all you gathered here.
Do not forget this; keep it in the center of your hearts.

The Six Kinds of Certainty and Mental Happiness

In a secluded place where *dakinis* naturally gather,
I am happy alone contemplating the Dharma.
To the warrior who has annihilated the self, I bow down.

From the state of the unborn mind springs no-death;
The idea of birth and death is liberated in its own place.
Having certainty about the view, my mind is happy;
If this happiness seems like happiness to you, Padampa,
    do likewise.

From the state of the nonmeditation of meditation
    springs no-distraction;
The idea of meditation and postmeditation is liberated in
    its own place.
Having certainty about meditation, my mind is happy;
If this happiness seems like happiness to you, Padampa,
    do likewise.

From the state of naturally occurring conduct springs no-
    ceasing;
The idea of artificial conduct is liberated in its own place.
Having certainty about conduct, my mind is happy;
If this happiness seems like happiness to you, Padampa,
    do likewise.

From the state of the unbestowed empowerment springs
    no-attainment;
The idea of the form of the deity is liberated in its own
    place.
Having certainty about empowerments, my mind is
    happy;
If this happiness seems like happiness to you, Padampa,
    do likewise.

From the state of the unguarded *samaya* springs no-
    impairment;
The idea of vows and guarding them is liberated in its
    own place.

Having certainty about *samaya*, my mind is happy;
If this happiness seems like happiness to you, Padampa,
do likewise.

From the state of no hope for the result springs no-fear;
The idea of hopes and fears is liberated in its own place.
Having certainty about the result, my mind is happy;
If this happiness seems like happiness to you, Padampa,
do likewise.

Distinguishing Happiness from Suffering

The *yogin* who, recognizing the essence of his own mind,
realizes the true nature, is always happy.
The practitioner who, pursuing delusion, increases his
misery, always suffers.

The yogin who, by resting within the uncontrived state,
realizes the unchanging nature, pure within its own
place, is always happy.
The practitioner who, pursuing feelings and thoughts,
accumulates attachments and aversions freely, always
suffers.

The *yogin* who, realizing all appearances to be the
dharmakaya, cuts through hopes, fears, and doubts, is
always happy.
The practitioner who, engaging in pretense and careless
actions, doesn't quell the eight worldly values, always
suffers.

The *yogin* who, recognizng everything to be mind, takes
all appearances as an aid, is always happy.
The practitioner who, having spent his life in distriction,
feels remorse at the time of death, always suffers.

The *yogin* who, inwardly having full realization, remains
within the true nature, in its own place, is always
happy.
The practitioner who, inwardly holding onto his desires,
yearns and yearns and wears fancy clothes, always
suffers.

The *yogin* who, having liberated thought processes in
their own place, has continuous meditation experience,
is always happy.
The practitioner who, pursuing words and terms, does
not determine the nature of his mind, always suffers.

The *yogin* who, having given up worldly activities, is
without selfishness and personal objectives, is always
happy.
The practitioner who, struggling to gather provisions, is
preoccupied with family and relatives, always suffers.

The *yogin* who, having inwardly turned away from
attachments, realizes everything to be an illusion, is
always happy.
The practitioner who, remaining on the path of
distraction, employs his body and speech as servants,
always suffers.

The *yogin* who, riding the horse of diligence, progresses
through the paths and *bhumis* to liberation, is always
happy.
The practitioner who, in the shackles of laziness, is
anchored to the depths of *samsara*, always suffers.

The *yogin* who, having cut through false assertions by
listening and reflecting, looks at his own mind as
entertainment, is always happy.
The practitioner who, professing to practice the Dharma,
engages in negative actions, always suffers.

The *yogin* who, having cut through hopes, fears, and
doubts, remains continuously within the intrinsic state,
is always happy.
The practitioner who, having handed over his
independence to others, ingratiates and flatters, always
suffers.

The *yogin* who, having cast all wants behind him,
continuously practices the divine Dharma, is always
happy.

Realizing Apparent Sounds to Be Like an Echo

I bow down at the feet of Marpa the Translator.
Realizing apparent sounds to be like an echo,

My yogic conduct is unceasing.
I have abandoned beautiful pretenses,
Fame—do what you please.

Having confidence that food and wealth are illusions,
I have dispersed the food and wealth I received.
Even if I receive nothing, I have no wishes.
Merit—do what you please.

Recognizing retinue and servants to be like magical
    emanations,
I do not flatter or court
The venerable scholars who come from all over.
Monks—do what you please.

Everything is the nature of equality,
But realizing attachments and aggrression to be the causes
    of suffering,
I have cut the bonds of longing.
Relatives—do what you please.

Dharmata is free from elaborations,
But the elaborations of clinging and attachment are one's
    own created suffering;
I have become free from the shackles of perceived and
    perceiver.
Craving—do what you please.

Within the natural luminosity of the innate mind
I do not see the stains of thoughts;
I have abandoned conceptual anlaysis.
Conventional terms—do what you please.

Mahamudra, Sung in Reply to Questions Asked by Three Scholars

When I meditate on *mahamudra*
I rest without any effort in reality, the fundamental state.
I rest relaxed in the state of nondistraction.
I rest with clarity in the state of emptiness.
I rest with awareness in the state of bliss.
I rest unmoving in the state of nonconceptuality.
I rest evenly in the state of various manifestations.

For the mind itself which rests like that,
Various kinds of certainty arise unceasingly.
The mind being self-luminous, activity is accomplished
   without effort.
The result not remaining as a mental aspiratiaon, my
   mind is happy.
Free from hopes, fears, and dualistic perceptions, I feel
   joyful.
Confusion arising as wisdom, I am bright and cheerful.

THE INNERMOST ESSENCE

JIGME LINGPA

ALONG WITH MAHAMUDRA, Ati is considered by Tibetan Buddhists to be the highest teaching, the culmination of the spiritual path. This "imperial *yana*," which in Tibetan is called Dzogchen, "the great perfection," was brought to Tibet in the eighth century by two great Indian teachers, the siddha Padmasambhava and the pandit Vimalamitra. In the fourteenth century, the manifold aspects and levels of Ati doctrine were reformulated by Longchen Rabjam, whose realization is said to have equaled that of the Buddha. The great *vidyadhara* ("knowledge holder") Jigme Lingpa (1730–1798) was the principal figure in the Ati lineage of recent centuries. He had three visions in which he received the transmission of Ati directly from Longchen Rabjam himself. Thereafter, he wrote many commentaries on Longchen Rabjam's principal writings in which he condensed and resystematized the tradition of Ati once again, giving it the form it has today.

In the Ati view, everything is complete and flawless as it is. Whatever occurs is the display of primordial wisdom mind and does not depart from that nature. This primordial awareness is the ground from which both confusion and enlightenment arise and into which they subside. Its nature is profound and brilliant emptiness, or void, and it is even more fundamental than buddhahood, since it has no bias even toward enlightenment. Ati is called the effortless vehicle, because it is said that abiding in its profound view, which is not different from enlightenment itself, is what the mind naturally does if it does not get drawn into any side trips. But the reader should not take this to mean that the spiritual path, with all its disciplines, is superfluous, and that all one has to do is put one's feet up and be enlightened. The effortlessness of Ati is a consummate discipline of simplicity, of constantly seeing within the complexities of mind the radiant and unbound essence of awareness itself. In the short introductory piece that follows, Jigme Lingpa gives us a pith impression of Ati, here called Maha Ati, "great Ati," as well as pointing to some of the many pitfalls that surround it.

THIS IS THE LION'S ROAR WHICH SUBDUES THE RAMPANT CON-fusions and misunderstandings of those meditators who have abandoned materialist attachments to meditate on the Innermost Essence.

The Maha Ati, which is beyond conceptions and transcends both grasping and letting go, is the essence of transcendental insight. This is the unchanging state of nonmeditation in which there is awareness but no clinging. Understanding this, I pay ceaseless homage to the Maha Ati with great simplicity.

Here is the essence of the Maha Ati Tantra,
The innermost heart of Padmakara's Teachings,
The life-force of the Dakinis.
This is the Ultimate Teaching of all the Nine Vehicles.[1]
It can be transmitted only by a Guru of the Thought Lineage
And not by words alone.
Nevertheless I have written this
For the Benefit of great meditators

---

[1] The nine vehicles are Shravakayana, Pratyekabuddhayana, Mahayana, Kriyayana, Upayana, Yogayana, Mahayogayana, Anuyana, and Atiyana.

Who are dedicated to the Highest Teaching.
This teaching was taken from the treasury of Dharmadhatu
And is not created out of attachment
To theories and philosophical abstractions.

First the pupil must find an accomplished Guru with whom
he has a good karmic link. The Teacher must be a holder of the
Thought Lineage Transmission. The pupil must have single-
minded devotion and faith, which makes possible the transmission of the Teacher's understanding.

The Maha Ati is of the greatest simplicity. It is what *is*. It
cannot be shown by analogy; nothing can obstruct it. It is without limitation and transcends all extremes. It is clearcut nowness, which can never change its shape or color. When you become one with this state, the desire to meditate itself dissolves;
you are freed from the chain of meditation and philosophy, and
conviction is born within you. The thinker has deserted. There
is no longer any benefit to be gained from "good" thoughts and
no harm is to be suffered from "bad" thoughts. Neutral
thoughts can no longer deceive. You become one with transcendental insight and boundless space. Then you will find signs of
progress on the Path. There is no longer any question of rampant confusions and misunderstandings.

Although this teaching is the King of the Yanas, meditators
are divided into those who are highly receptive to it, those who
are less receptive, and those who are quite unreceptive. The
most highly receptive pupils are hard to find, and it sometimes
happens that Teacher and pupil are unable to find a true meeting point. In such a case nothing is grained and misconceptions
may arise concerning the nature of Maha Ati.

Those who are less receptive begin by studying the theory
and gradually develop the feeling and true understanding.
Nowadays many people regard the theory as being the meditation. Their meditation may be clear and devoid of thoughts and
it may be relaxing and enjoyable, but this is merely the temporary experiencing of bliss. They think this is meditation and
that no one knows any better than them. They think, "I have
attained this understanding," and they are proud of themselves.
Then, if there is no competent Teacher, their experience is only
theoretical. As it is said in the Scriptures of Maha Ati: "Theory
is like a patch on a coat—one day it will come apart." People

285

often try to discriminate between "good" thoughts and "bad" thoughts, like trying to separate milk from water. It is easy enough to accept the negative experiences in life but much harder to see the positive experiences as part of the Path. Even those who claim to have reached the highest stage of Realization are completely involved with worldly concerns and fame. They are attracted by Devaputra.[2] This means they have not realized the self-liberation of the six senses. Such people regard fame as extraordinary and miraculous. This is like claiming that a raven is white. But those who are completely dedicated to the practice of Dharma without being concerned about worldly fame and glory should not become too self-satisfied on account of their higher developments of meditation. They must practice the Guru Yoga throughout the four periods of the day in order to receive the blessings of the Guru and to merge their minds with his and open the eye of insight. Once this experience is attained, it should not be disregarded. The Yogi should thenceforth dedicate himself to this practice with unremitting perseverance. Subsequently his experience of the Void will become more peaceful, or he will experience greater clarity and insight. Or again, he may begin to realize the shortcomings of discursive thoughts and thereby develop discriminating wisdom. Some individuals will be able to use both thoughts and the absence of thoughts as meditation, but it should be borne in mind that that which notes what is happening is the tight grip of ego.

Look out for the subtle hindrance of trying to analyze experiences. This is a great danger. It is too early to label all thoughts as Dharmakaya. The remedy is the wisdom of nowness, changeless and unfailing. Once freed from the bondage of philosophical speculation, the meditator develops penetrating awareness in his practice. If he analyzes his meditation and postmeditation experiences, he will be led astray and make many mistakes. If he fails to understand his shortcomings, he will never gain the free-flowing insight of nowness, beyond all concepts. He will have only a conceptual and nihilistic view of the Void, which is characteristic of the lesser Yanas.

It is also a mistake to regard the Void as a mirage, as though it were merely a combination of vivid perceptions and nothing-

---

[2] Devaputra personifies the evil force which causes attraction to sense objects.

ness. This is the experience of the lower Tantras, which might be induced by practice of the Svabhava Mantra. It is likewise a mistake, when discursive thoughts are pacified, to overlook the clarity and regard the mind as merely blank. The experience of true insight is the simultaneous awareness of both stillness and active thoughts. According to the Maha Ati teaching, meditation consists of seeing whatever arises in the mind and simply remaining in the state of nowness. Continuing in this state after meditation is known as "the postmeditation experience."

It is a mistake to try to *concentrate* on emptiness and, after meditation, intellectually to regard everything as a mirage. Primordial insight is the state which is not influenced by the undergrowth of thoughts. It is a mistake to be on guard against the wandering mind or to try and imprison the mind in the ascetic practice of suppressing thoughts.

Some people may misunderstand the term *nowness* and take it to refer to whatever thoughts happen to be in their mind at the moment. *Nowness* should be understood as being the primeval insight already described.

The state of nonmeditation is born in the heart when one no longer discriminates between meditation and nonmeditation and one is no longer tempted to change or prolong the state of meditation. There is all-pervading joy, free from all doubts. This is different from the enjoyment of sensual pleasures or from mere happiness.

When we speak of "clarity," we are referring to that state which is free from sloth and dullness. This clarity, inseparable from pure energy, shines forth unobstructed. It is a mistake to equate clarity with awareness of thoughts and the colors and shapes of external phenomena.

When thoughts are absent, the meditator is completely immersed in the space of nonthought. The "absence of thoughts" does not mean unconsciousness or sleep or withdrawal from the senses, but simply being unmoved by conflict. The three signs of meditation—clarity, joy and absence of thoughts—may occur naturally when a person meditates, but if an effort is made to create them the meditator still remains in the circle of Samsara.

There are four mistaken views of the Void. It is a mistake to imagine that the Void is merely empty without seeing the wild space of nowness. It is a mistake to seek the Buddha-nature

(Dharmakaya) in external sources without realizing that now-ness knows no path or goal. It is a mistake to try to introduce some remedy for thoughts without realizing that thoughts are by nature void and that one can free oneself like a snake un-winding. It is also a mistake to hold a nihilistic view that there is nothing but the Void, no cause and effect of karma and no meditator nor meditation, failing to experience the Void which is beyond conceptions. Those who have had glimpses of reali-zation must know these dangers and study them thoroughly. It is easy to theorize and talk eloquently about the Void, but the meditator may still be unable to deal with certain situations. In a Maha Ati text it is said: "Temporary realization is like a mist which will surely disappear." Meditators who have not studied these dangers will never derive any benefit from being in strict retreat or forcibly restraining the mind, nor from visualizing, reciting mantras or practicing Hatha Yoga. As is said in the *Phagpa Düdpa Sutra,*

A Bodhisattva who does not know the real meaning of
    solitude,
Even if he meditates for many years in a remote valley
    full of poisonous snakes
Five hundred miles from the nearest habitation,
Would develop overweening pride.

If the meditator is able to use whatever occurs in his life as the Path, his body becomes a retreat hut. He does not need to add up the number of years he has been meditating and does not panic when "shocking" thoughts arise. His awareness re-mains unbroken, like that of an old man watching a child at play. As is said in a Maha Ati text: "Complete realization is like unchanging space."

The Yogi of Maha Ati may look like an ordinary person, but his awareness is completely absorbed in nowness. He has no need of books because he sees apparent phenomena and the whole of existence as the Mandala of the Guru. For him there is no speculation about the stages on the Path. His actions are spontaneous and therefore benefit all sentient beings. When he leaves the physical body his consciousness becomes one with the Dharmakaya, just as the air in a vase merges with the sur-rounding space when the vase is broken.

Chase Them Away!

31

PATRUL RINPOCHE

TRANSLATED BY HERBERT V. GUENTHER

PATRUL RINPOCHE (1808–1887), one of the most revered masters of the Nyingma lineage of Tibetan Buddhism, was a great exemplar of the "over-the-hill" style of Ati masters. He liked to refer to himself as a "raggedy old man" or an "old dog." In this poem, apparently written when he was indeed an old man, he looks back on his life and inner development and "tells it like it is." Clearly in a mind such as Patrul's, great humor and utter matter-of-factness are completely inseparable.

WHEN THIS OLD DOG WAS LIVING IN SOLITUDE
After hearing the words of the trusty World-Protector,
He had the desire to speak likewise.

When first I met my teacher supreme,
I had the feeling of having found what I wanted
Like a merchant having reached the golden isle:
That's what is meant by engaging oneself in the many
    topics and their investigation.

When later I met my teacher supreme, I had the feeling
   of there being danger for me
Like a criminal facing the judge:
That's what is meant by getting a sound scolding.
If now I meet my teacher supreme,
I have the feeling of meeting with an equal
Like pigeons sleeping in a temple:
That's what is meant by keeping one's distance.

When first I heard instructions,
I had the feeling of wanting to turn them immediately
   into action
Like a hungry person pouncing on food:
That's what is meant by making an experience of it.
When later I heard instructions,
I had the feeling of great uncertainty
Like words spoken far away:
That's what is meant by not having got rid of notions.
When now I hear instructions,
I have the feeling of disgust
Like someone being made to eat his vomit again:
That's what is meant by having no desire to ask
   questions.

When first I went into solitude,
I had the feeling of my mind being at ease
Like a traveler having reached his own house:
That's what is meant by enjoying one's stay.
When later I went into solitude,
I had the feeling of not being able to stay
Like a beautiful girl living alone:
That's what is meant by frequently coming and going.
When now I go into solitude,
I have the feeling of it being a nice place to stay
Like an old dog about to die under some shelter:
That's what is meant by tying up a corpse for disposal.

When first I thought about vision,
I had the feeling of becoming overjoyed the loftier it grew
Like a wild bird searching for its nest:
That's what is meant by giving good advice.
When later I thought about vision,

I had the feeling of being lost
Like someone who has reached a crossroad:
That's what is meant by remaining silent.
When now I think about vision,
I have the feeling of my head spinning
Like an old man telling stories to children:
That's what is meant by not believing it.

When first I thought about meditation,
I had the feeling of delight in the joy and happiness it
    brought
Like the meeting of a man and woman of similar
    temperament:
That's what is meant by tasting the very essence of
    meditation.
When later I thought about meditation,
I had the feeling of being exhausted and tired
Like a weak person crushed by a heavy burden:
That's what is meant by short-lived meditation.
When now I think of meditation,
I have the feeling of it not lasting for a moment
Like a needle being balanced on a stone:
That's what is meant by having no desire for meditation.

When first I thought about conduct,
I had the feeling of being constrained by constraints
Like a wild horse put into harness:
That's what is meant by showing off.
When later I thought about conduct,
I had the feeling of being free to do what I liked
Like an old dog that has broken loose from the stake it
    was tied to:
That's what is meant by constraints having slipped.
When now I think about conduct,
I have the feeling of it not being important
Like a harlot with no shame:
That's what is meant by there being neither happiness
    nor misery.

When first I thought about the goal,
I had the feeling of its attainment being something
    valuable

Like a cheat praising his merchandise:
That's what is meant by having great expectations and
    desires.
When later I thought about the goal,
I had the feeling of it being something far away
Like the ocean extending from here to there:
That's what is meant by having little dedication.
When now I think about the goal,
I have the feeling of being without means
Like a thief when the night is over:
That's what is meant by having cut off all expectations.

When first I gave a talk,
I had the feeling of being clever and important
Like beautiful girls parading in the marketplace:
That's what is meant by desiring to give talks.
When later I gave a talk,
I had the feeling of being quite familiar with any topic
Like an old man telling worn stories over and again:
That's what is meant by being loquacious.
When now I give a talk,
I have the feeling of overstepping my limits
Like an evil spirit harassed by spells:
That's what is meant by being embarrassed.

When first I partook in debates,
I had the feeling of making a reputation for myself
Like someone instituting legal action against an
    obnoxious adversary:
That's what is meant by giving vent to righteous
    indignation.
When later I partook in debates,
I had the feeling of searching for the definite meaning
Like an upright judge looking for an honest witness:
That's what is meant by concentrating one's capacity.
When now I partake in debates,
I have the feeling that whatever is said will do
Like a liar roaming about the countryside:
That's what is meant by everything just being fine.

When first I wrote treatises,
I had the feeling of the words arising immediately

Like the *siddha* composing the *Dohas:*
That's what is meant by naturalness.
When later I wrote treatises,
I had the feeling of forcing the words together
Like a skilled person fashioning his poems:
That's what is meant by expressing things beautifully.
When now I write treatises,
I have the feeling of futility
Like an inexperienced person drawing a road map:
That's what is meant by not wasting ink and paper.

When first I gathered with intimate friends,
I had the feeling of competitiveness
Like young men having met for an archery contest:
That's what is meant by loving and hating.
When later I gathered with intimate friends,
I had the feeling of being in accord with all
Like whores having come to a fair:
That's what is meant by having many friends.
When now I gather with intimate friends,
I have the feeling of not fitting into the human herd
Like a leper having ventured into a crowd:
That's what is meant by staying alone.

When first I saw wealth,
I had the feeling of momentary joy
Like a child gathering flowers:
That's what is meant by not hoarding riches and wealth.
When later I saw wealth,
I had the feeling of there never being enough
Like water being poured into a pot with a broken bottom:
That's what is meant by making small efforts to gain
   something.
When now I see wealth,
I have the feeling of its being a heavy burden
Like an old beggar with too many children:
That's what is meant by rejoicing in having nothing.

When first I hired attendants and servants,
I had the feeling of having to give them lots of work
Like hired workmen gathering in a row:
That's what is meant by having good intentions.

When later I hired attendants and servants,
I had the feeling of losing my independence
Like child monks serving their superiors:
That's what is meant by severing all ties.
When now I hire attendants and servants,
I have the feeling that whatever I have is lost
Like a thievish dog having been let into one's house:
That's what is meant by doing things by yourself alone.

When first disciples came,
I had the feeling of self-importance
Like a servant having occupied the master's seat:
That's what is meant by a job well done.
When later disciples came,
I had the feeling of my mind and thoughts having some
    purpose
Like a guest having been accorded the seat of honor:
That's what is meant by doing what is advantageous.
When now disciples come,
I have the feeling of having to scowl at them
Like demons rising from the wilderness:
That's what is meant by chasing them away with stones.

The Refined Essence of
Oral Instructions

32

PADMASAMBHAVA

RECORDED BY YESHE TSOGYAL

PADMASAMBHAVA (FL. eighth century) is considered by Tibetans to have been a second Buddha. In fact, he was thought to be the simultaneous incarnation of Shakyamuni Buddha and the transcendental buddha Amitabha. He is venerated by all Tibetan Buddhists under the name Guru Rinpoche ("Precious Guru"). He was the main force behind the first spreading of the Buddha Dharma in Tibet. The Tibetan king Trisong Deptsen (755–797) had invited an Indian pandit, Shantirakshita, to Tibet to teach the Buddha Dharma, but Shantirakshita encountered so much resistance from local elements, including deities and demons inhabiting the lakes and mountains of Tibet, that help was needed. Padmasambhava was invited to Tibet to quell the resistance. He converted all the deities and demons into protectors of the Buddha Dharma, then gathered many disciples, especially twenty-five great ones. The chief among the twenty-five great disciples was the princess of Kharchen, Yeshe Tsogyal (757–817). As the present selection tells us, from her eighth year on, Yeshe Tsogyal followed the great master (called here by another of his many names, Orgyen Padmakara) like his shadow.

These instructions of Padmasambhava to Yeshe Tsogyal presume a background understanding about what happens at the time of dying that is familiar to Tibetan Buddhists. As described, the five elements—earth, water, fire, air, and space—which constitute all things, and thus of course each individual being, dissolve into each other. After certain other processes, the individual's subtle consciousness leaves the body and enters an in-between state known as the *bardo*, in a subtle body known as a bardo body. This bardo body has such properties as passing through solid obstructions and flying anywhere with the speed of thought. In the bardo, the subtle consciousnesses undergoes all manner of extremely vivid experiences both intensely horrific and vastly peaceful. Then, after a period traditionally given as forty-nine days, rebirth occurs. The bardo between death and birth is regarded as crucial, because depending on the composure and insight of the subtle consciousness in the face of its intense experiences (which are in turn in part linked to the force and nature of previous karma), enlightenment or insanity (or any state in between) and a consequent rebirth drawn from a very broad range of possibility—from very fortunate to very unfortunate—occur.

HOMAGE TO THE MASTER.

Lady Tsogyal of Kharchen served the nirmanakaya Orgyen Padmakara from her eighth year, accompanying him as a shadow follows a body.

When the master was about to leave Tibet for the land of the rakshas, I, Lady Kharchen, having offered a mandala of gold and turquoise and having turned a wheel of gathering, implored: Oh, Great Master! You are leaving to tame the rakshas. I am left behind here in Tibet. Although I have served you for a long time, master, this old woman has no confidence about the time of death. So I beseech you to kindly give me an instruction condensing all teachings into one, which is concise and easy to practice.

The great master replied: Devoted one with a faithful and virtuous mind, listen to me.

Although there are many profound key points of body, rest free and relaxed as you feel comfortable. Everything is included in simply that.

Although there are many key points of speech such as breath control and mantra recitation, stop speaking and rest like a mute. Everything is included in simply that.

Although there are many key points of mind such as concentrating, relaxing, projecting, dissolving, and focusing inward, everything is included in simply letting it rest in its natural state, free and easy, without fabrication.

The mind doesn't remain quietly in that state. If one wonders, Is it nothing?, like haze in the heat of the sun, it still shimmers and flashes forth. But if one wonders, Is it something? it has no color or shape to identify it but is utterly empty and completely awake—that is the nature of your mind.

Having recognized it as such, to become certain about it, that is the view. To remain undistracted in the state of stillness, without fabrication or fixation, that is the meditation. In that state, to be free from clinging or attachment, accepting or rejecting, hope or fear, toward any of the experiences of the six senses, that is the action.

Whatever doubt or hesitation occurs, supplicate your master. Don't remain in places of ordinary people; practice in seclusion. Give up your clinging to whatever you are most attached to as well as to whomever you have the strongest bond with in this life, and practice. Like that, although your body remains in human form, your mind is equal to the buddhas'.

At the time of dying, you should practice as follows.

By earth dissolving in water, the body becoms heavy and cannot support itself. By water dissolving in fire, the mouth and nose dry up. By fire dissolving in wind, body heat disappears. By wind dissolving in consciousness, one cannot but exhale with a rattle and inhale with a gasp.

At that time, the feelings of being pressed down by a huge mountain, being trapped within darkness, or being dropped into the expanse of space occur. All these experiences are accompanied by thunderous and ringing sounds. The whole sky will be vividly bright like an unfurled brocade.

Moreover, the natural forms of your mind, the peaceful, wrathful, semiwrathful deities, and the ones with various heads fill the sky, within a dome of rainbow lights. Brandishing weapons, they will utter "Beat! beat!" "Kill! kill!" "*Hung! Hung!*" "*Phat! Phat!*" and other fierce sounds. In addition, there will be light like a hundred thousand suns shining at once.

At this time, your innate deity will remind you of awareness, saying, Don't be distracted! Don't be distracted! Your innate demon will disturb all your experiences, make them collapse, and utter sharp and fierce sounds and confuse you.

At this point, know this: The feeling of being pressed down is not that of being pressed by a mountain. It is your own elements dissolving. Don't be afraid of that! The feeling of being trapped within darkness is not a darkness. It is your five sense faculties dissolving. The feeling of being dropped into the expanse of space is not being dropped. It is your mind without support because your body and mind have separated and your breathing has stopped.

All experiences of rainbow lights are the natural manifestations of your mind. All the peaceful and wrathful forms are the natural forms of your mind. All sounds are your own sounds. All lights are your own lights. Have no doubt about that. If you do feel doubt, you will be thrown into samsara. Having resolved this to be self-display, if you rest wide awake in luminous emptiness, then simply in that you will attain the three kayas and become enlightened. Even if you are cast into samsara, you won't go there.

The innate deity is your present taking hold of your mind with undistracted mindfulness. From this moment, it is very important to be without any hope and fear, clinging and fixation, toward the objects of your six sense faculties as well as toward fascination, happiness, and sorrow. From now on, if you attain stability, you will be able to assume your natural state in the bardo and become enlightened. Therefore, the most vital point is to sustain your practice undistractedly from this very moment.

The innate demon is your present tendency for ignorance, your doubt and hesitation. At that time, whatever fearful phenomena appear such as sounds, colors, and lights, don't be fascinated, don't doubt, and don't be afraid. If you fall into doubt for even a moment, you will wander in samsara, so gain complete stability.

At this point, the womb entrances appear as celestial palaces. Don't be attracted to them. Be certain of that! Be free from hope and fear! I swear there is no doubt that you will then become enlightened without taking further rebirths.

At that time, it is not that one is helped by a buddha. Your own awareness is primordially enlightened. It is not that one is harmed by the hells. Fixation being naturally purified, fear of samsara and hope for nirvana are cut from the root.

Becoming enlightened can be compared to water cleared of sediments, gold cleansed of impurities, or the sky cleared of clouds.

Having attained spacelike dharmakaya for the benefit of oneself, you will accomplish the benefit of sentient beings as far as space pervades. Having attained sambhogakaya and nirmanakaya for the welfare of others, you will benefit sentient beings as far as your mind pervades phenomena.

If this instruction is given three times to even a great sinner such as one who has killed his own father and mother, he will not fall into samsara even if thrown there. There is no doubt about becoming enlightened.

Even if you have many other profound teachings, without an instruction like this, you remain far away. Since you don't know where you may wander next, practice this with perseverance.

You should give this oral instruction to recipients who have great faith, strong diligence, and are intelligent, who always remember their teacher, who have confidence in the oral instructions, who exert themselves in the practice, who are stable-minded and able to give up concerns for this world. Give them this with the master's seal of entrustment, the yidam's seal of secrecy, and the dakini's seal of entrustment.

Although I, Padmakara, have followed many masters for three thousand six hundred years,[1] have requested instructions, received teachings, studied and taught, meditated and practiced, I have not found any teaching more profound than this.

I am going to tame the rakshas. You should practice like this.

---

[1] The years here reflect the ancient way of counting summer and winter seasons each as one year.

Mother, you will become enlightened in the celestial realm. Therefore persevere in this instruction.

Having spoken, Guru Rinpoche mounted the rays of the sun and departed for the land of the rakshas. Following that, Lady Tsogyal attained liberation. She committed this teaching to writing and concealed it as a profound treasure. She made this aspiration: In the future, may it be given to Guru Dorje Lingpa. May it then benefit many beings.

This completes the Sacred Refined Essence Instruction, the reply to questions on self-liberation at the moment of death and in the bardo.

SAMAYA, SEAL, SEAL, SEAL.

Rebirth in the Buddhist Tradition 33

REGINALD A. RAY

REGINALD RAY HAS SPECIALIZED, AMONG other things, in the Buddhist doctrine of reincarnation. He is not only an academic but an experienced practitioner of Tibetan Buddhism. Here he unfolds for us in clear terms the Buddhist understanding of death and rebirth, and especially the phenomenon of the *tulku,* or "reincarnated lama," who make a conscious journey through the death-and-rebirth process so as to be born again for the benefit of others.

AMONG THE WORLD RELIGIOUS, BUDDHISM MAY BE UNIQUE IN the amount of attention it devotes to the understanding of birth, death, and the question of subsequent existence, or, as these phenomena are collectively termed in the tradition, reincarnation (*punarbhava*). Most Westerners think of reincarnation as a popular Asian belief according to which people are born over and over in accordance with the law of karma. While this understanding is essentially accurate, it misses two other key dimensions of the doctrine: first, the fact that reincarnation works between lifetimes as well as operating constantly in ordinary life; and second, that reincarnation functions differently for ordinary people and for saints. Here the Buddhist theory of reincarnation is discussed in these major dimensions: the movement from one life to another among ordinary people, within the context of ordinary life, and as it functions among saints.

It is well known that Buddhism typically takes a practical approach to religious questions, and this is true also in the case of reincarnation. Buddhism not only theorizes about these phenomena but explores them experientially. This exploration is made possible through a variety of meditation techniques that render the mind increasingly sensitive and extend its awareness beyond the limits of a normal person's consciousness. This has enabled Buddhist meditators to learn and to infer many things about death and rebirth that are not amenable to scientific measurement and the collective and standardized kinds of verification it provides. In the following pages, the experiential dimension of reincarnation is examined through reference to lore surrounding Buddhist saints, past and present.

Buddhism, like other religions, takes an interest in death and rebirth not only for the sake of the dying and the dead, but also to help the living. The Buddhist teachings about death and rebirth have traditionally been used to counsel the dying, provide understanding and acceptance to the bereaved, and even help the deceased person continue on his or her journey. These same teachings also include meditation practices that people may perform not only to prepare themselves for their own deaths, but also to explore the very ground of the mind itself. In Tibet, for example, an advanced practice involved a meditation duplicating the experience of psychological dissolution that occurs at death. Through consciously traversing this unknown and frightening territory, the meditator could pass beyond conditioned consciousness to an experience of the unconditioned, radiant, and unobstructed foundation of the mind itself.

Ordinary Reincarnation: Death and Rebirth in Successive Lives

According to Buddhism, when the physical body dies, one's mind—actually consciousness in a subtle form—separates from it. In life, the consciousness is shaped and conditioned according to karmic tendencies accumulated over countless lifetimes.

At death, the subtle consciousness carries these karmic tendencies along with it as it travels toward rebirth. In dying, after
successive cessation of the senses, consciousness retreats to its
resting place in the heart center. For an ordinary person, there
is a gradual decline of conscious awareness, and at the moment
of death there is a blackout, similar to falling asleep. After a
period of time, one awakens without realizing, initially, that
death has occurred. However, then, the texts say, certain experiences reveal what has happened. One attempts to talk to one's
family or friends, but they show no awareness of one's presence
or words. One may stand in the sun but see no shadow. One
may walk in the sand but leave no footprints. Eventually one
realizes that one has separated from life, has died.

Then there follows an after-death state which may be momentary or last a long time. According to the Tibetan tradition,
death initiates a period usually specified as forty-nine days, during which one exists in the *bardo*, the state between death and
rebirth. This is a purely mental existence. Consciousness has
only a very subtle, mind-made body. In this state, one continues to have experiences. Because they are not grounded in
physical existence, they can be extraordinarily vivid, outlandish,
and frightening. During this period, the ordinary consciousness
seeks desperately to connect itself again to a physical incarnation, to reaffirm its existence. In this process, it seeks the familiar—in other words, it seeks the same kind of situation it had
at the moment of death. In Buddhist terms, it seeks to connect
with a situation that reflects its own karmic state at death.

In seeking a familiar body and familiar surroundings, the
consciousness is attracted to a man and woman whose union
can produce an embryo capable of providing the sought-for
karmic continuity. According to Buddhism, pregnancy takes
place at a time when the female can become pregnant and, in
addition, there is a consciousness seeking the karmic situation
that would be provided by the pregnancy. When these conditions are met, "fertilization" occurs, the woman becomes pregnant, and the seeking consciousness has a new home.

Not everyone takes rebirth in a human body. The accumulated karma of some consciousnesses leads them to be drawn to
other realms of existence. In Buddhism, six realms are known,
all conditioned by karma and all samsaric, but differing in the
relative amount of suffering or happiness in each. These are

divided into the three lower realms (of hell beings, hungry ghosts, and animals) and the three higher realms (of humans, demigods, and gods).

The lowest of the three lower realms is that of the hot and cold hells (*naraka*) characterized by intense aggression and suffering. Consciousnesses bearing karma arising from previous uncontrolled anger, aggression and harming of others are reincarnated in the hell realm, which reflects this state of mind. Above that is the realm of the hungry ghosts (*preta*), marked by a feeling of great physical and psychological poverty and by intense hunger and longing. Karma arising from lives driven by desire, avarice, and greed that sees others only as a means of satisfaction brings rebirth here. Also reborn here are consciousnesses of people whose lives were prematurely cut short and who were unable to relinquish their attachment to them. These spirits wander among the living for years or even centuries, frequenting places they knew, trying to contact the living, seeking to satisfy their unfulfilled state.

The highest of the three lower realms is the animal realm, characterized by ignorance and set behavior. Born here are consciousnesses that previously lived in patterns of dullness and stupidity, willfully ignoring anything beyond their routine, thus causing harm to others or failing to respond to their needs.

In the three lower realms, suffering heavily predominates. In the three higher realms, there is less suffering and more happiness. Immediately above the animal realm is that of the humans (*manusya*), characterized by a relative balance between suffering and happiness. The human realm is the most advantageous for enlightenment, and it is only here that one may become a buddha. The advantage of the human realm is that in the realms above it, there is so much happiness that beings are not motivated to change their situation, while in the realms below it, there is so much suffering that beings are unable to get sufficient distance from it to learn and change. In the human realm alone there is enough suffering to provide motivation for spiritual development, yet not so much that beings are entirely crushed by it.

Above the human realm are those of the gods (*deva*) and the demigods (*asura*), characterized by great happiness and a very long lifespan. Rebirth in these two higher realms is the positive result of kindness and generosity in previous lifetimes. How-

ever, in spite of their positive state of being, the beings in these
two realms are still within the grasp of *samsara*, for their attachment to their state produces karmic seeds for their eventual
downfall.

Rebirth in the

Buddhist

Tradition

Ordinary Reincarnation from Moment to Moment within One Life

The doctrine of reincarnation as operating from one life to another is connected with a more subtle understanding of reincarnation as governing the very workings of the mind itself.
Buddhism teaches that the notion of a solid and continuous "I"
or self is not given in reality, but is instead an idea that we
superimpose upon our fundamentally impermanent and discontinuous experience. Yet we are deeply committed to the idea
of an existent self because we crave to be, to exist, to continue,
to be more and more, to gain power and control, not to cease,
not to die. It is the discrepancy between our attempts to insist
on a solid self and the fact that no such self actually exists that
produces the continuous suffering of human existence. When
reality will not be what we want and try to make it be, we suffer.
The more we deny what we in fact experience, the more intense
our suffering, the more we struggle, and the more egocentric,
neurotic, self-serving, and mean-spirited we become.

The experience of impermanence and discontinuity, which
all people feel, however subliminally, reflects the perception of
an exceptionally clear intelligence. This is the intelligence, inherent in all beings, that perceives things as they are (*yatha-
bhutam*). This perception or intelligence is more basic than ego;
it is what is called Buddha nature (*buddha-gotra*). Buddha nature is fundamental to being human. By contrast, the belief in
a self is adventitious, incidental, and relatively superficial. The
belief in a continuous self can more or less obscure the Buddha
nature, but it can never destroy, harm, or even taint it. However
much we may try to deny what is true (that there is no self)
and attempt to insist on what is not true (that there is one), we
can never entirely succeed. The more neurotic we are in this
sense, the more we must struggle to maintain our illusion and
the more we harm others in the process.

The conventional notion of death is, according to Buddhism, inseparably linked with the idea of an "I" or self, for it presupposes the idea of a self that now truly exists and will, at a certain point, cease to exist. What death means to us is the cessation of the self that we conceive ourselves to be. And yet this cessation of the self occurs constantly, in every moment of existence. The idea of a self (and the "I" is no more than an idea), like every other concept that we have, arises, dwells momentarily, and ceases. In other words, that death of the self that we so fear is part and parcel of our experience at each moment. Yet we do not acknowledge this, our of fear of nonexistence, out of willful ignorance, and out of the momentum of avoidance strategies, known as karma, that we have developed over countless lifetimes. Yet, as mentioned, each of us is subliminally aware of this constant death of the self in each moment, which is why we are so afraid of physical death.

Each moment of life, then, contains the death of our cherished self, and this death is followed by a rebirth, based on ignorance and karmic formations, of another "incarnation," so to speak, of that idea of a self. This process of death and reincarnation in each moment, according to Buddhism, is fundamentally no different from the process that occurs when we physically die and are reincarnated. The process is exactly the same except that in the moment-to-moment death and rebirth, we take the same physical organism as the support for our concept of self (our physical body in this life). When we physically die, we must seek another physical support, another body.

An important question remains unanswered. If there is no continuous self, then what provides the continuity from one moment to the next and one life to the next? Obviously there is some kind of continuity—none of us becomes a completely different person in each moment, and Buddhism insists on a karmic continuity from life to life. Simply put, it is nothing more than an idea—an idea of the self—that is reborn over and over. It is each person's firmly held belief that he or she exists as a substantial and continuous entity, maintained by ignoring the reality of the situation. This ignoring is supported by particular patterns of avoidance that carry over from moment to moment and from life to life. The carryover is of an illusion, not of a substantial reality. Each moment of illusion is allowed to condition and give rise to a subsequent moment of illusion with the same structure. But still, from moment to moment there is a gap in which the illusory idea of self could be allowed to fall through. This succession of discontinuous but karmically linked ideas of self is called a life stream (Skt. *samtana;* Tib. *rgyud*). This life stream contains all the effects of previous actions and, through ignorance, these are bound into one ongoing series of rebirths. Each arising of consciousness is conditioned by the previous arising and in turn sets up conditions for a subsequent arising.

However, once ignorance is shattered through the experience of enlightenment, the life stream will no longer be held together. To be sure, enlightened people will live for a time before the karmic momentum of their bodily existence exhausts itself. However, when they die, they will not be reborn. The idea of a self, supported by ignorance, will have dissipated with enlightenment. Without the idea of a self, there will be no rebirth. It is interesting that even the moment-to-moment "reincarnation" of such people, which lasts until the physical death of their current body, does not operate as it does in ordinary persons. This is illustrated by the biographies of realized masters, which typically depict them as unpredictable and lacking the normal continuity of personality that most of us associate with individuality.

Extraordinary Reincarnation: Tulkus, or Incarnate Lamas

Rebirth into the six realms usually occurs as a result of the blind force of karma, resulting in an uncontrollable compulsion to regain the territory of ego. However, some people are reborn in the six realms out of a different motivation. These are individuals who, through spiritual practice, have come to advanced realization. Such people have lost much or all of their karmic momentum for rebirth in samsara and, unless some other factor entered the picture, would cease to be reborn altogether.

Buddhism teaches that insight into reality is automatically accompanied by compassion. Each progressively widening glimpse of wisdom is accompanied by a deeper sense of kindness and mercy toward other beings. The development of compassion leads naturally to an aspiration to help those sentient beings still trapped in the cycle of birth and death. Followers of Mahayana Buddhism act upon this aspiration by taking the bodhisattva vow to continue to be reborn within samsara until all beings have attained enlightenment. Among the more realized of these bodhisattvas, this vow leads to continued rebirth within the six realms, even long after the egoistic compulsion for rebirth has ceased. Since attachment to the idea of ego no longer provides the "glue" holding together the bodhisattva's "life stream," some other force must perform that function. It is now the bodhisattva's aspiration and vow that hold the life force together in one continuity, enabling him or her to continue to be reborn.

Buddha Shakyamuni, prior to his enlightenment was such a high-level bodhisattva. Since the Buddha, there have been innumerable other realized persons who have similarly taken rebirth out of compassion. Some of these have been Buddhists and some not. Within Buddhism, these reborn bodhisattvas have often been identified and even sometimes formally recognized. In India, for example, the great tantric saints (siddhas) were often considered reincarnations (nirmanakaya) of this type. In India, there developed the notion of a formally recognized line of successive incarnations of the same saint. In other words, a saint would die, would be reborn, and would be recognized as a reincarnation of the decreased master. Tucci mentions the case of the great siddha (tantric saint) Nagarjuna as an example of this type. The notion of a recognized line of successive incarnations of a particular saint was further developed in Tibet in the tradition of tulkus, or incarnate lamas. It is worth examining the tulku tradition in some detail, as a primary example of the Buddhist notion of reincarnation among saints.

In the Mahayana tradition of Tibet, when a holy person died, it was believed that, in accordance with his bodhisattva vow, he would take rebirth somewhere in or near Tibet to continue working for the benefit of sentient beings. After a certain length of time had elapsed after his death, a search would be undertaken to find the reincarnation. Once found, the child—sometimes as young as eighteen months—would be officially recognized. If, as was often the case, his predecessor had been the abbot of a monastery or complex of monasteries, he would be installed again in his former position and educated so that, when he reached majority, he could fully assume the responsibilities of his previous incarnation.

The Tibetan term *tulku* (*sprul-sku;* Skt. *nirmanakaya*) is composed of two parts, *ku* (*sku;* Skt. *kaya*) and *tul* (*sprul;* Skt. *nirmana*). *Ku* in Tibetan is an honorific term for "body" and indicates not an ordinary body but one that is pure, without ignorance, without neurosis. *Tul* refers to something that is created or fashioned. The term *tulku,* like its corresponding Sanskrit term, *nirmanakaya,* literally indicates a physical being who is completely realized. Strictly speaking, in fact, the term denotes the human incarnation of a buddha who is fully enlightened.

In its application to Tibetan masters, the term *tulku* is not necessarily to be taken literally. For one thing, all tulkus are considered to be bodhisattvas who, however high their realization, are still traversing the path toward the full and complete enlightenment of a buddha. In addition, Tibetan tradition acknowledges several different levels of tulkus. Only those few in the very highest category are understood to be enlightened (although even for them the cosmic enlightenment of a buddha still lies ahead).

The first chapter of a highly realized tulku's life actually begins with the death and after-death existence of his previous incarnation. Unlike an ordinary person, when a high-level bodhisattva dies, he does not lose all awareness but remains in a state of lucidity and peace. Resting in this state, bardo experiences are seen not as threats, but as manifestations of the energy of being. Not compelled to rebirth out of fear or desire, but drawn to it out of compassion for sentient beings, the high-level bodhisattva chooses a situation in which he will be able to continue his work of helping beings.

Because in Tibetan Buddhism tulkus play a central role in the organization and spiritual life of the monastic community and its relations with the laity, the process of locating an incarnation is considered of utmost importance. The recognition of tulkus is approached through a multifaceted process. Most important in this process is the intuition of a great guru, a master with unobstructed perception who perhaps had known the previous incarnation and could tell, by simply looking at a young child, whether he was the authentic reincarnation. Intuition might also come in the form of visions or dreams.

Sometimes visions are sought by those entrusted with recognition of tulkus at certain sacred places. One such place was the lake Lamoi Lhato near Lhasa, famous for providing various kinds of visions and spiritual direction. In the recognition of His Holiness, the fourteenth Dalai Lama, for example, the regent went to this lake and, meditating, received a decisive vision, enabling the new Dalai Lama to be found.

The insight, dreams, and visions of gifted gurus form the core of the process of recognizing reincarnations, but other factors also provide important direction and confirmation. Sometimes phenomena surrounding the previous incarnation's death provide initial indications of where to look for the new incarnation. Sometimes the identification of tulkus is aided by indications given by a particular master before his death. Among the heads of the major order of Karmapa incarnations, for example, it is traditional for the departing master to leave a letter with sometimes quite precise information concerning the identity of his next incarnation and how he is to be found.

Important indications are also sometimes given by the parents of an incarnation. The entry of a tulku's consciousness into his future mother's womb is said to be marked by unusual phenomena. The mother of a child believed to be a tulku is typically asked if she experienced anything unusual around the time of her child's conception. One tulku's mother, for example, a poor shepherdess in eastern Tibet, reported that conception had been marked by a dream of a being entering her body in a flash of light.

The birth of a tulku is also said to be accompanied by unusual phenomena, and anything unusual, noticed by parents, relatives, and villagers at the time of a possible tulku's birth is noted down. There may be phenomena such as flowers blooming out of season, a rainbow appearing in the sky, water turning to milk or relatives having unusual dreams.

In the first few years of life, young tulkus often show unusual behavior, such as recognizing and showing affection for close friends and disciples of their previous incarnation; knowing, without having been shown, how to perform various customary and ritual actions; and sitting quietly for long periods of time. Those seeking to determine the authenticity of a tulku would look carefully for phenomena of this sort.

Once there is some confidence that an incarnation has been

located, he is subjected to tests to see whether he can correctly identify objects belonging to his previous incarnation. One guru, Chögyam Trungpa, Rinpoche, reported how he was tested, at the age of eighteen months: "Pairs of several objects were put before me, and in each case I picked out the one that had belonged to the tenth Trungpa tulku; among them were two walking sticks and two rosaries; also, names were written on small pieces of paper, and when I was asked which piece had his name on it, I chose the right one."

In a similar fashion, the prospective fourteenth Dalai Lama was shown two black rosaries, two yellow rosaries, two ritual drums, and two walking sticks. One of each of these had belonged to the previous Dalai Lama and, in each case, the young child picked out the correct object.

Once recognized, a newly recognized tulku is usually brought to his monastery, with his mother if he is very young. Here he undergoes various kinds of training. We are told that among particularly high tulkus, education sometimes seems as much a matter of remembering something that had been previously known as learning something new. The Dalai Lama tells us that when he picked out his previous incarnation's rosary and ritual drum, he placed the rosary around his neck and began to beat the drum, both in the prescribed manner. He also remarks that sometimes young tulkus are able to chant texts which they have not yet learned, at least in this life. Trungpa Rinpoche reports that when it came time for him to learn the Tibetan alphabet, he was able to master it in one lesson.

Within the Buddhist context, such phenomena are understood as natural manifestations of the clarity and awareness maintained by tulkus through the experiences of death, the intermediate state, and rebirth. Ordinary people could have a similar recollection of their previous lives, except that death and its aftermath, leading to rebirth, are experienced as terrifying and traumatic, blotting out memories of previous existence.

Rebirth in the

Buddhist

Tradition

GLOSSARY

Entries in this glossary were adapted from Ingrid Fischer-Schreiber, Franz-Karl Ehrhard, and Michael S. Diener, *The Shambhala Dictionary of Buddhism and Zen* (Boston: Shambhala Publications, 1991); Nālandā Translation Committee under the direction of Chögyam Trungpa (trans.), *The Rain of Wisdom* (Boston and London: Shambhala Publications, 1980); and Yeshe Tsogyal, *The Lotus-Born: The Life Story of Padmasambhava*, trans. Erik Pema Kunsang (Boston and London: Shambhala Publications, 1993).

ABHIDHARMA (Skt., Pali Abhidhamma). "Special teaching," the third part of the Buddhist canon (*see* Tripitaka). The Abhidharma represents the earliest compilation of Buddhist philosophy and psychology. In it the teachings and analyses concerning psychological and spiritual phenomena contained in the discourses of the Buddha and his principal disciples are presented in a systematic order. It constitutes the dogmatic basis of the Hinayana and Mahayana.

ABHISHEKA (Skt.). "Anointing, consecration." The process, central for the methods of the Vajrayana, in which the disciple is empowered by the master to carry out specific meditation practices. Generally an *abhisheka* is accompanied by the reading of the corresponding *sadhana,* which authorizes the student to read and practice the corresponding text, as well as by an oral commentary by the master through which the proper mode of practice is assured.

ALAYA-VIJNANA (Skt.). "Storehouse consciousness." Central notion of the Yogachara school of the Mahayana, which sees in it the basic consciousness of everything existing—the essence of the world, out of which everything that is arises. It contains the experiences of individual lives and the seeds of every psychological phenomenon.

ANATMAN (Skt., Pali *anatta*). Nonself, nonessentiality; one of the three marks of everything existing. The *anatman* doctrine is one of the central teachings of Buddhism. It holds that no self exists in the sense of a permanent, eternal, integral, and independent substance. Thus the ego in Buddhism is no more than a transitory and change-able—and therefore suffering-prone—empirical personality put to-gether from the five aggregates (*skandhas*).

ANITYA (Skt., Pali *anicca*). "Impermanence." Transitoriness or im-permanence is one of the three marks of existence. Impermanence is the fundamental property of everything conditioned—that which arises, dwells, and passes away. From it derive the other two marks of existence, suffering and egolessness (*duhkha* and *anatman*).

ARHAT (Skt., Pali *arahat*, Chin. *lohan*, Jap. *rakan*). "Worthy one," who has attained the highest level of the Hinayana, that of "no-more-learning" on the supramundane path, and who possesses the certainty that all defilements and passions have been extinguished and will not arise again in the future. The fruition of arhatship is *nirvana* with a vestige of conditions. The *arhat* attains full extinction immediately following this life.

ASURA (Skt.). Demon, evil spirit; "titan"; one of the six modes of existence, sometimes reckoned among the higher modes and some-times among the lower. In the sense of a higher mode of existence, *asura* refers to the lower gods who dwell on the slopes or summit of the world mountain Sumeru or in castles of air. Seen as a lower mode of existence, the *asuras* are the enemies of the gods, belonging to the sensual desire realm.

ATI (Skt., Tib. *dzogchen*). "Great perfection." The primary teaching of the Nyingmapa school of Tibetan Buddhism. This teaching is con-sidered by its adherents to be the definitive and most secret teaching of Shakyamuni Buddha. It is called "great" because there is nothing more sublime; it is called "perfection" because no further means are necessary. According to the experience of Ati practitioners, purity of mind is always present and needs only to be recognized. The tradition of Ati was brought to Tibet in the eighth century by Padmasambhava and Vimilamitra; in the fourteenth century it was synthesized by Longchenpa into a unified system. The condensation of this system by Jigme Lingpa (1730–1798) remains an authoritative expression of the great perfection tradition up to the present day.

ATMAN (Skt.). According to the Hindu understanding, the real im-mortal self of human beings. In Buddhism the existence of an *atman* is denied: neither within nor outside of physical and mental manifes-

313

tations is there anything that could be designated as an independent, imperishable essence. (*See also* anatman; skandha.)

AVADHUTI (Skt.). The central channel of energy in the illusory (subtle) body. When the life force enters this channel, the resolution of duality is attained.

AVIDYA (Skt., Pali *avijja*). Ignorance or delusion. *Avidya* is the first part in the nexus of conditionality (*pratitya-samutpada*), which leads to entanglement in the world of *samsara* as well as to the three poisons (passion, aggression, and ignorance).

Avidya is considered the root of everything unwholesome in the world and is defined as ignorance of the suffering-ridden character of existence. It is that state of mind that does not correspond to reality, that holds illusory phenomena for reality, and brings forth suffering. Ignorance occasions craving (*trishna*) and is thereby the essential factor binding beings to the cycle of rebirth. According to the Mahayana view, *avidya* with regard to the emptiness (*shunyata*) of appearances entails that a person who is not enlightened will take the phenomenal world to be the only reality and thus ignore the essential truth.

BARDO (Tib.). Intermediate state between death and the next rebirth or another of the transitional states of experience.

BHAVANA (Skt., Pali). Meditation, mind development; all those practices usually designated as meditation.

BHIKSHU (Skt., Pali *bhikku*). Beggar, monk, male member of the Buddhist Sangha who has entered homelessness and received full ordination. In ancient times the *bhikshus* formed the nucleus of the Buddhist community, since according to the early Buddhist view, only a person who had renounced the world could reach the supreme goal, nirvana. The main activities of *bhikshus* are meditating and presenting the Dharma. They are not allowed to work. The basic principles of the monastic life are poverty, celibacy, and peaceableness. The lifestyle is governed by the rules laid down in the Vinaya.

BHIKSHUNI (Skt., Pali *bhikkuni*). Nun, fully ordained female member of the Buddhist Sangha. The life of nuns is similar to that of monks, but more strictly regulated. The number of nuns, compared with that of monks, is extremely small.

BHUMI (Skt.). Each of the ten stages that the *bodhisattva* must go through to attain buddhahood: very joyful, stainless, luminous, radiant, difficult to conquer, face to face, far-reaching, immovable, having good intellect, and cloud of dharma.

BODHI (Skt., Pali). "Enlightened." In the Hinayana, *bodhi* is equated with the perfection of insight into, and realization of, the Four Noble Truths; this perfection means the cessation of suffering.

By contrast, in the Mahayana, *bodhi* is mainly understood as wisdom based on insight into the unity of *nirvana* and *samsara* as well as of subject and object. It is described as the realization of *prajna*, awakening to one's own buddha-nature, insight into the essential emptiness (*shunyata*) of the world, or omniscience and perception of suchness (*tathata*).

BODHICHITTA   (Skt.). "Mind of enlightenment." Relative *bodhichitta* is the aspiration, nurtured by limitless compassion, to attain enlightenment for the sake of helping others. Absolute *bodhichitta* is direct perception of the true nature of phenomena, which is emptiness (*shunyata*).

BODHISATTVA   (Skt.). "Enlightenment being." In Mahayana Buddhism, a bodhisattva is a being who seeks buddhahood through the systematic practice of the perfect virtues (*paramitas*) but renounces complete entry into *nirvana* until all beings are saved. The determining factor for his action is compassion, supported by highest insight and wisdom (*prajna*). A bodhisattva provides active help, is ready to take upon himself the suffering of all other beings, and to transfer his own karmic merit to other beings. The way of a bodhisattva begins with arousing the thought of enlightenment and taking the bodhisattva vow. The career of a bodhisattva is divided into ten stages (*bhumis*). The bodhisattva ideal replaced in Mahayana the Hinayana ideal of the *arhat,* whose effort is directed toward the attainment of his own liberation, since this was regarded as too narrow and ego-oriented.

BUDDHA   (Skt., Pali). "Awakened one." 1. A person who has achieved the enlightenment that leads to release from the cycle of existence (*samsara*) and has thereby attained complete liberation (*nirvana*). The content of his teaching, which is based on the experience of enlightenment, is the four noble truths. A buddha has overcome every kind of craving (*trishna*); although he still has pleasant and unpleasant sensations, he is not ruled by them and remains untouched by them within. After his death he is not reborn again. The buddha of our age is Shakyamuni, although he is not the first and only buddha. Six buddhas are known to have preceded him, and fourteen are predicted to follow him.

2. The historical Buddha, born in 563 BCE, the son of a prince of the Shakyas, whose small kingdom in the foothills of the Himalayas lies in present-day Nepal. His first name was Siddhartha, his family name Gautama. Hence he is also called Gautama Buddha. During his life as a wandering ascetic, he was known as Shakyamuni, the "Sage of the Shakyas." In order to distinguish the historical Buddha from the transcendent buddhas (*see* buddha 3), he is generally called Shakyamuni Buddha or Buddha Shakyamuni.

3. The "buddha principle," which manifests itself in the most various forms. Whereas in Hinayana only the existence of one buddha in every age is accepted, for the Mahayana there are countless transcendent buddhas. According to the Mahayana teaching of the *trikaya,* the buddha principle manifests itself in three principal forms, the so-called three bodies (*see* trikaya). In this sense the transcendent buddhas represent embodiments of various aspects of the buddha principle.

CHAKRA (Skt.). "Wheel, circle." One of the centers of subtle or refined energy in the illusory body. They concentrate, transform, and distribute the energy that streams through them. Though chakras have correspondences on the bodily level (for example, head, throat, heart, and navel), these are not identical with them but belong to another level of phenomenal reality.

CH'AN (Chin.). *See* Zen.

DAKINI (Skt.). A wrathful or semiwrathful female deity (*yidam*), signifying compassion, emptiness, and knowledge.

DEVA (Skt., Pali). "Shining one." A celestial being or god; one of the inhabitants of one of the good modes of existence who live in fortunate realms of the heavens but who, like all other beings, are subject to the cycle of rebirth. The gods are allotted a long, happy life as a reward for previous good deeds; however, precisely this happiness constitutes the primary hindrance on their path to liberation, since because of it they cannot recognize the truth of suffering (*see* Four Noble Truths).

DHARMA (Skt., Pali *dhamma*). A central notion of Buddhism, used in various meanings.

1. The cosmic law, the "great norm," underlying our world; above all, the law of karmically determined rebirth.

2. The teaching of the Buddha, who recognized and formulated this "law"; thus the teaching that expresses the universal truth. The Dharma in this sense existed already before the birth of the historical Buddha, who is no more than a manifestation of it. This is the Dharma in which a Buddhist takes refuge.

3. Norms of behavior and ethical rules (*see* shila; vinaya).

4. Manifestation of reality, of the general state of affairs; thing, phenomenon.

5. Mental content, object of thought, idea—a reflection of a thing in the human mind.

6. Term for the so-called factors of existence, which the Hinayana considers to be the building blocks of the empirical personality and its world.

DHARMAKAYA (Skt.). *See* trikaya.

DHARMATA (Skt.) The nature of the *dharmas*, the essence of everything. Philosophical concept of the Mahayana. Synonymous with *tathata*, suchness.

DHYANA (Skt., Pali *jhana*, Chin. *ch'an-na* or *ch'an*, Jap. *zenna* or *zen*). Meditation, absorption. In general, any absorbed state of mind brought about through concentration (*samadhi*). Such a state is reached through the entire attention dwelling uninterruptedly on a physical or mental object of meditation; in this way the mind passes through various stages in which the currents of the passions gradually fade away.

DOHA (Skt.). A type of verse or song spontaneously composed by Vajrayana practitioners as an expression of their realization.

DUHKHA (Skt., Pali *dukkha*). Suffering; a central concept in Buddhism, which lies at the root of the Four Noble Truths. *Duhkha* not only signifies suffering in the sense of unpleasant sensations, but also refers to everything, both material and mental, that is conditioned, that is subject to arising and passing away, that is comprised of the five *skandhas*, and that is not in a state of liberation. Thus everything that is temporarily pleasant is suffering, since it is subject to ending. *Duhkha* arises because of desire and craving and can be overcome by the elimination of desire. The means to bring about the extinction of suffering is shown by the Eightfold Path.

EIGHTFOLD PATH (Skt. *ashtangika-marga*, Pali *atthangika-magga*). The path leading to release from suffering. The eight parts of the path are (1) right view, based on understanding of the Four Noble Truths and the nonindividuality of existence (*anatman*); (2) right resolve, in favor of renunciation, good will, and nonharming of sentient beings; (3) right speech, or avoidance of lying, slander, and gossip; (4) right livelihood, or avoidance of professions that are harmful to sentient beings, such as butcher, hunter, weapons or narcotics dealer; (6) right effort, or cultivation of what is karmically wholesome and avoidance of what is karmically unwholesome; (7) right mindfulness, or ongoing mindfulness of body, feelings, thinking, and objects of thought; and (8) right concentration, which finds its highpoint in meditative absorption.

FOUR NOBLE TRUTHS (Skt. *arya-satya*, Pali *ariya-satta*). The basis of the Buddhist teaching. They are (1) the truth of suffering, (2) the truth of the origin of suffering, (3) the truth of the cessation of suffering, (4) the truth of the path that leads to the cessation of suffering.

The first truth says that existence is characterized by suffering (*duhkha*) and does not bring satisfaction. Everything is suffering: birth, sickness, death; coming together with what one does not like; separating from what one does like; not obtaining what one desires;

and the five aggregates (*skandhas*) of attachment that constitute the personality.

The second truth gives as the cause of suffering craving or desire, the thirst (*trishna*) for sensual pleasure, for becoming and passing away. This craving binds beings to the cycle of existence (*samsara*).

The third truth says that through elimination of craving, suffering can be brought to an end.

The fourth truth gives the Eightfold Path as the means for ending suffering.

GANACHAKRA   (Skt.). A ritual feast, a practice in which desire and sense perceptions are made part of the path. By celebrating the phenomenal world, practitioners simultaneously extend their understanding of sacredness and further surrender ego.

GURU   (Skt.). Teacher, particularly a spiritual master.

HINAYANA   (Skt.). The "small vehicle," in which the practitioner concentrates on basic meditation practice and an understanding of basic Buddhist doctrines such as the Four Noble Truths. *See also* Theravada.

JETSUN   (Tib.). Honorific Tibetan term applied to revered teachers.

KANNON   (Jap., also spelled Kanzeon or Kwannon; Chin. Kuan-yin; Skt. Avalokiteshvara). One of the most important bodhisattvas of the Mahayana; the Bodhisattva of Compassion.

KARMA   (Skt., Pali *kamma*). "Deed." According to the doctrine of cause and effect, our present experience is a product of previous actions and volitions, and future conditions depend on what we do in the present. Actions may be classified in three ways: (1) wholesome—tending toward higher realms of *samsara,* or in the presence of an enlightened attitude, toward liberation; (2) unwholesome—tending to perpetuate confusion and pain; and (3) neutral.

Karma originates from the false belief in an ego, which prompts a chain reaction of seeking to protect territory and maintain security. Virtuous action can lead to better states, but the chain reaction process itself can only be cut and transcended by insight and discipline. Karma can be precise down to the minute details of body, mind, and environment. There is "group karma" of families and nations as well as individual karma.

KAYA   (Skt.). *See* trikaya.

KLESHA   (Skt., Pali *kilesa*). "Trouble, defilement, passion"; any of the factors, particularly conflicting emotions, that dull the mind and are the basis for all unwholesome actions and thus bind people to the cycle of rebirth (*samsara*). The attainment of arhathood (*see* arhat) signifies the extinction of all *kleshas*.

LAMA (Tib.). "None above"; in Tibetan Buddhism a religious master, or guru, venerated by his students, since he is an authentic embodiment of the Buddhist teachings. The term *lama* is used for the Sanskrit *guru* in the traditional Indian sense, but includes still further meanings. For the Vajrayana, the lama is particularly important, since his role is not only to teach rituals but also to conduct them.

As spiritual authority, he can be the head of one or several monasteries and possess political influence. The spiritual "value" of the *lama* is indicated by the honorific title *rinpoche* ("precious jewel"), which is bestowed upon especially qualified masters. Today, however, *lama* is often used as a polite form of address for any Tibetan monk, regardless of the level of his spiritual development.

LOJONG (Tib.). "Mind-training." Specifically, the practice of cultivating *bodhichitta* outlined by the Kadampa slogans, introduced into Tibet by the great Indian Buddhist teacher Atisha Dipankara Shrijnana (982–1054).

LOKA (Skt.). "World." A term used in reference to the traditional division of the universe into various worlds, generally a threefold division into heaven, earth, and hell, which are subdivided into six realms. Heaven contains the god realm and the jealous god (*asura*) realm; earth, the human realm and the animal realm; hell, the hungry ghost (*preta*) realm and the hell realm. The six realms correspond to six psychological states respectively: bliss, jealousy and lust for entertainment, passion and desire, ignorance, poverty and possessiveness, and aggression and hatred.

MADHYAMAKA (Skt.) A Mahayana school, founded by the Indian teacher Nagarjuna, which emphasizes the doctrine of *shunyata*.

MAHASIDDHA (Skt.). Roughly "great master of perfect capabilities." In the Vajrayana, a yogi who has mastered the teachings of the Tantras. He distinguishes himself through certain magical powers (*siddhis*), which are visible signs of his enlightenment. Best known is the group of eighty-four *mahasiddhas*, among whom were men and women of all social classes; their model of highly individual realization strongly influenced Tibetan Buddhism.

MAHAYANA (Skt.). "Great vehicle." One of the three great bodies of Buddhist doctrine, the others being the Hinayana, "small vehicle," and the Vajrayana, "indestructible vehicle." The Mahayana emphasizes the emptiness of all phenomena, compassion, and the acknowledgment of universal buddha-nature. The ideal figure of the Mahayana is the bodhisattva; hence it is often referred to as the bodhisattva path.

MANDALA (Skt.). "Circle, arch, section." A symbolic representation of cosmic forces in two- or three-dimensional form, which is of considerable significance in the tantric Buddhism of Tibet.

MANJUSHRI (Skt., Jap. *Monju*). "He Who Is Noble and Gentle." The bodhisattva of wisdom, one of the most important figures of the Buddhist pantheon.

MANTRA (Skt.). A power-laden syllable or series of syllables that manifests certain cosmic forces and aspects of the buddhas; sometimes it is also the name of a buddha. Continuous repetition of mantras is practiced as a form of meditation in many Buddhist schools; it plays a considerable role in the Vajrayana. Here *mantra* is defined as a means of protecting the mind. In the transformation of "body, speech, and mind" that is brought about by spiritual practice, mantra is associated with speech. Recitation of mantras is often done in connection with detailed visualizations and certain bodily postures.

MUDRA (Skt.). "Seal, sign." A bodily posture or a symbolic gesture. In Buddhist iconography every buddha is depicted with a characteristic gesture of the hands, which corresponds to natural gestures (of teaching, protecting, and so on) and also to certain aspects of the Buddhist teaching or of the particular buddha depicted. In the Vajrayana, *mudras* accompany the performance of liturgies and the recitation of mantras. They also help to actualize certain inner states in that they anticipate their physical expression; thus they assist in bringing about a connection between the practitioner and the buddha visualized in a given practice (*sadhana*).

NAGA (Skt.). "Serpent." The "dragon," a beneficent half-divine being, which in spring climbs into the heavens and in winter lives deep in the earth. *Naga* or *mahanaga* ("great dragon") is sometimes used as a synonym for the Buddha or for the sages who have matured beyond rebirth. *Nagarajas* ("dragon kings" or "dragon queens") are water deities who govern springs, rivers, lakes, and seas. In many Buddhist traditions the *nagas* are water deities who in their sea palaces guard Buddhist scriptures that have been placed in their care because humanity is not yet ripe for their reception.

NIDANA (Skt.). *See* pratitya-samutpada.

NIRMANAKAYA (Skt.). *See* trikaya.

NIRVANA (Skt., Pali *nibbana*, Jap. *nehan*). "Extinction." The goal of spiritual practice in all branches of Buddhism. The term *nirvana* does not indicate annihilation, but rather entry into another mode of existence. In the understanding of early Buddhism, it is departure from the cycle of rebirths (*samsara*) and entry into an entirely different mode of existence. It requires completely overcoming the three unwholesome roots—desire, hatred, and delusion—and ending active volition. It means freedom from the determining effect of karma. *Nirvana* is unconditioned; its characteristic marks are absence of arising, subsisting, changing, and passing away.

PARAMITA (Skt.). "That which has reached the other shore," the transcendental. The *paramitas*, generally translated as "the perfections," are the virtues perfected by a bodhisattva in the course of development. There are six of these: (1) *dana-paramita* (generosity), (2) *shila-paramita* (discipline), (3) *kshanti-paramita* (patience), (4) *virya-paramita* (energy or exertion), (5) *dhyana-paramita* (meditation), (6) *prajna-paramita* (transcendental knowledge).

PARINIRVANA (Skt., Pali *parinibbana*). "Total extinction." Synonym for *nirvana*. *Parinirvana* is often equated with *nirvana* after death, but can also refer to *nirvana* before death. Sometimes *parinirvana* simply means the death of a monk or nun.

PHOWA (Tib.). Ejection of consciousness at the moment of death.

PITAKA (Skt.). *See* tripitaka.

PRAJNA (Skt., Pali *panna*, Jap. *hannya*). "Transcendental knowledge" or "wisdom." A central notion of the Mahayana referring to an immediately experienced intuitive wisdom that cannot be conveyed by concepts or in intellectual terms. The definitive moment of *prajna* is insight into emptiness *(shunyata)*, which is the true nature of reality. The realization of prajna is often equated with the attainment of enlightenment and is one of the essential marks of buddhahood. *Prajna* is also one of the "perfections" *(paramitas)* actualized by bodhisattvas in the course of their development.

PRATITYA-SAMUTPADA (Skt., Pali, *patichcha-samuppada*). "Conditioned arising" or "interdependent arising." The doctrine of conditioned arising says that all psychological and physical phenomena constituting apparent individual existence are interdependent and mutually condition each other; this at the same time describes what entangles sentient beings in *samsara*.

The chain of conditioned arising is, together with the *anatman* doctrine, the core teaching of all Buddhist schools. Attainment of enlightenment and thus realization of buddhahood depends on comprehending this doctrine.

Pratitya-samutpada consists of twelve links *(nidanas)*: (1) ignorance, which conditions (2) formations or impulses, which precede actions. These can be good, bad, or neutral and are related to physical, verbal, and psychological actions. In turn they condition (3) consciousness in the next life of the individual. This consciousness reenters another womb after the death of an individual who has not been liberated and instigates there the arising of (4) "name and form," the psychological and physical factors, i.e., a new empirical being constituted by the five *skandhas*. Which womb the consciousness chooses is determined by its qualities, which in turn depend upon the formations or impulses. Interdependently, (5) the six bases arise. These are the six object realms of the senses, which present themselves to the being after its birth, thus conditioning (6) contact with its environment. This contact invokes (7) sensation, out of which develops, for someone who is ignorant in the Buddhist sense, (8) craving. Ignorance and craving lead, after the death of the individual, to (9) clinging to a womb, where (10) a new becoming is set in motion. This is followed by (11) birth, which again comes to an end in (12) old age and death. The entire chain of conditions thus covers three existences: 1–2 relate to the previous existence, 3–7 relate to conditioning of the present existence, 8–10 to the fruits of the present existence, and 11–12 to the future life. Although conditioned arising has been described here in terms of life and death, it also applies to the phenomena and situations of this life.

PRATYEKABUDDHA (Skt., Pali *pachcheka-buddha*). "Solitary awakened one." A term for an awakened one (buddha) who has attained enlightenment on his own and only for himself. Meritorious qualities, such as omniscience, or the ten powers, which characterize a fully enlightened one, are not ascribed to him. In the levels of sainthood, he is placed between the *arhats* and the buddhas who have attained complete enlightenment.

PRETA (Skt., Pali *peta*). "Departed one." These so-called hungry ghosts constitute one of the three negative modes of existence. *Pretas* are beings whose karma is too good for rebirth in the hells but too bad for rebirth as an *asura*. Greed, envy, and jealousy can, according to the traditional view, lead to rebirth as a *preta*. *Pretas* suffer the torment of hunger, because their bellies are immense but their mouths only as big as the eye of a needle. They are also subject to various other tortures.

RAKSHA (Skt.). More or less evil spirits. Three types are distinguished: harmless beings; titans, or enemies of the gods; and demons and devils, who inhabit cemeteries and harass human beings.

RINPOCHE (Tib.). *See* lama.

RINZAI (Jap., Chin. *Lin-chi*). Name of one of the most important schools of Ch'an (Zen), and one of the two schools of Zen still active in Japan. In the Rinzai school, primarily *kanna* Zen ("Zen of the contemplation of words") and thus koan practice are stressed as an especially fast way to the realization of enlightenment.

ROSHI (Jap.). "Old [venerable] master"; title of a Zen master. Traditional training in Zen takes place under a *roshi,* who can be monk or layperson, man or woman. It is the task of the *roshi* to lead and inspire students on the way to enlightenment, for which, naturally, the prerequisite is that the roshi has already experienced profound enlightenment.

SADHANA   (Skt.). Derived from *sadh*, "to arrive at the goal" and meaning roughly "means to completion or perfection." In Vajrayana Buddhism a *sadhana* is a particular type of liturgical text and the meditation practices presented in it. *Sadhana* texts describe in detail deities to be experienced as spiritual realities and the entire process from graphic visualization of them to dissolving them into formless meditation. Performing this type of religious practice, which is central to Tibetan Buddhism, requires empowerment and consecration by the master for practice connected with the particular deity involved. Part of this is transmission of the mantra associated with the deity.

SAMADHI   (Skt., Jap. *sanmai* or *zanmai*). "Establish, make firm." Collectedness of the mind on a single object through (gradual) calming of mental activity. *Samadhi* is a nondualistic state of consciousness in which the consciousness of the experiencing "subject" becomes one with the experienced "object." This state of consciousness is often referred to as "one-pointedness of mind," but this expression can be misleading if it calls up the image of "concentration" on one point on which the mind is "directed." In *samadhi*, the mind is neither straining to concentrate on one point, nor is it directed from here (subject) to there (object), which would be a dualistic mode of experience.

SAMAYA   (Skt.). "Coming together." The Vajrayana principle of commitment, whereby the student's total experience is bound to the path.

SAMSARA   (Skt.). "Journeying." The "cycle of existences," a succession of rebirths that a being goes through within the various modes of existence until liberation is attained. Imprisonment in *samsara* is conditioned by the three "unwholesome roots": hatred, craving, and delusion. The type of rebirth within *samsara* is determined by the karma of the being. In the Mahayana, *samsara* refers to the phenomenal world and is considered to be essentially identical with *nirvana*.

SAMSKARA   (Skt., Pali *sankhara*). "Impression, consequence." Generally translated as "formations," "mental formational forces," or "impulses." *Samskara* is the fourth of the *skandhas* and the second link in the chain of conditioned arising *(pratitya-samutpada.)* Formations include all volitional impulses or intentions that precede an action. Since actions can be physical, verbal, or mental, impulses that are physical, verbal, and mental are distinguished. Their presence is the condition for a new rebirth. If they are absent, no karma is produced and no further rebirths take place. In addition they determine the type of rebirth, since they can be good, bad, or neutral, and their quality conditions the consciousness that arises—according to the doctrine of conditioned arising—through them, that seeks a womb after the death of a being, and that brings about the existence of a new empirical person.

SANGHA (Skt.). "Crowd, host." The Buddhist community. In a narrower sense the Sangha consists of monks, nuns, and novices. In a wider sense the Sangha also includes lay followers.

SHAKYAMUNI (Skt.). "Sage of the Shakya Clan"; epithet of Siddhartha Gautama, the founder of Buddhism, the historical Buddha, who belonged to the Shakya clan. Siddhartha received this epithet after he had separated himself from his teachers and resolved to find the way to enlightenment by himself.

SHAMATHA (Skt.). "Dwelling in tranquillity." A basic meditation practice common to most schools of Buddhism, whose aim is the taming and sharpening of the mind by means of coming back again and again to meditative discipline. Shamatha is developed as a springboard for insight *(vipashyana)*, seeing the transparency of experiences rather than solidifying them.

SHASTRA (Skt.). "Instruction, textbook." A type of Buddhist text; generally a commentary or a philosophical treatise.

SHIKANTAZA (Jap.). "Nothing but *(shikan)* precisely *(ta)* sitting *(za)*." A form of the practice of *zazen* in which there are no more supportive techniques of the type beginners use, such as counting the breath or a koan.

SHILA (Skt., Pali *sila*). "Obligations, precepts." A general term for discipline or one of the ethical guidelines that in Buddhism determine the behavior of monks, nuns, and lay persons and that constitute the precondition for any progress on the path of awakening *bodhi*. The ten shilas for monks and nuns and novices are (1) refraining from killing, (2) not taking what is not given, (3) refraining from prohibited sexual activity, (4) refraining from unjust speech, (5) abstaining from intoxicants, (6) abstaining from solid food after noon, (7) avoiding music, dance, plays, and other entertainments, (8) abstaining from the use of perfumes and ornamental jewelry, (9) refraining from sleeping in high, soft beds, (10) refraining from contact with money and other valuables. The first five *shila*s apply also to Buddhist laypersons, who on certain days observe the first eight.

SHRAVAKA (Skt.). "Hearer." Originally a reference to the personal students of the Buddha or students in general. In the Mahayana, it means those students who, in contrast to *pratyekabuddha*s and bodhisattvas, seek personal enlightenment and can attain this only by listening to the teaching and gaining insight into the Four Noble Truths and the irreality of phenomena.

SHUNYATA (Skt., Pali *sunnata*, Jap. *ku*). "Emptiness, void." Central notion of Buddhism. Ancient Buddhism recognized that all composite things are empty, impermanent, devoid of an essence, and characterized by suffering. In the Hinayana emptiness is only applied to the "person"; in the Mahayana, on the other hand, all things are regarded as without essence. *Shunyata* does not mean that things do not exist but rather that they are nothing besides appearances. In the Vajrayana, it is equivalent to the feminine principle—unborn, unceasing, like space.

SIDDHA (Skt.). "Perfect, complete." An enlightened master in the tantric tradition. *Siddha* has the connotation of one who, besides being realized on the absolute level, is in tune with the magical possibilities of the phenomenal world.

SIDDHI (Skt.). "Perfect abilities." In the context of Buddhist yoga as it is practiced especially in the Vajrayana, perfect mastery over the powers of the body and of nature. The Vajrayana is acquainted with eight ordinary *siddhi*s: (1) the sword that renders unconquerable, (2) the elixir for the eyes that makes gods visible, (3) fleetness in running, (4) invisibility, (5) the life-essence that preserves youth, (6) the ability to fly, (7) the ability to make certain pills, (8) power over the world of spirits and demons. Enlightenment is differentiated from these eight as the sole "extraordinary" or supreme *siddhi*. In the biographies of the eighty-four *mahasiddhas*, the attainment of these abilities is described in detail.

SIX REALMS. *See* loka.

SKANDHA (Skt., Pali *khanda*). "Group, aggregate, heap." One of the five aggregates, which constitute the entirety of what is generally known as "personality." They are (1) form, (2) sensation, (3) perception, (4) mental formations, and (5) consciousness. These aggregates are frequently referred to as "aggregates of attachment," since (excluding the case of *arhats* and buddhas) craving or desire attaches itself to them and attracts them to itself; thus it makes of them objects of attachment and brings about suffering.

SOTO (Jap., Chin. *Ts'ao-tung*). With the Rinzai school, one of the two most important schools of Zen in Japan. The Soto school heavily stresses *mokusho* Zen ("Zen of silent enlightenment") and thus also the practice of sitting meditation (*see* shikantaza).

SUTRA (Skt., Pali *sutta*, Jap. *kyo*). "Thread." A discourse of the Buddha. The sutras are collected in the second part of the Buddhist canon (*see* Tripitaka), the Sutra-pitaka, or "Basket of the Teachings." The sutras have been preserved in Pali and Sanskrit as well as in Chinese and Tibetan translations.

TANTRA (Skt.). "Continuum, thread." A general concept for the basic activity of the Vajrayana and its systems of meditation. Also a term for various kinds of texts (medical tantras, astrological tantras, etc.)

TATHAGATA (Skt., Pali). "Thus-gone." One who on the way of truth has attained supreme enlightenment. It is one of the ten titles of the Buddha, which he himself used when speaking of himself or other buddhas.

THERAVADA (Pali). "Teaching of the elders of the order." The Hinayana school (also called the Pali school), founded in and brought to Ceylon in 250 B.C.E. Today the Theravada is widespread in the countries of Southeast Asia and regards itself as the school closest to the original form of Buddhism. The emphasis in the Theravada is on the liberation of the individual, which takes place through one's own effort in meditation, and through observing the rules of moral discipline and leading a monastic life.

TRIKAYA (Skt.). "Three bodies." Refers to the three bodies possessed by a buddha according to the Mahayana view. The basis of this teaching is the conviction that a buddha is one with the absolute and manifests in the relative world in order to work for the welfare of all beings. The three bodies are: (1) *Dharmakaya* ("body of the great order"), the true nature of the Buddha, which is identical with transcendental reality, the essence of the universe. The *dharmakaya* is the unity of the Buddha with everything existing. At the same time it represents the Dharma, the teaching expounded by the Buddha. (2) *Sambhogakaya* ("body of delight"), the body of buddhas who in a "buddha-paradise" enjoy the truth that they embody. (3) *Nirmanakaya* ("body of transformation"), the earthly body in which buddhas appear to people in order to fulfill the buddhas' resolve to guide all beings to liberation.

TRIPITAKA (Skt., Pali *Tipitaka*). "Three Baskets." The canon of Buddhist scriptures, consisting of three parts: the Vinaya-pitaka, the Sutra-pitaka, and the Abhidharma-pitaka. The first "basket" contains accounts of the origins of the Buddhist Sangha as well as the rules of discipline regulating the lives of monks and nuns. The second is composed of discourses said to have come from the mouth of Buddha or his immediate disciples. The third part is a compendium of Buddhist psychology and philosophy.

TRISHNA (Skt., Pali, *tanha*). "Thirst, craving, desire." A central notion of Buddhism. *Trishna* is the desire that arises through the contact between a sense organ and its corresponding object. It is the cause of attachment and thus of suffering (*duhkha*); it binds sentient beings to the cycle of existence (*samsara*).

TULKU   (Tib.). "Transformation body." In Tibetan Buddhism, a term for a person who, after certain tests, is recognized as the reincarnation of a previously deceased person.

UPASAKA   (Skt., Pali). "One who sits close by." Buddhist lay adherent who takes refuge in the Buddha, the Dharma, and the Sangha, and who vows to observe the five *shilas*.

UPAYA   (Skt.). Skill in means or method. 1. The ability of a bodhisattva to guide beings to liberation through skillful means. All possible methods and ruses from straightforward talk to the most conspicuous miracles could be applicable. 2. Skill in expounding the teaching.

VAJRA   (Skt., Tib. *dorje*). "Adamantine, diamond." In general, the term *vajra* conveys the sense of what is beyond arising and ceasing and hence indestructible. A *vajra* is also a ritual scepter used in Vajrayana practice.

VAJRAYANA   (Skt.). "Diamond Vehicle." A school of Buddhism that arose, primarily in northeastern and northwestern India, around the middle of the first millennium. It developed out of the teachings of the Mahayana and reached Tibet, China, and Japan from Central Asia and India along with the Mahayana. It is characterized by a psychological method based on highly developed ritual practices.

VIDYA   (Skt.). "Knowledge, teaching." There are two types of *vidya:* (1) lower knowledge, or intellectually acquired knowledge, and (2) higher knowledge, or intuitive, spiritual experience, which leads to enlightenment, liberation, and realization of the supreme reality.

VINAYA   (Skt., Pali). "Discipline." The third part of the Tripitaka, containing the rules and regulations for the communal life of monks and nuns.

VIPASHYANA   (Skt., Pali *vipassana*). Insight, clear seeing; intuitive cognition of the three marks of existence, namely, the impermanence, suffering, and egolessness of all physical and mental phenomena. In Mahayana, *vipashyana* is seen as analytical examination of the nature of things that leads to insight into the true nature of the world— emptiness (*shunyata*). Such insight prevents the arising of new passions. *Vipashyana* is one of the two factors essential for the attainment of enlightenment; the other is *shamatha* (calming the mind).

VIRYA   (Skt., Pali *viriya*). Energy, will power, the basis of which is indefatigable exertion to bring about wholesomeness and avoid unwholesomeness, and to transform impure into pure.

YIDAM   (Tib.). "Firm mind." In Vajrayana Buddhism, a personal deity, whose nature corresponds to the individual psychological makeup of the practitioner. *Yidams* are manifestations of the *sambho-*

gakaya (*see* trikaya) and are visualized in meditative practice. They can take on either a peaceful or wrathful form of manifestation.

YOGA   (Skt.). "Yoke." The actual integration of learning into personal experience. In Vajrayana Buddhism, a general reference to meditation practices.

YOGACHARA SCHOOL   (Skt.). "Application of yoga." A school of Mahayana Buddhism founded by Maitreyanatha, Asanga, and Vasubandhu, emphasizing the primacy of experience.

YOGI   (Skt.). A tantric practitioner. A male practitioner is called a *yogin;* a female practitioner, a *yogini.*

ZAZEN   (Jap., Chin. *tso-ch'an*). From *za,* "sitting" and *zen,* "absorption." Meditative practice taught in Zen as the most direct way to enlightenment.

ZEN   (Jap., Chin. *ch'an*). A school of Mahayana Buddhism that developed in China in the sixth and seventh centuries. More than any other school, Zen stresses the primary importance of the enlightenment experience and teaches the practice of *zazen*—sitting as the shortest, but also the steepest, way to awakening.

BIBLIOGRAPHY: SUGGESTED FURTHER READINGS

PART ONE
The Life of the Buddha and the Spread of Buddhism

Kohn, Sherab Chödzin. *The Awakened One: A Life of the Buddha.* Boston & London: Shambhala Publications, 1994.

Nyanamoli, Bhikku. *Life of the Buddha.* Kandy: Buddhist Publication Society, 1972.

PART TWO
Basic Teachings

Byrom, Thomas, trans. *The Dhammapada.* New York: Vintage, 1976.

Goenka, S. N., *The Art of Living.* San Francisco: HarperSanFrancisco, 1987.

Goldstein, Joseph. *The Experience of Insight: A Simple and Direct Guide to Buddhist Meditation.* Boston & London: Shambhala Publications, 1987.

Goldstein, Joseph, and Jack Kornfield. *Seeking the Heart of Wisdom: The Path of Insight Meditation.* Boston & London: Shambhala Publications, 1987.

Katagiri, Dainin. *Returning to Silence: Zen Practice in Daily Life.* Boston & London: Shambhala Publications, 1988.

Kornfield, Jack. *Living Buddhist Masters.* Boulder: Prajña Press, 1983.

Rahula, Walpola. *What the Buddha Taught.* New York: Grove Press, 1962.

Sangharakshita. *A Survey of Buddhism.* London: Windhorse, 1987.

Thera, Nyanaponika. *The Heart of Buddhist Meditation.* York Harbor, Me.: Samuel Weiser, 1973.

———. *Vision of Dhamma: The Buddhist Writings of Nyanaponika Thera.* York Harbor, Me.: Samuel Weiser, 1987.

Warren, Clarke. *Buddhism in Translation.* New York: Dover, 1986.

PART THREE
The Teachings of the Great Vehicle

MAHAYANA

Chang, C. C. *A Treasury of Mahayana Sutras.* State College: Pennsylvania State University Press, 1983.

Chödrön, Pema. *The Wisdom of No Escape and the Path of Loving-Kindness.* Boston & London: Shambhala Publications, 1991.

Conze, Edward, ed. *Buddhist Scriptures.* Harmondsworth: Penguin, 1959.

————. *Buddhist Texts through the Ages.* Boston & London: Shambhala Publications, 1990.

Gyatso, Tenzin, the Fourteenth Dalai Lama. *A Flash of Lightning in the Dark of Night: A Guide to the Bodhisattva's Way of Life.* Boston & London: Shambhala Publications, 1994.

Hanh, Thich Nhat. *Being Peace.* Berkeley: Parallax Press, 1987.

————. *Peace Is Every Step: The Path of Mindfulness in Everyday Life.* New York: Bantam, 1991.

Kongtrul, Jamgon. *The Great Path of Awakening: A Commentary on the Mahayana Teaching of the Seven Points of Mind Training.* Trans. Ken McLeod. Boston & London: Shambhala Publications, 1987.

Luk, Charles, trans. *Vimalakirti Nirdesa Sutra.* Boston & London: Shambhala Publications, 1990.

Price, A. F., and Wong Mou-lam, trans. *The Diamond Sutra and the Sutra of Hui-neng.* Boston & London: Shambhala Publications, 1990.

Shantideva. *A Guide to the Bodhisattva's Way of Life.* Trans. Stephen Batchelor and Sherpa Tulku. Dharamsala: Library for Tibetan Works and Archives, 1979.

Suzuki, D. T. *The Lankavatara Sutra.* London: Routledge & Kegan, Paul, 1932.

Zopa, Lama. *Transforming Problems into Happiness.* Boston: Wisdom Publications, 1993.

ZEN

Beck, Charlotte Joko. *Everyday Zen: Love and Work.* New York: Harper, 1989.

Blofeld, John, trans. *The Zen Teaching of Huang Po: On the Transmission of Mind.* New York: Grove Press, 1975.

Cleary, Thomas, trans. *Rational Zen: The Mind of Dogen Zenji.* Boston & London: Shambhala Publications, 1992.

Kapleau, Philip. *The Three Pillars of Zen.* New York: Anchor, 1989.

Reps, Paul. *Zen Flesh, Zen Bones: A Collection of Zen and Pre-Zen*
Writings. Rutland, Vt.: Charles E. Tuttle, 1989.

Soho, Takuan. *The Unfettered Mind: Writings of the Zen Master to the Sword Master*. New York: Kodansha, 1986.

Suzuki, Shunryu. *Zen Mind, Beginner's Mind*. New York: Weatherhill, 1971.

Tanahashi, Kazuaki, ed. *Moon in a Dewdrop: Writings of Zen Master Dogen*. San Francisco: North Point Press, 1985.

PART FOUR
The Tantric Teachings

Allione, Tsultrim. *Women of Wisdom*. New York: Penguin, 1988.

Chang, C. C., trans. *One Hundred Thousand Songs of Milarepa*. 2 vols. Boston & London: Shambhala Publications, 1989.

Fremantle, Francesca, and Chögyam Trungpa, trans. *The Tibetan Book of the Dead: The Great Liberation through Hearing in the Bardo*. Boston & London: Shambhala Publications, 1987.

Lhalungpa, Lobsang P., trans. *The Life of Milarepa*. New York: Arkana, 1992.

Padmasambhava. *Dakini Teachings: Padmasambhava's Oral Teachings to Lady Tsogyal*. Trans. Erik Pema Kunsang. Boston & London: Shambhala Publications, 1990.

Trungpa, Chögyam. *Cutting Through Spiritual Materialism*. Boston & London: Shambhala Publications, 1987.

———. *Journey without Goal: The Tantric Wisdom of the Buddha*. Boston & London: Shambhala Publications, 1985.

———. *The Myth of Freedom and the Way of Meditation*. Boston & London: Shambhala Publications, 1976.

Tsogyal, Yeshe. *The Lotus Born: The Life Story of Padmasambhava*. Trans. Erik Pema Kunsang. Boston & London: Shambhala Publications, 1993.

Chapter 9, "Karma and Its Fruit": From *The Heart of Buddhist Meditation*, by Nyanaponika Thera (York Beach, Me.: Samuel Weiser, 1973; Kandy: Buddhist Publication Society, 1992). Reprinted by permission of Samuel Weiser, Inc., York Beach, ME 03910.

Chapter 10, "The Practice of Recollection": From *The Practice of Recollection: A Guide to Buddhist Meditation*, by Bhikku Mangalo (Boulder, Colo.: Prajna Press, 1978).

Chapter 11, "Unlimited Friendliness": Version of *The Metta Sutta*, by Gil Fronsdal, from *Teachings of the Buddha*, edited by Jack Kornfield with Gil Fronsdal. © 1993 by Jack Kornfield. Reprinted by arrangement with Shambhala Publications, Inc.

Chapter 12, "On Trust in the Mind": From *On Trust in the Mind*, by Seng-ts'an, translated by Burton Watson. Reprinted by permission of the translator.

Chapter 13, "The Heart Sutra": *The Heart Sutra*, translated by the Nālandā Translation Committee (Boulder & Halifax: Nālandā Translation Committee, 1975). Reprinted by permission of the Nālandā Translation Committee, 1619 Edward St., Halifax, Nova Scotia, Canada B3H 3H9.

Chapter 14, "Exchanging Oneself for Others": Translated by Glenn H. Mullin in accordance with an oral explanation received from Lama Chomdze Tashi Wangyal of Drepung Loseling at the Library of Tibetan Works and Archives, Dharamsala, 1979.

Chapter 15, "Loving-Kindness": From *The Wisdom of No Escape and the Path of Loving-Kindness*, by Pema Chödrön. © 1991 by Pema Chödrön. Reprinted by arrangement with Shambhala Publications, Inc.

Chapter 16, "The Bodhisattva Path": From *Cutting Through Spiritual Materialism*, by Chögyam Trungpa. © 1973 by Chögyam Trungpa. Reprinted by arrangement with Shambhala Publications, Inc.

Chapter 17, "The Sutra Called Flawless Purity": From *A Treasury of Mahayana Sutras*, by Garma C. C. Chang (University Park: Pennsylvania State University Press, 1983), pp. 37–40. © 1983 by the Pennsylvania State University Press. Reprinted by permission of the publisher.

Chapter 18, "Looking at Living Beings": From *The Vimalakirti Nirdesa Sutra*, translated and edited by Charles Luk (Boston: Shambhala Publications, 1990), chap. 7.

Chapter 19, "The Enlightenment of Hui-neng": From *The Diamond Sutra and the Sutra of Hui-neng*, translated by A.F. Price and Wong Mou-lam (Boston: Shambhala Publications, 1990), pp. 67–78.

Chapter 20, "To Forget the Self": From *The Way of Everyday Life: Zen Master Dogen's Genjokoan with Commentary by Hakuyu Taizan Maezumi* (Los Angeles: Center Publications, 1978).

Chapter 21, "Ten Bulls": From *Zen Flesh, Zen Bones: A Collection of Zen and Pre-Zen Writings,* compiled by Paul Reps (Rutland, Vt.: Charles E. Tuttle, 1989), pp. 165–67, 168–87.

Chapter 22, "Unfettered Mind": From *The Unfettered Mind,* by Takuan Soho, translated by William Scott Wilson, published by Kodansha International Ltd. © 1986 by Kodansha International Ltd. Reprinted by permission. All rights reserved.

Chapter 23, "Zen Mind, Beginner's Mind": From *Zen Mind, Beginner's Mind,* by Shunryu Suzuki (New York: Weatherhill, 1970). © Weatherhill, Inc.

Chapter 24, "Emptiness": From *Returning to Silence,* by Dainin Katagiri. © 1988 by Minnesota Zen Meditation Center. Reprinted by arrangement with Shambhala Publications, Inc., 300 Massachusetts Avenue, Boston, MA 02115.

Chapter 25, "Engaged Buddhism": Excerpted by permission from *Being Peace,* by Thich Nhat Hanh (Berkeley: Parallax Press, 1987).

Chapter 26, "The Tantric Practitioner": From *Journey without Goal: The Tantric Wisdom of the Buddha,* by Chögyam Trungpa. © 1981 by Chögyam Trungpa. Reprinted by arrangement with Shambhala Publications, Inc.

Chapter 28, "The Union of Joy and Happiness": "Mahamudra Upadesa," translated by Chögyam Trungpa in *The Myth of Freedom and the Way of Meditation,* by Chögyam Trungpa, edited by John Baker and Marvin Casper. © 1976 by Chögyam Trungpa. Reprinted by arrangement with Shambhala Publications, Inc.

Chapter 29, "Songs of Milarepa": From *Songs of Milarepa,* translated by Karma Tsultrim Palmo. © Elizabeth Callahan.

Chapter 30, "Ati: The Innermost Essence": Selection by Jigme Lingpa from *Mudra,* by Chögyam Trungpa. © 1972 by Chögyam Trungpa. Reprinted by arrangement with Shambhala Publications, Inc.

Chapter 31, "Chase Them Away!": From *Wind Horse,* translated by Herbert V. Guenther and edited by R. Davidson. Reprinted by permission of Asian Humanities Press, Berkeley, Calif.

Chapter 32, "The Refined Essence of Oral Instructions": From *Dakini Teachings: Padmasambhava's Oral Instructions to Lady Tsogyal,* recorded and concealed by Yeshe Tsogyal, revealed by Nyang Ral Nyima Oser and Sangye Lingpa, translated by Erik Pema Kunsang. © 1990 by Erik Hein Schmidt. Reprinted by arrangement with Shambhala Publications, Inc.